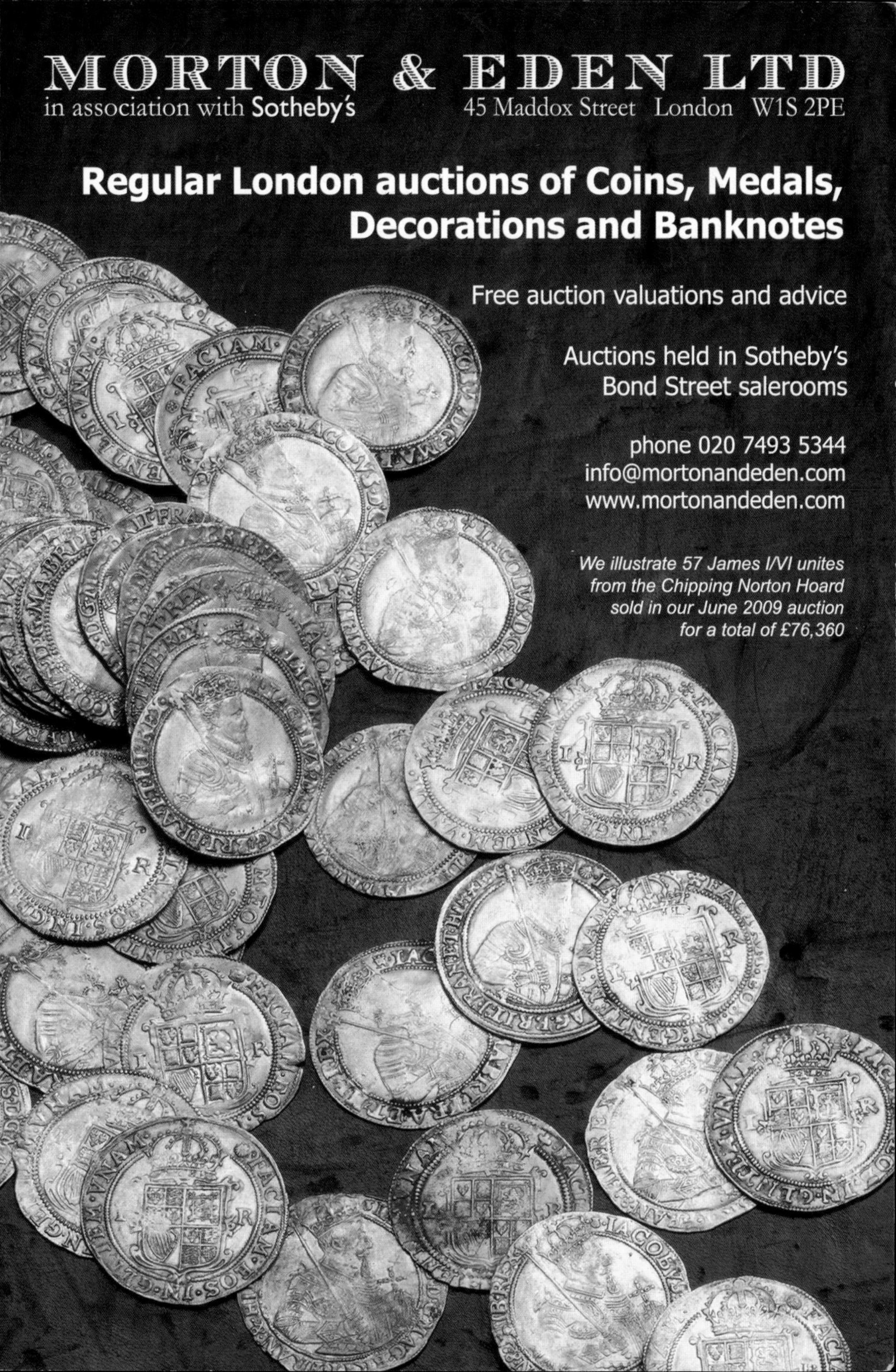
MORTON & EDEN LTD
in association with Sotheby's
45 Maddox Street London W1S 2PE
Regular London auctions of Coins, Medals, Decorations and Banknotes
Free auction valuations and advice
Auctions held in Sotheby's Bond Street salerooms
phone 020 7493 5344
info@mortonandeden.com
www.mortonandeden.com
We illustrate 57 James I/VI unites from the Chipping Norton Hoard sold in our June 2009 auction for a total of £76,360

THE

COIN YEARBOOK 2010

Edited by

John W. Mussell, FRGS

and the Editorial Team of COIN NEWS

ISBN–978–1 870 192 93 4

A Token TITLE

Published by

TOKEN PUBLISHING LIMITED

Orchard House, Duchy Road, Heathpark, Honiton, EX14 1YD

Telephone: 01404 46972 Fax: 01404 44788

e-mail: info@tokenpublishing.com. Website: http://www.tokenpublishing.com

Printed in Great Britain by JF Print, Sparkford

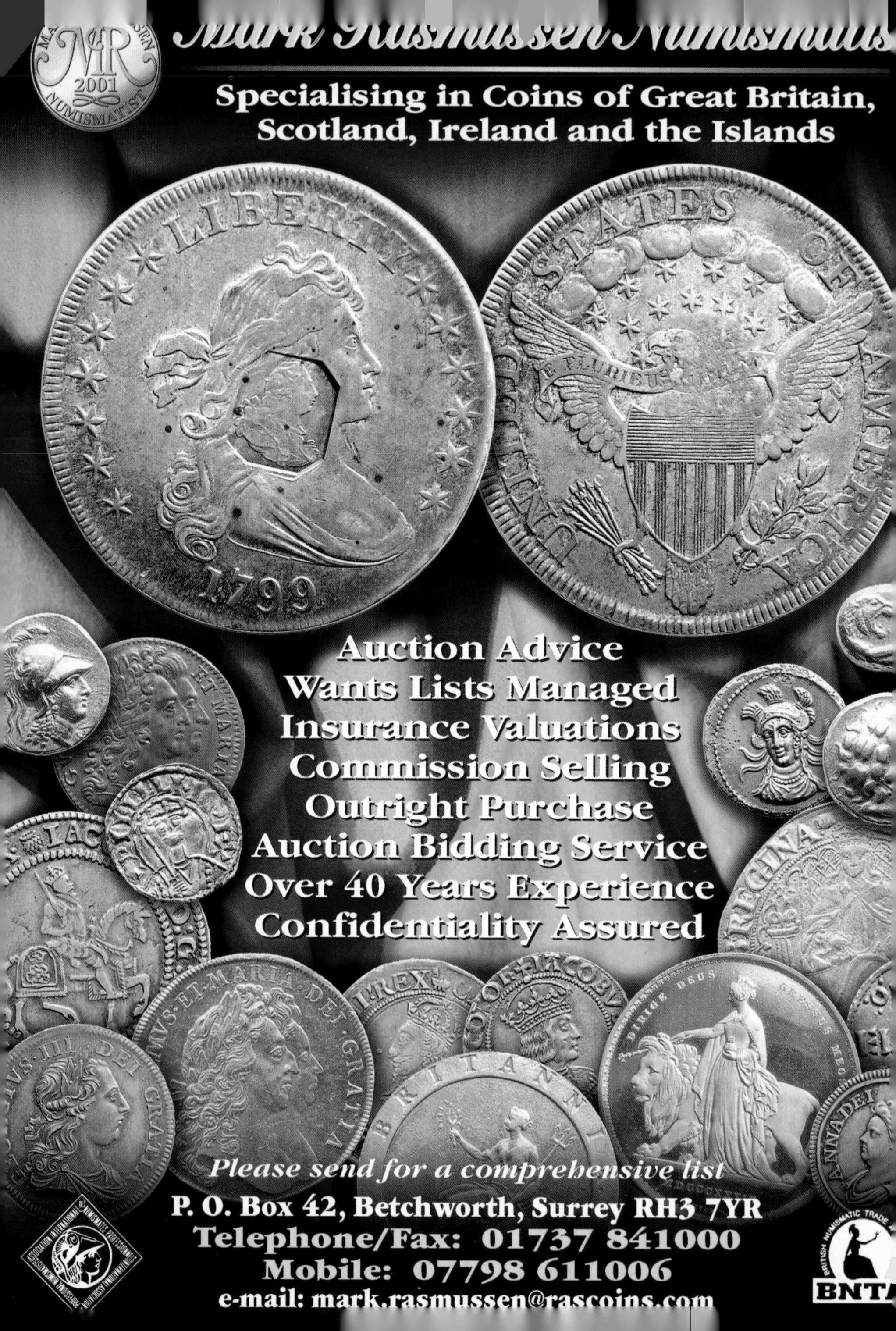

Mark Rasmussen Numismatis
MR 2001 NUMISMATIST
Specialising in Coins of Great Britain, Scotland, Ireland and the Islands
Auction Advice
Wants Lists Managed
Insurance Valuations
Commission Selling
Outright Purchase
Auction Bidding Service
Over 40 Years Experience
Confidentiality Assured
Please send for a comprehensive list
P. O. Box 42, Betchworth, Surrey RH3 7YR
Telephone/Fax: 01737 841000
Mobile: 07798 611006
e-mail: mark.rasmussen@rascoins.com
BNTA

Contents

Foreword

THIS latest edition of the acclaimed COIN YEARBOOK is being written against the backdrop of a world in financial turmoil, all around us are talks of doom and gloom and prophecies that the world as we know it is sure to come to an end any time soon. In fact such talk has been around for well over a year and whilst Britain, and numerous other countries, have indeed been struggling in the wake of the "credit crunch" and have been caught firmly in the teeth of a global recession there are sure signs that, as we enter the last quarter of 2009, the worst is in fact behind us and that "normal service" could well be resumed soon. However many of us in the coin hobby could actually be excused for wondering just what all the hype has been about because if we are absolutely honest here we haven't really been as badly affected as many other sectors of society. Whilst I am sure individual collectors have suffered, jobs have been lost, belts tightened etc. the fact remains that actually the hobby, and the coin trade, has enjoyed something of a boom time recently. The reasons behind this are simple to understand and have been covered extensively in COIN NEWS in recent months—as the stock market started to fall and house prices went into a tailspin those who still had money, and there were a number despite what the Great British Press might say, started looking around for alternative investments—coins, and more specifically gold, were an obvious choice. As the YEARBOOK goes to press gold stands at $955 an oz, a few dollars short of the records of last year but when you take into account that the US$ stands at $1.60 to the GB£ rather than the $2 of 2008 you will realise that in fact gold is reaching heights rarely seen before. This is inevitably proving a lure for investors, and gold coins are disappearing from dealers' list and trays faster than ever. However it isn't only gold that's benefitting, with those in the know eschewing the bullion pieces and reaching for those with more numismatic appeal, safe in the knowledge that whilst their house might be losing money daily and the Stock Market can no longer guarantee returns, coins at least seem to be relatively safe. That said, as we go to press both the Stock and Housing markets are rallying, so whether the investors are still as keen on coins when the 2011 YEARBOOK comes out remains to be seen.

Important though this boom has been for the coin hobby it isn't actually the key numismatic story of the year—that accolade has to go to the (in)famous "undated" 20 pence that somehow got released from the Royal Mint. Most will know the story by now—in short the pre-April 2008 20p obverse (the old design) was married to the post-April 2008 reverse (new design) leaving a mule with no date—and readers of COIN NEWS will know that we broke the story in December 2008. However in July 2009 the National Press got hold of it and suddenly numismatics was news. Admittedly this level of mistake is very rare for the Mint, not since 1983 and the New Pence/Two Pence has such an error occurred and so it was newsworthy, especially as suddenly the public could look for something in their change that was worth far, far more than face value. Just how interested the public were was unexpected to say the least with the story continuing to run long after most would have expected it to fade away—a *Mail on Sunday* article about this coin and others to look out for which casually mentioned COIN NEWS resulted in over 3,000 enquiries and requests for free samples in the Token Publishing office. Proof once more that if you strip away the "academic" level of our hobby there are far more people interested in coins than perhaps they will admit.

This level of interest should increase over the next couple of years with the promise of the 2012 Olympics and the ambitious coin programme embarked on by the Royal Mint in the run up to the games. Britain's biggest ever commemorative coin programme has now been launched with a key product being the "Celebration of Britain", an 18 strong silver proof collection "celebrating the heritage and highlighting the achievements, physical character and identity of Great Britain". The first six of these featuring such Icons of Britain as the clock tower housing Big Ben, Stonehenge, The Angel of the North, The Flying Scotsman, The Globe Theatre and Sir Isaac Newton. This series runs parallel to another programme destined to capture the imagination of everyone and not just those with deep pockets—that for the "public designed" 50 pences. This started off with a competition, open to all UK residents early in 2009, with a view to finding designs for 29 coins due to be issued at the rate of one a month from March 2010 running up to the opening of the Games themselves in 2012. Each coin will represent a different sport from the Olympics and Paralympics and with such a short circulation time they are sure to prove immensely popular amongst serious collectors and the general public alike. There are also rumours of other numismatic plans for the run up to the Games although at the time of writing none are set in stone.

One thing is certain—that with the interest in the "dateless 20p" still not waning (internet auction sites are still selling them well), the continued desire to seek alternative investments and the high profile launch of so many new coins for the Olympics, the hobby of coin collecting is destined to stay very much in the public eye in the coming months and years and we look forward to welcoming as many new collectors into the fold as possible. For those of you who are reading a COIN YEARBOOK for the first time—and judging by the huge increase in sales of the 2009 edition (which we had to reprint having sold out in February) and the pre-orders for this edition there are many of you out there—we do hope that this will inspire you to take up the hobby seriously—we promise you it can be a great deal of fun and we will do what we can to help.

Of course we ourselves need help from time to time, the hobby being as varied and interesting as it is and we would once again like to extend our thanks to all those who have helped with the compilation of this new edition of the COIN YEARBOOK. In particular we would like to thank Elizabeth Cottam and Chris Rudd for their input and help with the Celtic Section, Mike Vosper for the Roman Section, Stephen Mitchell of Studio coins for helping out with the Hammered coinage, Roy Norbury of West Essex Coins for the Milled, Nick Swabey for his help with the Maundy sets and oddments and Patrick Mackenzie for his work on the decimals. We would also like to once again thank Andrew Auld of West Wicklow coins and Declan O'Kelly of Cathedral Stamps, Dublin for their assistance with the Irish section.

Finally a reminder: as mentioned above, the volatility of the price of precious metals is an important factor to take into consideration when referring to the price guide in this publication. A rise or fall in the price of gold, for example, can drastically alter the market price of a gold sovereign, although truly numismatic items tend not to be so easily affected. Therefore, remember that the prices for gold coins are accurate at the time this publication is printed (September 2009), but over the course of the year they may go up or even down.

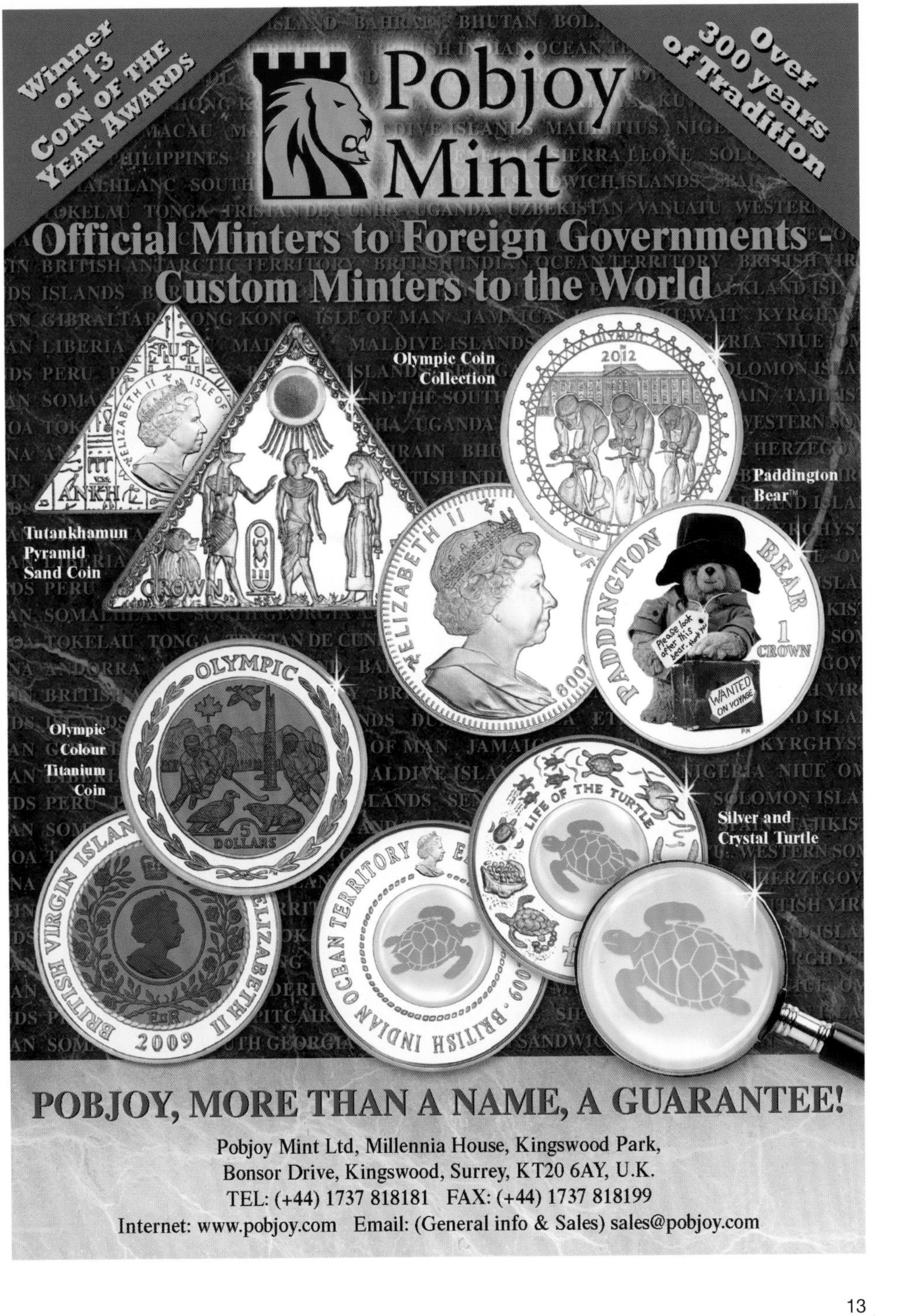
Winner of 13 COIN OF THE YEAR AWARDS
Pobjoy Mint
Over 300 years of Tradition
Official Minters to Foreign Governments - Custom Minters to the World
Olympic Coin Collection
Tutankhamun Pyramid Sand Coin
Paddington Bear™
Olympic Colour Titanium Coin
Silver and Crystal Turtle
POBJOY, MORE THAN A NAME, A GUARANTEE!
Pobjoy Mint Ltd, Millennia House, Kingswood Park,
Bonsor Drive, Kingswood, Surrey, KT20 6AY, U.K.
TEL: (+44) 1737 818181 FAX: (+44) 1737 818199
Internet: www.pobjoy.com Email: (General info & Sales) sales@pobjoy.com

Market review

by JOHN ANDREW

The round-up of the Summer Sales in COIN NEWS began for 2008, "The market continues to be buoyant with quality coins fetching very strong prices". Indeed, that was the message for most of the year. Coins have had a good run for several years now. Unlike the 1970s when they had an "alternative investment" appeal, the market is not investment orientated, but is built on a solid foundation of collector interest. The boom years of the 1970s all ended in tears in the early 1980s when investors left the market in droves and there were more sellers than buyers

Milled sovereigns have remained popular over our period of review (July 1, 2008 to June 30, 2009). At Lockdales on July 13 there was a very interesting 1879 Sydney mint shield back sovereign. The obverse legend reads VIOTORIA as opposed to VICTORIA. The O instead of a C in the Queen's name was not an actual O, but the die crack at this point has filled the curve between the limbs of the C so it appears to be an O. The piece was offered with an estimate of £200–£300—it was contested to a remarkable £1,350, therefore demonstrating that any "variety" of a sovereign is sought after.

There was another Australian surprise at Bonhams on July 16. A New South Wales 15 pence or "dump" of 1813 was offered in a somewhat sorry state. The crown and date are clear, while the obverse legend is only partly so. However, there is a cut on both the crown and the flan. The reverse is worn. Having noted these defects, the cataloguer's overall grading was "generally fine" and the estimate was set at £600–£900. It sold for £4,935.

On September 24, DNW had its first £1 million coin sale. The highlight was a base metal coin that was among a group of early American coins consigned to the event by an old English family. An ancestor had brought the coins to the UK in the late 17th century. The star was an outstanding 1776 Continental Dollar struck in pewter. The piece is most attractive and is virtually as struck. Regarded as the first coin issued by the United States of America, it is a popular piece. It is believed that around 80 Continental Dollars have survived. It sold for nearly three times its top estimate at £80,500.

Some cracking English coins were offered. Top price was paid for a 1656 Cromwell broad (pictured on p.15). Apart from a few light scratch marks in the fields, the piece is in extremely fine or better condition. It sold for a hammer price of £9,500—which is £10,925 with the premium. In February 1982, a comparable specimen sold at Glendining's for a hammer price of £9,200. Are coins a good investment? It depends what you pay for them!

Russian coins were on a roller-coaster at Baldwin's on September 24. The auctioneer Seth Freeman said after the event, "It seems that even the mundane is in demand in the Russian world as lots sold for double, triple and ten times their estimates. The English vendor was fairly much speechless when we told him the price his collection had sold for." Seth was not exaggerating; indeed he was playing down the buoyancy of the market. For example, half a dozen silver poltina of Alexander II (1855–81) were offered in very fine to extremely fine state. None was illustrated and the estimate was £250–£300. They sold for a staggering £6,900. The Russian coins sold for nearly seven times expectations at £209,099.

However, markets do not climb forever upwards. The highlights of Spink's sale on September 24/25 were four mid-19th century Hong Kong dollar-size patterns. Estimated at sums ranging from £100,000–120,000 to £130,000–150,000 each, none found buyers. The auctioneer, Richard Bishop, commented that the general feeling was that the Hong Kong market was not as buoyant as it was. The market was probably more cautious about high-ticket coins, but nevertheless the demand for quality coins was still healthy. Possibly these coins were estimated too highly at the insistence of the vendor? However, the roll continued for Russian material when a couple of scruffy quarter-kopecks dated 1720 and 1722 sold for £9,070, which was 60 times the top estimate. Polish coins were also sought.

Russian coins really made the news at St James's Auctions on November 6 when the unique and legendary Russian Elizabeth I gold 20 roubles of 1755 (pictured left)—the largest 18th century Russian denomination—was offered. Prior to the auction several offers had been made to purchase the piece—including one for £1 million. However, given the presale interest in the piece, the auction house advised its client to proceed with the auction. The coin sold for £1.7825 million, a new world record for a non-US coin. Contrary to rumours, the purchaser did pay for the coin. Indeed, he is delighted with his acquisition.

However, not everything was buoyant. There were quite a few unsold lots at the sale. The largest number was in the British section where 160 out of 613 lots did not find buyers. A percentage in excess of 25 is high, although, compared to the art market in general, things could have been much worse. At Christie's auction of Islamic objects on October 7, only 47 per cent of lots sold. Admittedly, many of the coins that did not sell at St James's Auctions were run-of-the-mill specimens or specialities such as silver patterns of Charles II copper. However, there were also a number of high profile choice coins. For example, an extremely rare proof 1830 pattern sovereign estimated at £10,000–£13,500.

Some superb specimens sold, but below their lower estimate. For example a splendid 1658 Oliver Cromwell halfcrown in about mint state was offered with a guide of

£3,500–£4,000. This estimate was punchy. However, it proved too much for the day. Clearly the auctioneer was given discretion and the hammer fell at £2,700, or £3,105 with Premium. The *2009 Coin Yearbook* price for an EF specimen is £3,250. However, a choice shilling of the same date and grade was offered with a guide of £2,750–£3,250 against a *Coin Yearbook* EF price of £2,250. The piece sold for a hammer price of £3,500 (£4,025 with the Premium).

Interestingly, there were not so many dealers at this sale. This could indicate that the trade was not particularly anxious to add to stock. This caution was understandable. There had also been a great deal of good British material offered around that time. The basics of economics are that supply and demand interact to determine price. It was clear that collectors were still in the market for good material. Of course, unlike the trade, collectors do not buy just because something is "a good buy"—they only buy what they want at the price they consider is "right".

The St James's Auctions sale appeared to be a blip when the world was in financial turmoil. At the end of November, Spink's general sale went well. Spink received hundreds of bidding slips for this sale. Many were for 5–15 lots with a total spend of a few thousand pounds. Auctioneer Richard Bishop could not help but wonder whether they had been left by individuals who felt more comfortable buying coins than making traditional financial investments or bank deposits in those troubled times. Certainly the Alan Shipman Collection of Sovereigns did well. The highlight here was an 1828 sovereign (pictured), one of the key dates in the series. Apart from light marks, the piece is in nearly extremely fine condition. Specimens in this state are extremely rare. The piece was contested to £12,750. The coin had passed through Spink's rooms in 1991 when the buyer paid £2,530 and again in 1997 when the price was £3,860 (both cases including the Buyer's Premium at 10 per cent).

It was clear by early 2009 that the only soft element of the market appeared to be Russian material. However, given that market's meteoritic rise in the last few years, this was hardly surprising. However, in other areas the common theme from the auction houses was that the market was strong and there was a shortage of good material. There was a Catch-22 situation. Prospective vendors did not want to sell anything from their collections because they did not know what to do with the money they would realise. Collectors felt more confident adding to their collections than to their portfolios. It was very noticeable that gold was not as plentiful in the sales as it was a year previously. Gold is regarded as a safe haven in times of trouble. The fact of the matter was that it was probably a good time to dispose of unwanted items—the market was certainly hungry across the board.

By May, things were back to normal at St James's Auctions. An Elizabeth I sixth issue gold crown was offered bearing the tun mintmark of 1592–5. The cataloguer's note simply read, "A charming piece". It is virtually as struck and has a rich red tone (pictured). The piece was estimated at an undemanding £4,500–5,500 against a *Standard Catalogue* price of £3,500 for a VF specimen. While one would expect the coin to "sell well", I doubt if anyone anticipated what the successful buyer would have to pay to secure this gem. It sold to a collector for £19,550.

So, what can one conclude about the market?

The market for British coins is strong. There were a few wobbles before Christmas, which was nothing compared to the mayhem in the financial markets. Coins that appeal can fetch extremely high sums, while those without a "wow factor" may not be fought over. However, let's take a look at what the professionals have to say.

IAN GOLDBART, Managing Director of A. H. Baldwin & Sons Ltd

Looking back over the last year, I suppose, with the global economic turmoil, the coin market could have gone either way. As it turns out, top quality coins have gone from strength to strength. The number of new and existing collectors visiting our Adelphi Terrace showroom has continued to grow and our fixed priced lists have been greeted with great enthusiasm. Despite the global instability and uncertainty within the larger and more traditional investment markets, such as shares, bonds and property and the concerns about banks and their very low interest paid on deposits, our auctions in London, New York and Hong Kong have been well attended and hammer prices strong.

The coin market has benefited because it is relatively small, has not been ramped up, has a natural supply constraint of high quality rarities and unlike the aforementioned larger traditional markets, appears to be completely unleveraged. While collectors continue to exhibit a passion for coins, we see our market growing and remaining strong.

STEPHEN FENTON, St James's Auctions

The market continues to show no signs of stopping, with existing world record prices being regularly shattered at St James's. The best example was in November 2008 when £1,782,500 was paid for the legendary Russian 20 Roubles of Catherine the Great. This auction also set a record for a coin sale in the UK, with a grand total realised of over £3,200,000. Then in May 2009 amongst a superb selection of pattern coins being offered, £184,000 was paid for the pattern George III 1770 five guineas by John Tanner, in a sale which totalled over £1,206,000, with some 10 per cent of the lots being sold via live bidding over the internet—a rapidly growing area.

TOM EDEN, Morton & Eden

The July 2008/June 2009 season represented our best year to date in terms of turnover—some £4.25 million for coins and medals. English coins as well as the ancient and Islamic series have fared very well. The December 2008 sale included the second part of the Carroll F. Wales collection of Byzantine coins, bringing the final total to just over £225,000. The June 2009 sale saw the disbursal of the Chipping Norton hoard of gold unites of James I with all 57 coins finding new homes for a total of £76,360—some 10 per cent over our expectations. We are well-known for selling Renaissance medals and plaquettes and in June 2009 we sold a magnificent plaquette of The Entombment by the important Paduan sculptor Riccio for £126,500. Finally, Russian coins and medals have brought consistently strong prices, especially in the latter category.

NIMROD DIX, Dix Noonan Webb

The results of the nine auctions we have held in the first half of 2009 emphasize the fundamental strength in the market not only for coins and military medals but also for other areas of collectables like tokens and banknotes. In the current economic climate it is hard to think of another asset class that has held its value to the same degree. It is quite clear that demand for top quality pieces far exceeds supply and that so long as this situation remains we will see continued strength in this market.

GRAEME MONK, Croydon Coin Auctions

We at Croydon cannot comment on the various record prices that have been reached recently, as that is not the field that we deal in. We can say that over the last year, we have seen a great increase in the number of people taking an interest in coins. There are lots of new customers, and many old friends are returning. We consistently have over 50 people in the room. The market strength is not only at the top quality end of the market, but right the way down to bags of what years ago might have been called junk. We have recently sold above average pre-47 silver at 20 times face plus 5 per cent buyers premium. Crowns have performed well, with nice 1927 proofs hitting £200, and even a Fair/GFair £75. Edward VII is not far behind, as they are now fetching £200 including premium. Pennies are a strong growth area; the late Laurie Bamford's collection's untimely appearance on the market heightened interest and they have never looked back. Michael Gouby's imminent book will only add fuel to the fire; perhaps there is still room for further increases. The poor stock market performance, and low interest rates have certainly encouraged collectors and others to put more money into coins, and at the time of writing there seems no sign whatever of any weakness in the market. There seem to be more potential buyers than sellers.

STEPHEN LOCKETT, London Coins

The period had the very significant back drop of the "credit crunch" which saw massive collapses in traditional investment vehicles such as the stock market and at one point threatened an entire meltdown of the free world's banking and financial system. One result of this which affected our market was a rush to gold as a safe haven, as many collector coins are made from gold this had a positive knock on affect for us with new clients entering the market and established collectors not wishing to sell or adding to their collections. We noticed also a strong growth in interest in certified coins, currently high quality copies of many British Coins are flowing into the UK from the Far East and the guarantee of authenticity the encapsulated product offers is a growing attraction.

RICHARD BEALE, Warwick & Warwick

This has been our most successful year selling coins and banknotes, with the economic situation having a positive effect. Many clients faced with minimal interest rates on their savings and the volatility of stocks and shares have spent considerable sums on coins and banknotes. The rise in the value of gold has also had a very positive effect with people cashing in on their collections of gold coins. The popularity and appeal of coin and banknote collecting has continued unabated with many younger people taking up the hobby, ensuring a very healthy market for basic and more advanced material.

SPOKESPERSON, Spink

The demand for high grade and rare coins has remained very strong. The rise in gold prices combined with falling returns from other forms of investment seems to suggest that active buying by private collectors has been supplemented by some investment-focused buying. As a consequence we have seen high prices being realised for rare gold coins as seen with a 1828 Sovereign changing hands for £12,750 against a £6,000–£8,000 estimate in November. More recently we have seen hammered gold reflecting a similar pattern of excellent prices. In March, a very rare Henry VIII George Noble made £32,900 (est. £15,000–18,000) whilst in June an equally rare Henry VI second reign Half Noble made £9,300 (est. £3,000–4,000). European gold coins also showed a similar pattern with a rare Maltese 4 Zecchini of 1705 making £21,375 (est. £4,000–6,000). Other areas have also remained strong, particularly Anglo-Saxon hammered silver. The March sale of the John Marshall collection showed that the market for Ancient Greek and Roman coins is also very strong. Overall the market has performed exceptionally well in all categories with the only exception being Russian, where a level of overdue realism seems to have reasserted itself in recent months.

Museum archive

Every month in COIN NEWS we are privileged to feature one of the rare items from the Royal Mint 's own private Museum at Llanstrisant. The collection represents one of the most impressive numismatic collections in the world, featuring outstanding rarities alongside the currency we all use in our every day lives. Here we have chosen a few of the items we have featured as a "snap shot" of the Museum's treasures.

Swann Cabinets

When the Royal Mint collection was re-arranged and re-housed in the early 1970s, Graham Dyer took the decision to use cabinets made by Mr Swann as the most appropriate way in which to keep a national collection. It was not just because the cabinets were handsome and exquisitely well made but also because they represented a practical way of storing many thousands of coins. The intervening years have revealed the decision to commission 80 cabinets from Mr Swann to have been an extremely wise one.

Tim Swann was a true craftsman. He will be well known to collectors as the maker of cabinets of exceptional quality and through his career he was responsible for supplying the needs of several important museum collections, including cabinets for the Royal Collection of coins and medals at Windsor. He died in July 2007 but he will long be remembered amongst collectors and curators through the quality of craftsmanship he left behind.

Henry VIII silver trial plate

The connection between a monarch and the appearance or nature of the coinage has waxed and waned over the centuries. Henry VIII, as well as being famous for influencing many aspects of national life, left his mark on the coinage by debasing it as a way of raising money. Silver in particular suffered, with the fineness being reduced markedly over the debasement period and, not only is the evidence to be seen in the coins, it is also there in the trial plates that were made at the time.

A trial plate is a way of testing the precious metal content of a coin. At below 800 fine this one was made to a standard of silver well below the sterling fineness of 925 and shows the degree to which the arrangements for the debasement were formalised.

The Quarter-sovereign

In Spring 2009, the Royal Mint issued quarter-sovereigns for the first time as legal currency. Precedents for the initiative are to be found in the lower value gold coins of the 18th century but more particularly in the beautifully prepared pattern quarter sovereigns of 1853. The Royal Mint collection contains specimens of both types that were produced, one bearing a prominent denominational value and the other an exquisitely drawn shield of the Royal Arms. It was an interesting proposal aired by Sir John Herschel as Master of the Mint but which foundered on fears that the coin would wear too quickly and other practical considerations also mitigated against its release. Having an eye to the requirements of circulation did not arise in relation to the quarter-sovereigns issued in 2009 and their release has presented an opportunity to extend the range of gold coins.

Wax model of Britannia by William Wyon

The designers of coins and medals work in many different ways. Some carve directly into plaster, some model in clay or wax and these days three-dimensional computer design software offers another option. In the 18th and 19th centuries artists often built up a relief composition by modelling wax on slate, an exquisite example of which is pictured here. The piece, which measures 55 mm, is the work of the famous 19th-century engraver William Wyon and depicts the figure of Britannia with shield and trident standing in front of the prow of an ornately decorated ship. The purpose for which it was made has never quite been determined and it seems that the design did not make it through to being developed as a struck medal. Whatever lay behind the commission, however, it demonstrates clearly the manner in which William Wyon worked up medallic designs and also the remarkable level of detail he was able to capture by modelling in wax.

Trial Fifty Pence Piece

Shaped coins—shapes that are other than round—are nothing new. The Chinese, as with so much else, were there well before western Europe, while for England the Civil War siege pieces of the 17th century are an early example of experimentation with this idea. Britain had to wait until the 1930s, however, and the issue of the 12-sided threepence for its first multi-sided coin of regular issue and thereafter there was much more to come from many other countries. The idea to issue the world's first equilateral-curve heptagon as part of Britain's new decimal currency came originally from H. G. Conway, the technical member of the Decimal Currency Board who was at that time President of the Institute of Mechanical Engineers. The item illustrated here, which is inscribed with his name, is a trial piece from very early in the process of development. The fifty pence has since become an extremely popular coin and it is only right that on at least one coin the unsung hero of its introduction is celebrated.

Edward VIII Crown

The recent unveiling of the designs by Matthew Dent for the new coinage caused quite a stir in the numismatic world and beyond. How often, after all, does a story about the British coinage command front-page coverage in The Times? The modern celebration of heraldry that the new designs represent calls to mind an heraldic design from the reign of Edward VIII by the acknowledged master of the genre George Kruger Gray.

In May 1936 quite serious consideration was given to a design for the crown, serious enough indeed that it was to make it all the way through to this extremely rare pattern uniface piece now in the Royal Mint collection. The beautifully composed shield of the Royal Arms was, however, upstaged by elaborate mantling judged to be far too fussy; and such was the profusion of heraldic detail that the satellite national floral emblems were all but lost—the daffodil appearing particularly indistinct. Although rejected, it still stands as a testament to Kruger Gray's heraldic imagination.

LONDON COINS
DEALERS AND AUCTIONEERS
FREE VALUATIONS AND APPRAISALS
* English Milled Coins
* British Hammered Coins
* World Coins
* Roman and Ancient Coins
* Proof Sets
* Royal Mint Issues
* Paper Money
* Medals
* Gold Coins, Sovereigns, Guineas and Krugerrands
* Tokens
* Bonds and Shares
Free Catalogues
'How To Sell Your Coins' Information Pack
See our website for our stock of choice English coins
www.londoncoins.co.uk
Four auctions every year
4-6 Upper Street South
New Ash Green, Longfield, Kent, DA3 8JJ
Tel: 01474 871464

Monarchs of England

Here we list the Kings and Queens from Anglo-Saxon times to the present, with the dates of their rule. Before Eadgar became the King of all England the country had been divided up into small kingdoms, each with their own ruler.

ANGLO-SAXON KINGS

The Anglo-Saxon monarchs ruled over the various kingdoms which existed in England following the withdrawal of the Romans in the 5th century AD. The most prominent kingdoms in the land were Kent, Sussex, Wessex, Mercia and Northumbria. Each kingdom produced its own coinage but in 973 Eadgar introduced a new coinage that became the standard for the whole of the country.

Eadgar, penny

Eadgar (959–975)
Edward the Martyr (975–978)
Aethelred II (978–1016)
Cnut (1016–1035)
Harold I (1035–1040)
Harthacanut (1035–1042)
Edward the Confessor (1042–1066)
Harold II (1066)

Cnut and his penny.

Stephen.

NORMAN KINGS

The Normans came to Britain from their native France following the establishment of a kingdom in Sicily and southern Italy. An expedition led by the powerful Duke William of Normandy culminated in the battle of Hastings in 1066 where he defeated Harold II and was proclaimed King of All England. Their influence spread from these new centres to the Crusader States in the Near East and to Scotland and Wales in Great Britain, and to Ireland. Today their influence can be seen in their typical Romanesque style of architecture.

William I (1066–1087)
William II (1087–1100)
Henry I (1100–1135)
Stephen (1135–1154)

William I, penny

PLANTAGENETS

The Plantagenet kings of England were descended from the first House of Anjou who were established as rulers of England through the Treaty of Wallingford, which passed over the claims of Eustace and William, Stephen of Blois's sons, in favour of Henry of Anjou, son of the Empress Matilda and Geoffrey V, Count of Anjou.

Henry II.

Henry II (1154–1189)
Richard I (1189–1199)
John (1199–1216)
Henry III (1216–1272)
Edward I (1272–1307)
Edward II (1307–1327)
Edward III (1327–1377)
Richard II (1377–1399)

Henry II, penny

Henry IV.

HOUSE OF LANCASTER

The House of Lancaster, a branch of the English royal House of Plantagenet, was one of the opposing factions involved in the Wars of the Roses, the civil war which dominated England and Wales during the 15th century. Lancaster provided England with three Kings

Henry IV (1399–1413)
Henry V (1413–1422)
Henry VI (1422–1461)

Henry IV, halfpenny

HOUSE OF YORK

The House of York was the other branch of the House of Plantagenet involved in the disastrous Wars of the Roses. Edward IV was descended from Edmund of Langley, 1st Duke of York, the fourth surviving son of Edward III.

Edward IV (1461–1483 and again 1471–83)
Richard III (1483–1485)

Edward IV.

Henry VII.

TUDORS

The House of Tudor was an English royal dynasty that lasted 118 years, from 1485 to 1603. The family descended from the Welsh courtier Owen Tudor (Tewdwr). Following the defeat of Richard III at Bosworth, the battle that ended the Wars of the Roses, Henry Tudor, 2nd Earl of Richmond, took the throne as Henry VII.

Henry VII (1485–1509)
Henry VIII (1509–1547)
Edward VI (1547–1553)
Mary (1553–1558)
Philip & Mary (1554–1558)
Elizabeth I (1558–1603)

Henry VII, angel.

STUARTS

The House of Stuart ruled Scotland for 336 years, between 1371 and 1707. Elizabeth I of England's closest heir was James VI of Scotland via her grandfather Henry VII of England, who was founder of the Tudor dynasty. On Elizabeth's death, James Stuart ascended the thrones of England and Ireland and inherited the English claims to the French throne. The Stuarts styled themselves "Kings and Queens of Great Britain", although there was no parliamentary union until the reign of Queen Anne, the last monarch of the House of Stuart.

James I (1603–1625)
Charles I (1625–1649)
The Commonwealth (1653–1658)
Charles II (1660–1685)
James II (1685–1688)
William III & Mary (1688–1694)
William III (1694–1702)
Anne (1702–1714)

James I, crown.

James I.

George I.

HOUSE OF HANOVER

The House of Hanover was a Germanic royal dynasty which ruled the Duchy of Brunswick-Lüneburg and the Kingdom of Hanover. George Ludwig ascended to the throne of the Kingdom of Great Britain and Ireland through the female line from Princess Elizabeth, sister of Charles I.

George I (1714–1727)
George II (1727–1760)
George III (1760–1820)
George IV (1820–1830)
William IV (1830–1837)
Victoria (1837–1901)

George I, two guineas.

HOUSES OF SAXE-COBURG-GOTHA AND WINDSOR

The name Saxe-Coburg-Gotha was inherited by Edward VII from his father Prince Albert, the second son of the Duke of Saxe-Coburg-Gotha and husband of Victoria. During World War I the name was changed to Windsor to avoid the Germanic connotatiion.

Edward VII (1901–1910)
George V (1910–1936)
Edward VIII (1936)
George VI (1936–1952)
Elizabeth II (1952–)

Edward VII, shilling.

Edward VII.

Tel: 01543 473073 1.00pm - 6.30pm Mon-Fri	**J. WELSH** P.O. Box 150, Burton-on-Trent Staffs DE13 7LB All Coins Banked, No Callers.	Est. 1968 Fax No. (24 hrs - 7 days) 01543 473234

COINS FOR SALE

*(*P.O.R .... PRICE ON REQUEST)*

HAMMERED GOLD
- HVII ANGEL A/UNC ..... *P.O.R.
- HVII ANGEL NVF S.2187 ..... P.O.R.
- JMS I LAUREL AUNC S2638C ..... P.O.R.
- JMS I UNITE S2618 NVF ..... P.O.R.
- JMS I UNITE GVF+ S2618 ..... P.O.R.
- JMS I UNITE EF S2618 MM ROSE ..... P.O.R.
- JMS I LAUREL EF/AUNC S2638A ..... P.O.R.
- CHS I UNITE VF/VF+ S2687 ..... P.O.R.
- CHS I UNITE GVF+ S2687 ..... P.O.R.
- CHS I UNITE GVF+ S2694 RARE ..... P.O.R.
- ELIZ I ANGEL A/UNC S2531 ..... P.O.R.

2 GUINEAS
- 1684 CHS II VF+ ..... P.O.R.
- 1700 GN SUP. BU ..... P.O.R.
- 1738 GEO II BU GEM ..... P.O.R.
- 1740/39 GEO II GEM AUNC ..... P.O.R.

GUINEAS
- 1673 NEF NICE S.3318 ..... P.O.R.
- 1673 EF RARE ..... P.O.R.
- 1687 NEF NICE S.3319 RARE ..... P.O.R.
- 1694 W+MARY A/UNC EX. RARE ..... P.O.R.
- 1715 GEO I NVF/VF £750
- 1716 NEF ..... P.O.R.
- 1726 GEO I NICE ABU EX. RARE ..... P.O.R.
- 1727 GEO II EF, EX. RARE ..... P.O.R.
- 1745 LIMA NEF EX. RARE ..... P.O.R.
- 1751 NEF RARE £950
- 1758 BU PR LIKE ..... P.O.R.
- 1766 NICE ABU/BU EX. RARE ..... P.O.R.
- 1772 ABU RARE £950
- 1772 UNC RARE ..... P.O.R.
- 1775 SUPERB BU/FDC ..... P.O.R.
- 1787 NICE UNC £800
- 1789 BU £850
- 1790 ABU/BU RARE £650
- 1791 ABU £450
- 1794 NICE BU £750
- 1795 BU £750
- 1798 BU £695
- 1799 BU EX. RARE ..... P.O.R.

SOVEREIGNS

GEORGE III
- 1820 BU PR. LIKE £1650
- 1820 EF/ABU OPEN 2 NICE £975

GEORGE IV
- 1821 NEF £650
- 1821 EF NICE £950
- 1821 NICE ABU £995
- 1822 GVF £575
- 1822 NICE ABU £995
- 1824 GVF £525
- 1825 ABU BARE HEAD £1250
- 1825 BARE HEAD, GVF+ £595
- 1825 B. HD. VF+ £495
- 1826 BU GEM RARE £1950
- 1826 NICE EF/ABU £975
- 1826 GVF £495
- 1827 NVF/VF £450
- 1827 BU GEM £1950
- 1829 NVF/VF RARE £495
- 1829 NICE VF+ £550
- 1830 VF SCARCE £525
- 1830 ABU/BU £950

WILLIAM IV
- 1832 F/GF £395
- 1832 SUPERB BU ..... ONLY £1850
- 1832 BU GEM ..... ONLY £1650
- 1833 ABU £1400
- 1833 NEF NICE EF RARE £950
- 1837 NICE EF £850

VICTORIA 1837—1887

YOUNG HEAD SHIELD REV.
- 1838 VF RARE £995
- 1844 NEF/EF £475
- 1848 VF £250
- 1846 GVF+ RARE £350
- 1846 EF NICE V. RARE £475
- 1847 EF £350
- 1849 VF RARE £250
- 1852 BU RARE £450
- 1855 GVF £225
- 1855 WWI BU GEM RARE £495
- 1855 BU RARE £450
- 1856 NICE ABU RARE £395
- 1857 EF/ABU RARE £275
- 1860 VF £195
- 1863 BU D14 ..... £325
- 1864 BU RARE DN37 ..... £375
- 1865 EF RARE D13 ..... £250
- 1866 EF/ABU DN6 ..... £250
- 1866 SUPERB BU £450
- 1866 SYD AUS. NVF/VF £250
- 1868 VF D.H. £225
- 1869 EF £195
- 1869 BU GEM £325
- 1871 EF D.30 ..... £225
- 1871 L NICE ABU £225
- 1871 SYD NICE ABU RARE £295
- 1872 L ABT BU D59 ..... £240
- 1872 L BU D90 ..... £295
- 1872 L ABT BU/BU D.86 ..... £225
- 1872 L VF £195
- 1873 SYD. ABU/BU £275
- 1873 SYD BU GEM £450
- 1875 SYD BU £350
- 1875 SYD NICE BU £350
- 1875 SYD. BU GEM £395
- 1877 S BU GEM £350
- 1879 SYD BU GEM £350
- 1880 SYD. BU GEM RARE £475
- 1887-2009 ..... ON LIST

CROWNS
- 1658 CROMWELL VIR. UNC ..... P.O.R.
- 1662 ROSE BELOW FINE £140
- 1678 VF EXT. RARE £750
- 1679 CHS II FINE, 4TH B £125
- 1679 CAP-T. PRIMO FINE £125
- 1680 4TH BUST FINE £150
- 1688 JMS II VF, RARE £475
- 1688 JMS II GF £250
- 1692 W+MARY GVF RARE £1500
- 1692/2 W+MARY NICE NVF/VF £695
- 1696 NEF NICE £595
- 1696 GVF+ £295
- 1700 NICE GVF+ RARE £750
- 1739 NICE GVF+ £750
- 1743 GVF £650
- 1743 EF LOVELY LIGHT TONE £1500
- 1751 GEM ABT UNC LOV. COL ..... P.O.R.
- 1770 RUSS RBLE ABU £250
- 1780 MARIA, THER. BU £13
- 1804 BE DOLL BU GEM £595
- 1804 BC DON BU NICE £550
- 1804 BE DEM. BU GEM PR. LIKE £595
- 1804 BE DON GVF+ £240
- 1804 BE DOLL NEF £225
- 1818 LVIII SUPERB BU PR. LIKE £575
- 1818 LVIII SUPERB UNC LOV. COL £595
- 1818 LIX GEM UMC NICE TONE £595
- 1818 LVIII UNC LIGHT TONE £350
- 1819 LIX UNC £295
- 1820 NICE VF £75
- 1820 NEF £125
- 1821 NICE VF £75
- 1822 TERT. NICE VIR. UNC £675
- 1822 TERT. GVF+ RARE £150
- 1822 TERT. VF+ £95
- 1822 TERT. GF £48
- 1822 TERT. NVF £55
- 1844 NICE GVF+ £175
- 1844 NICE EF/AUNC £395
- 1844 GVF £95
- 1845 NICE NEF £175
- 1845 EF/ABU NICE £495
- 1845 EF NICE TONE £295
- 1845 NICE ABU/BU ..... ONLY £675
- 1845 SMALL DATE EF/AUNC £595
- 1847 Y. HD, SUPERB UNC £2250
- 1887 EF NICE £45
- 1887 GVF+ £30
- 1887 EF/ABU £55
- 1887 VIR. UNC NICE TONE £65
- 1887 UNC TONED £85
- 1888 NAR. DATE NICE BU £175
- 1889 BU NICE £95
- 1890 SUPERB BU LT. TONE £225
- 1890 GF £14
- 1890 NVF/VF £18
- 1890 VF £25
- 1891 EF/ABU RARE £95
- 1891 F/GF £15
- 1893 LVI VF+ £25
- 1893 LVI NEF/EF £45
- 1893 LVII NVF RARE £45
- 1893 LVI NVF/VF £22
- 1893 LVI VF £25
- 1893 LVI GVF+ £35
- 1893 LVI NEF £40
- 1893 LVI NEF/EF £55

ON MAIN LIST

MORE UK GOLD, FOREIGN GOLD, 2/6, 2/-, 1/- 6D, 3DS, MDY SETS, COPPER, SETS, ETC.

IF YOU WOULD LIKE TO RECEIVE MY FREE SALES LIST OF ENGLISH, GOLD, SILVER, COPPER AND FOREIGN COINS, (A VERY WIDE RANGE (1200 – 2009). PLEASE WRITE, TELEPHONE OR FAX ME

2009 Proof Britannia Sets NOW AVAILABLE
Allgold Of Sevenoaks
Specialist in the supply of English gold coins
Investment Gold
Rare Coins
Royal Mint and Pobjoy Mint Latest Gold coin issues
Rare and Scarce Sovereigns
3 & 4 Coin Gold Proof sets from 1982
www.allgoldcoins.co.uk
Extensive online store
We are the south's leading specialist in the supply of high quality sovereigns and modern proof sets including date runs, rare and scarce coins from 1817 - date. We offer free help and advice to all collectors and investors. If you are looking to Buy / Sell or just want information on your coins, we are always happy to help!
Sovereigns 1817–2010
Coin Accessories & Books
Treasury and Bank of England Banknotes (1694-2008)
Ebay Auctions
24hr Live Gold Price and charts
P.O. Box 260, Wallington, SM5 4AH
Tel: 0844 544 7952
E-Mail: sales@allgoldcoins.co.uk
BRITISH NUMISMATIC TRADE ASSOCIATION
EUROCARD MasterCard
VISA

Sovereign
an iconic image

Each month in COIN NEWS Clive King of Allgold gives tips on the sovereign market. Here he gives an overview of this popular coin.

The Revival of the Sovereign

So why the explosion in sovereign collecting? Long gone are the days that you could walk into your local bank and buy them, in fact up until the Millennium apart from rare sovereigns they were pretty much out of fashion. Then in 2000 came exemption from VAT in the UK, and most importantly the internet, which gave the opportunity to millions to purchase coins from the comfort of their living room. Low interest rates meant that money was not appreciating greatly in savings accounts and the new breed of the investor collector was born. Of course this did not only benefit the sovereign market but antiques, other coins and stamps, all saw booms in interest. However, it completely rejuvenated the sovereign. Indeed in 2000 interest in the sovereign prompted the Royal Mint to revive the bullion issue not seen since 1982 and it is now in its tenth consecutive year of production and looks set to continue.

Many of those entering the world of sovereign collecting today do so with one eye on investment for the future as well as their interest in coins, which they may have held since a child. Such has been the interest in the market since the turn of the millennia that it has lead to significant changes in availability and values of some sovereigns, with previously unnoticed varieties being discovered all the time. It should also be remembered that another reason for renewed interest in the sovereign is the recent dramatic increase in the price of gold which looks set to continue.

Modern Sovereigns

The year 1816 was a landmark for British coinage. The mint was moved from the Tower of London to a new site on Tower Hill and steam powered minting machinery built by Boulton and Watt replaced the old hand operated presses. Significantly, new coinage was produced with an intrinsic value substantially below the face value of each coin—the first official token coinage in the world. In 1817, after an absence of 213 years, sovereigns were minted to replace the guinea. The new coins, valued at 20 shillings (the same as the original rate of over three centuries earlier), were accompanied by half sovereign issues and pattern five and two pound pieces. All were minted to the 22 carat (91.6 per cent) fineness standard previously used for the guinea.

Mints and Mintmarks

The discovery of large quantities of gold in the Australian colonies in the 1850s, led to the establishment of the Sydney Branch of the Royal Mint in 1855. The first "Sydney Mint" sovereigns and half sovereigns issued by this mint were

Reverse of the Victoria, Young Head sovereign with Sydney mintmark.

unique in the history of the British Empire. In a situation which has not been repeated since, the coins carried a design which was completely different from that of the standard British issue but by 1871 it was decreed that all coins produced at the colonial mints should carry the standard Shield and St George designs. A small "S" mintmark was placed below the shield to designate the Sydney Mint issues. On "St. George" issues, the mintmark appeared on the obverse below the bust. The Melbourne Mint commenced operations in 1872 ("M" mintmark) and Perth in 1899 ("P" mintmark). A Jubilee head design of Queen Victoria was placed on the obverse in 1887. Colonial "S", "M" and "P" mintmarks for "St. George" gold coins were moved to the reverse on the ground just above the date. In 1908 (Edward VII's reign), the Canadian Mint ("C" mintmark) at Ottawa began producing sovereigns. For a single year in 1918, the Indian Mint ("I" mintmark) at Bombay produced a sovereign. The last of the colonial mints to issue gold coins—Pretoria in South Africa ("SA" mintmark)—began producing sovereigns and half sovereigns in 1923 (George V's reign).

Coin Grading

The importance of accurate grading cannot be underestimated, if you are new to sovereign collecting you should become acquainted with terms such as Fine (F), Very Fine (VF), Extremely Fine (EF) and Uncirculated (Unc or BU) and know how to recognise them. We would always recommend purchasing sovereigns from reputable dealers who will give you advice and, if members of the British Numismatic Trade Association, are committed to giving fair and accurate gradings. Collectors should be wary of buying coins on internet auction sites where dealers have little or no reputation and often provide poor quality pictures and overgrade hoping to obtain vastly inflated values.

Fakes and Forgeries

There are many sovereigns which have either been altered or copied to fool the uninitiated and even more experienced collectors can get caught out. The quality of forgeries varies greatly from poorly struck plated lead coins which hardly resemble the original to extremely sophisticated copies. One of the most often seen forgery is the removal of the mint mark on the 1917 sovereign to produce what appears to be a perfect 1917 London struck coin which is, of course, very rare. The collector should be very wary of any 1917 London sovereign being sold other than by a reputable dealer and the coin's provenance should be obtained as this will be needed when the coin is resold if full value is to be achieved. Another type of fake to watch out for are the excellent copies made in Lebanon in the 1970s. These are mainly of early sovereigns such as George III, George IV and William IV. The most common of these are the 1822 George IV sovereigns which are almost indistioguishable from the original, but the biggest giveaway is that they appear in fantastic uncirculated condition: even the edges are sharp, like a coin that would have been struck in the 1970s! So as a general rule beware of coins that appear too cheap or come from an unknown source, as well as early sovereigns which appear to look new. In particular do not buy a 1917 London Sovereign without proof of its genuineness.

The different head types of Queen Elizabeth II and the reverses of the 2002 and 2005 sovereigns..

MANDELA
A LONG
WALK TO
FREEDOM
NELSON ROLIHLAHLA

View of the bay

WILLIAM McCREATH offers some advice when it comes to the internet

In the eleven years that I've been registered on eBay the number of numismatic items listed has grown enormously as has the variety of items on offer, from the very common to the very rare and everything in-between, they will all appear at some time or another. eBay is a very rich hunting ground for those who are interested in items that are off the beaten track: countermarked coins, tokens, error coins and notes, old contemporary counterfeits, etc.—the variety on offer simply can't be found in any other one place. Buying these types of items holds few dangers for bidders as they are often in low grade but still desirable, so with a little caution it's difficult to go wrong. Very rare countermarked coins are occasionally offered by sellers who are unaware of how rare they are, which can give the informed collector the chance to bag a real bargain. Very rare tokens can sometimes be had cheaply, the reason being that few own reference books about tokens compared to books about coins.

Bidding on mainstream items is entirely a different matter however, and extreme caution has to be exercised along with doing some homework before bidding. If a seller regularly lists nothing but "high grade" coins or notes, a collector should be asking themselves "where does the seller get their stock from?", especially if they seem to be happy to frequently sell at "bargain" prices. It is astounding that this question does not even cross the mind of many collectors as they merrily bid away, snapping up what they see as bargain after bargain from the same seller. One eBay seller regularly buys mostly UK banknotes in the lower grades off eBay, irons them, and then successfully sells them on eBay a few weeks later as rare high grade notes, very often making a very handsome profit. Why their happy band of buyers have not noticed what's going on is mystifying in the extreme. I would recommend only buying high grade notes if they are of recent vintage, especially if a seller offers nothing but alleged high grade notes. A few other sellers have now jumped on this bandwagon as they see this seller doing very well . . . one bad apple etc.

A large number of coins listed are overgraded, no surprise perhaps. Coins in no better than Fine condition can be found listed as being EF, or commonly a somewhat vague "high grade", which should be a red flag for prospective bidders. A silver coin that appears to have original lustre may have been "dipped" which can sometimes gives them a matt appearance, so watch out for this especially if the majority of a seller's silver coins have this look. Coins that to an experienced collector look to have been cleaned or even harshly polished can still find inexperienced happy buyers. Hopefully regular readers of *COIN NEWS* will know better. I would recommend completely ignoring the stated grade and judge from the photographs—if they are of poor quality then do not bid as the seller is possibly trying to hide something. Good quality digital cameras are now not expensive so there is no excuse for dark or fuzzy pictures. I find it useful to compare eBay coin photographs to the photographs of similar coins in dealers' lists and in auction catalogues, as this can give a very good idea if they are overgraded or not.

If a seller has the items that they have sold hidden as "private" in their feedbacks, thus making it impossible to find out what an item was, they may have a good reason for hiding this information so they should perhaps be avoided. Unfortunately a 100 per cent positive feedback record for a seller no longer counts as much as it once did. It would seem that as inexperienced buyers now appear to be in the majority, so they give positives to bad sellers when they should be giving strong negatives.

Recommending to never bid on a coin from a seller in China might be considered extreme, and perhaps unfair to honest sellers in that country, but there are huge numbers of fake coins being made in China for sale to collectors and some are very convincing. They range from 1977 crowns that are dated 1877 to USA trade dollars. Some sell for suitably low prices but some sell for hundreds of pounds to soon-to-be-disappointed buyers. Also some of these fakes are re-appearing as genuine coins offered by unscrupulous sellers. Unfortunately as these coins are not identified as copies in any way, and they are very convincing, only experience at handling the real thing can help the buyer. As they are being made on an industrial scale the fakes will by now outnumber the genuine population of some rare coins, so buy from sellers in China only if the item is cheap and the postage charge not extortionate and you enjoy a gamble with long odds.

It's not all depressing news when it comes to the mainstream numismatic items listed on eBay, but good news can be thin on the ground. It may be possible to find a few sellers who do accurately grade the coins they list for sale and if that few are found use should be made of eBay's "saved sellers" feature.

The chance of a bargain can be had when a seller offers a rare variety that they don't recognise. Just hope that you are one of just a few that have spotted it and bid at the last possible moment, but not more than you are prepared to pay. Placing a very high last minute "must have" bid is a very risky business because if another bidder does the same the winning bid could be close to your maximum. Very rare notes or scarce serial numbers on notes can also be found where the seller is unaware of their status. There are many active banknote collectors on eBay so there may be some competition, but a last minute bid may win the day.

"Buy the book before the coin, and read it" is advice that's often given to beginners, and very sound advice it is. Collectors may not consider eBay as a source of reference material but they should. In addition to the usual well-known standard references, very often auction catalogues can be found, and with a bit of luck they may come complete with the prices realised. For a specialist collector an auction catalogue containing their speciality can be a mine of information that is not available in any other single publication. There is a subsection for publications in the coins section but a search in the general "books" category for your chosen subject may reveal additional items.

Numismatic ephemera is another topic worth searching for, as a gem or two might be found such as Decimal Currency Board booklets and leaflets from the 1960s and 1970s, old dealers' lists, old magazines, old banking letters perhaps signed by a high ranking bank official whose signature appeared on notes—there are endless possibilities.

There is always a large variety of cheques listed on eBay (or checks if the seller lives in North America, so if searching for items from your home town search for it with "cheque" and "check"). Cheque collectors will be spoilt for choice with prices from just a few pounds to around £50 for a single rare cheque. Another side-line could be old savings banks, which can be of interest to both coin and banknote collectors: the sturdy metal "home safe" types turn up regularly, occasionally unused in the original cardboard box. Finding one with a key could be useful as most that contain a few coins have no key and there could be a rare date penny in there.

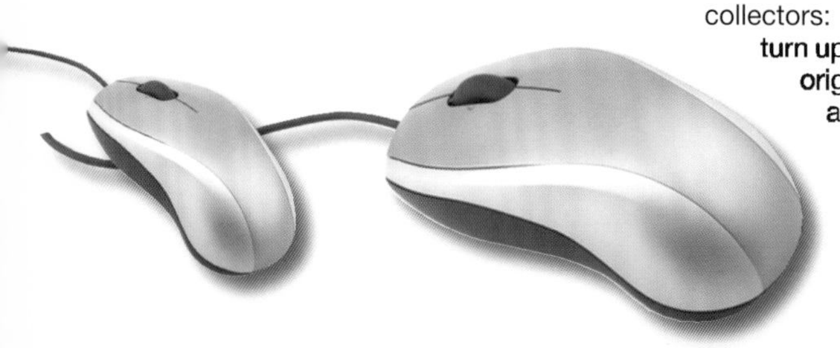

In the not too distant future it may become virtually impossible to find accurately graded coins and notes on eBay as more and more good sellers give up selling on the site. They find it frustrating when they get a low price for their accurately graded coins, achieving just Fine prices for VF coins, while bad sellers find it easy to get high prices for their overgraded coins, achieving EF prices for VF coins. Some long term eBay coin sellers who used to offer accurately graded coins that sold for fair prices are now offering overgraded coins. This seems to be a case of, "if you can't beat them, join them". We are now getting closer to the stage where the only people buying so-called "high grade" coins and banknotes through eBay are those who have no idea of how an accurately graded coin or note should look. A knowledgeable collector has little chance of bidding success if many are willing to pay EF money for VF coins or notes.

I sometimes wonder if the buyers of these overgraded coins and notes have had a shock when they eventually try to sell them to dealers or other collectors who recognise their true grade.

ASK!

ASK YOURSELF AT LEAST SOME OF THESE QUESTIONS BEFORE BIDDING ON A NUMISMATIC ITEM ON EBAY . . .

How can a seller have an un-unending supply of old high grade notes or coins?

How can a seller afford to frequently sell at below a likely dealer's buying price if the coins they offer are accurately graded?

Why does a seller keep some information private?

Why are this seller's coin photographs always dark or fuzzy or too small?

Do I really want that coin from a seller in China?

Dates
on coins

The vast majority of modern coins bear the date prominently on one side. In most cases dates are expressed in modified Arabic numerals according to the Christian calendar and present no problem in identification. There have been a few notable exceptions to this general rule, however. Morocco, for example, has used European numerals to express dates according to the Moslem calendar, so that a coin dated 1321 actually signifies 1903. Dates are almost invariably written from left to right—even in Arabic script which writes words from right to left. An exception, however, occurred in the Philippines quarto of 1822 where the date appeared as 2281, and the "2"s back to front for good measure.

	ARABIC-TURKISH	CHINESE, JAPANESE KOREAN, ANNAMESE (ORDINARY)	CHINESE, JAPANESE KOREAN, ANNAMESE (OFFICIAL)	INDIAN	SIAMESE	BURMESE
1	١	一	壹	१	๑	၁
2	٢	二	貳	२	๒	၂
3	٣	三	叁	३	๓	၃
4	٤	四	肆	४	๔	၄
5	٥	五	伍	५	๕	၅
6	٦	六	陸	६	๖	၆
7	٧	七	柒	७	๗	၇
8	٨	八	捌	८	๘	၈
9	٩	九	玖	९	๙	၉
0	٠			०	๐	၀
10	١٠	十	拾		๑๐	
100	١٠٠	百			๑๐๐	
1000	١٠٠٠	千				

Dates in Roman numerals have been used since 1234 when this practice was adopted by the Danish town of Roskilde. Such Roman numerals were used sporadically throughout the Middle Ages and in later centuries and survive fitfully to this day. This was the system used in England for the first dated coins, the gold half-sovereigns of Edward VI struck at Durham House in 1548 (MDXLVIII). This continued till 1550 (MDL) but thereafter Arabic numerals were used, beginning with the half-crown of 1551. Notable exceptions of more recent times include the Gothic coinage of Queen Victoria (1847–87).

The first coin with the date in European numerals was a plappart of St Gallen, Switzerland dated 1424, but this was an isolated case. In 1477 Maria of Burgundy issued a guldiner which bore a date on the reverse, in the form of two pairs of digits flanking the crown at the top. The numerals in this instance were true Gothic, an interesting transition between true Arabic numerals and the modified Arabic figures now used in Europe. The Tyrolese guldengroschen of 1484–6 were the first coins to be regularly dated in European numerals and thereafter this custom spread rapidly.

For the numismatist, the problem arises when coins bear a date in the numerals of a different alphabet or computed according to a different era. Opposite is a table showing the basic numerals used in different scripts. The various eras which may be found in coin dates are as listed and explained opposite.

Hijra

The era used on Moslem coins dates from the flight of Mohammed from Mecca to Medina on July 15, 622 and is often expressed as digits followed by AH (*Anno Hegirae*). Moslems employ a lunar calendar of twelve months comprising 354 11/30 days. Tipu Sultan of Mysore in 1201 AH (the fifth year of his reign) introduced a new era dating from the birth of Mohammed in AD 570 and using a luni-solar system. Tipu also adopted the Hindu cycle of sixty years (the Tamil Brihaspate Cycle), but changed this two or three years later, from Hijra to Muludi.

Afghan coins used the lunar calendar until 1920 and during 1929–31, but at other times have used the solar calendar. Thus the Democratic Republic began issuing its coins in SH 1358 (1979).

To convert an AH date to the Christian calendar you must translate the Arabic into European numerals. Taking an Arabic coin dated 1320, for example, first deduct 3% (to convert from the Moslem lunar year to our solar year). This gives 39.6 which, rounded up to the nearest whole number, is 40. Deduct 40 from 1320 (1280), then add 622. The answer is 1902.

There have been a few notable exceptions. Thus the Khanian era of Ilkhan Ghazan Mahmud began on 1st Rajab 701 AH (1301). This era used a solar calendar, but was shortlived, being confined to coins of Mahmud and his nephew Abu Said down to year 34 (1333).

The era of Tarikh Ilahi was adopted by the Mughal emperor Akbar in the thirteenth year of his reign (922 AH). This era dated from his accession on 5th Rabi al-Sani 963 AH (February 19, 1556). The calendar had solar months and days but no weeks, so each day of the month had a different name. This system was used by Akbar, Jahangir and Shah Jahan, often with a Hijra date as well.

Saphar

The era of the Caesars began on January 1, 38 BC and dated from the conquest of Spain by Augustus. Its use on coinage, however, seems to have been confined to the marabotins of Alfonso VIII of Castile and was expressed in both Latin and Arabic.

Samvat

The era of Vikramaditya began in 57 BC and was a luni-solar system used in some Indian states. Coins may be found with both Samvat and Hijra dates. Conversion to the Christian date is simple; merely subtract 57 from the Samvat to arrive at the AD date.

Saka

This originated in the southwestern district of Northern India and began in AD 78. As it used the luni-solar system it converts easily by adding 78 to the Saka date.

Nepal

Nepalese coins have used four different date systems. All coins of the Malla kings were dated in Nepal Samvat (NS) era, year 1 beginning in 881. This system was also used briefly by the state of Cooch Behar. Until 1888 all coins of the Gurkha dynasty were dated in the Saka era (SE) which began in AD 78. After 1888 most copper coins were dated in the Vikram Samvat (VS) era from 57 BC. With the exception of some gold coins struck in 1890 and 1892, silver and gold coins only changed to the VS era in 1911, but now this system is used for all coins struck in Nepal. Finally, dates in the Christian era have appeared on some commemorative coins of recent years.

Ethiopian

This era dates from August AD 7, so that EE 1885 is AD 1892. Ethiopian dates are expressed in five digits using Amharic numerals. The first two are the digits of the centuries, the third is the character for 100, while the fourth and fifth are the digits representing the decade and year. On modern coins dates are rendered in Amharic numerals using the Christian era.

Thailand

Thai coins mainly use the Buddhist era (BE) which dates from 543 BC, but some coins have used dates from the Chula-Sakarat calendar (CS) which began in AD 638, while others use a Ratanakosind Sok (RS) date from the foundation of the Chakri dynasty in AD 1781.

Hebrew

The coins of Israel use the Jewish calendar dating from the beginning of the world (Adam and Eve in the Garden of Eden) in 3760 BC. Thus the year 1993 is rendered as 5753. The five millennia are assumed in dates, so that only the last three digits are expressed. 735 therefore equates with AD 1975. Dates are written in Hebrew letters, reading from right to left. The first two characters signify 400 and 300 respectively, totalling 700. The third letter denotes the decades (*lamedh* = 30) and the fourth letter, following the separation mark (") represents the final digit (*heh* = 5). The Jewish year runs from September or October in the Christian calendar.

Dates from the creation of the world

This system was also used in Russia under Ivan IV. The dating system *Anno Mundi* (AM) was established by the Council of Constantinople in AD 680 which determined that the birth of Christ had occurred in 5508 AM. Ivan's coins expressed the date as 7055 (1447).

Dynastic dates

The system of dating coinage according to regnal years is a feature of Chinese and Japanese coins. Chinese coins normally have an inscription stating that they are coins of such and such a reign period (not the emperor's name), and during the Southern Sung dynasty this was joined by the numeral of the year of the reign. This system was continued under the republic and survives in Taiwan to this day, although the coins of the Chinese Peoples Republic are dated in western numerals using the Christian calendar.

Early Japanese coins bore a reference to the era (the title assumed by each emperor on his accession) but, like Chinese coins, could not be dated accurately. From the beginning of the Meiji era (1867), however, coins have included a regnal number. The Showa era, beginning in 1926 with the accession of Hirohito, eventually ran to sixty-three (expressed in western numerals on some denominations, in Japanese ideograms on others) to denote 1988, although the rest of the inscription was in Japanese characters.

Dynastic dates were used on Korean milled coins introduced in 1888. These bore two characters at the top *Kae Kuk* (founding of the dynasty) followed by quantitative numerals. The system dated from the founding of the Yi dynasty in 1392. Curiously enough, some Korean banknotes have borne dates from the foundation of the first dynasty in 2333 BC.

Iran adopted a similar system in 1975, celebrating the 15th anniversary of the Pahlavi regime by harking back to the glories of Darius. The new calendar dated from the foundation of the Persian Empire 2535 years earlier, but was abolished only three years later when the Shah was overthrown.

Political eras

France adopted a republican calendar in 1793 when the monarchy was abolished. Coins were then inscribed L'AN (the year) followed by Roman numerals, but later Arabic numerals were substituted. This continued to the year 14 (1806) but in that year the Emperor Napoleon restored the Christian calendar. The French system was emulated by Haiti whose coins dated from the revolution of 1803. The date appeared as AN followed by a number until AN 31 (1834) on some coins; others had both the evolutionary year and the Christian date from 1828 until 1850 (AN 47). Coins with a date in the Christian calendar appeared only in 1807–9 and then from 1850 onwards.

Mussolini introduced the Fascist calendar to Italy, dating from the seizure of power in October 1922. This system was widely employed on documents and memorials, but was first used on silver 20 lire coins of 1927 and then only in addition to the Christian date and appearing discreetly as Roman numerals. Subsequently it was extended to gold 50 lire and 100 lire coins in 1931 and the subsidiary coinage in 1936, being last used in the year XXI (1943).

Around the world

Listed here are the names of all the coins of the world, many of which have been around for hundreds of years, others are no longer in use. Some of the denominations have been introduced only recently, whilst others are familiar household words. A number of the names are shared by different countries and a few have even been used by different civilisations.

Abazi	Caucusus
Abbasi, Abbassi	Afghanistan, Georgia, Persia
Ackey	Gold Coast
Adli Altin	Ottoman Empire
Afghani	Afghanistan

Agnel	France
Agora (ot)	Israel
Ahmadi	Mysore, Yemen
Akce	Turkey
Akcheh	Turkestan
Albertusdaler	Denmark
Albus	German States, Swiss Cantons
Altin, Altun	Egypt, Turkey
Altinlik	Turkey
Altyn, Altynnik	Russia
Amani	Afghanistan
Amman Cash	Mewar Udaipur, Pudukota, India
Angel	England, Scotland, Isle of Man
Angelet	France
Angelot	France
Angster	Lucerne
Anna	Burma, India, Pakistan, Kenya, Muscat & Oman
Antoninianus	Rome
Ardite	Navarre
Argentino	Argentina
Ariary	Malagasy Republic
As	Rome
Asarfi	Nepal
Ashrafi	Afghanistan, Awadh, Bahawalpur, Egypt, Hyderabad
Asper	Algeria, Egypt, Libya, Trebizond, Tunisia, Turkey
Asses	Luxembourg
At	Laos
Atia	Portuguese India
Atribuo	Frankfurt
Att	Cambodia, Laos, Siam (Thailand)
August d'Or	Saxony
Augustale	Sicily
Aurar (plural Eyrir)	Iceland
Austral	Argentina
Avo	Macau, Timor
Bagarone	Bologna
Bagattino	Venice
Baggliangster	Lucerne

Baht	Thailand
Baiocco (plural **Baiocchi**)	Papal States
Baisa	Oman
Baiza	Kuwait
Baizah	Muscat & Oman
Balboa	Panama
Ban (plural **Bani** or **Banu**)	Roumania
Banica	Croatia
Barbarina	Mantua
Barbonaccio	Lucca
Barbone	Lucca
Barbuda	Portugal
Barilla	Philippines
Batzen	German States, Swiss Cantons
Bawbee	Scotland
Bazaruco	Portuguese India
Bazaruk	Dutch Settlements in India
Belga	Belgium
Benduqi	Morocco
Besa (plural **Bese**)	Ethiopia, Somalia
Beshlik	Soviet Central Asia

Bezant Byzantine Empire, Cyprus, Jerusalem
Bezzo Italian States
Bianco (plural **Bianchi**) Bologna, Papal States
Biche French Indian Settlements
Binio Roman Empire
Bipkwele Equatorial Guinea
Bir (r) Ethiopia
Bisti Caucasia
Bit Guyana, West Indies
Bitt Danish Virgin Islands
Black Dog Nevis
Blaffert Switzerland
Blanc France
Blodsklipping Sweden
Bluzger Swiss Cantons
Bodle Scotland
Bogach Yemen
Bolivar Venezuela
Boliviano Bolivia
Bolognino Papal States
Bonk Ceylon, Dutch East Indies
Bonnet Scotland
Boo Japan
Braspenning Flanders
Broad England
Bu Japan
Budju Algeria
Buqsha Yemen Arab Republic
Burbe(ns) Tunisia

Butut Gambia
Cache French Indian Settlements
Cagliareso Italian States
Calderilla Spain
Candareen China
Carbovanetz Ukraine
Carlin Sicily
Carlino Papal States
Carolin Austria,German States, Sweden
Cash China, Hong Kong, India, Mysore, Travancore, Turkestan, Vietnam
Cassathaler German States
Cauri Guinea
Ceitil Portugal
Cent Australia, Bahamas, Barbados, Belize, Bermuda, Botswana, British East Caribbean Territories, British Honduras, British North Borneo, British Virgin Islands, Brunei, Canada, Cayman Island, Ceylon, China, Cochin China, Cocos (Keeling) Islands, Cook Islands, Curacao, Cyprus, Danish West Indies, East Africa, Ethiopia, Fiji, French Indochina, Gilbert and Ellice Islands, Guyana, Hawaii, Hong Kong, Indonesia, Jamaica, Kenya, Kiao Chau (Kiatschau), Kiribati, Laos, Liberia, Malaya, Malaysia, Malta, Mauritius, Netherlands, Netherlands Antilles, Netherlands Indies, New Zealand, Nova Scotia, Panama, Prince Edward Island, Sarawak, Seychelles, Sierra Leone, Singapore, Solomon Islands, South Africa, Sri Lanka, Straits Settlements, Suriname, Swaziland, Tanzania, Trinidad and Tobago, Tuvalu, Uganda, United States of America, Virgin Islands, Zanzibar, Zimbabwe
Centas (plural **Centa, Centu**) Lithuania

Centavo Angola, Argentina, Bolivia, Brazil, Cape Verde Islands, Chile, Colombia, Costa Rica, Cuba, Dominican Republic, Ecuador, El Salvador, Guatemala, Guinea-Bissau, Honduras, Mexico, Mozambique, Nicaragua, Paraguay, Peru, Philippines, Portugal, Portuguese Guinea, Portuguese India, Puerto Rico, St Thomas and Prince Islands, Timor, Venezuela
Centecimo Bolivia
Cententionalis Roman Empire
Centesimo Bolivia, Chile, Dominican Republic, Ethiopia, Italian East Africa, Italy, Panama, Paraguay, San Marino, Somalia, Uruguay, Vatican
Centime Algeria, Antwerp, Belgian Congo, Belgium, Cambodia, Cameroon, Cochin China, Comoro Islands, Djibouti, France, French Equatorial Africa, French Guiana, French Indochina, French Oceania, French Polynesia, French Somali Coast, French West Africa, Guadeloupe, Guinea, Haiti, Laos, Monaco, Morocco, New Caledonia, Reunion,

Senegal, Switzerland, Togo, Tunisia, Vietnam, Westphalia, Yugoslavia, Zaire

Centimo Costa Rica, Mozambique, Paraguay, Peru, Philippines, Puerto Rico, St Thomas and Prince Islands, Spain, Venezuela

Centu Lithuania

Chaise Antwerp, Bavaria, France

Chervonetz (plural **Chervontzy**) Russia

Chetrum Bhutan

Cheun South Korea

Chiao China, Formosa, Manchukuo

Chi'en China

Chio China

Cho-gin Japan

Chomseh Yemen

Chon Korea

Christian d'Or Denmark

Chuckram Travancore

Colon Costa Rica, El Salvador

Condor Chile, Colombia, Ecuador

Cordoba Nicaragua

Cornado Spain

Cornuto Savoy

Coroa de Prata Portugal

Coroin Eire

Corona Austrian provinces of Italy, Naples

Coronato Castile, Naples

Couronne d'Or France

Crocione Italian States

Crossazzo Genoa

Crown Ascension, Australia, Bermuda, England, Ghana, Gibraltar, Ireland, Isle of Man, Jamaica, Jersey, Malawi, New Zealand, Nigeria, Rhodesia, Rhodesia and Nyasaland, St Helena, Scotland, Southern Rhodesia, Tristan da Cunha, Turks and Caicos Islands

Cruzadinho Brazil, Portugal

Cruzado Brazil, Portugal

Cruzeiro Brazil

Cuartillo, Cuartino Mexico

Cuarto Bolivia, Spain

Daalder Netherlands

DakBler Danish West Indies, Denmark, Sweden

Dam Afghanistan, India, Nepal

Daric Persia

Dauphin France

Decime France

Decimo Argentina, Chile, Colombia, Ecuador, Galapagos

Decussis Roman Republic

Dekadrachm Syracuse, Hellenistic kingdoms

Dekanummion Byzantine Empire

Dekobolon Greece

Demareteion Syracuse

Demer France

Demy Scotland

Denar Hungary

Denarius Rome

Denaro Italian States

Denga Russia

Dengi Roumania

Denier France and colonies, Haiti, Swiss Cantons

Denning Denmark

Deut Rhineland, Westphalia

Deutschemark Germany

Dhofari Riyal Yemen

Diamante Ferrara

Diamantino Ferrara

Dicken Swiss Cantons

Didrachm Greece

Dime Canada, Hawaii, USA

Dinar
Afghanistan, Algeria, Bahrain, Hejaz, Iraq, Kuwait, Morocco, Persia, Saudi Arabia, Serbia, Tunisia, Turkey, Yugoslavia

Diner Andorra

Dinero Peru, Spain

Diobol Greece

Dirham Jordan, Libya, Morocco, United Arab Emirates

Dirhem Dubai, Iraq, Morocco, Qatar

Dio, Diu Portuguese India

Disme USA

Dobla Genoa, Naples and Sicily

Doblado Spanish colonies

Doblenca, Doblenga Aragon, Barcelona

Dobler Mallorca

Doblon Chile, Spain, Urugay

Dobra St Thomas and Prince

Dodekadrachm Carthage

Doit Netherlands, Netherlands Indies, Indonesia

Dokdo Junagadh, Kutch, Nawanagar (Indian States)

Dollar Anguilla, Antigua and Barbuda, Australia, Bahamas, Belize, Bermuda, Canada, Cayman Islands, China, Cocos (Keeling) Islands, Cook Islands, East Caribbean Territories, Fiji, Great Britain, Grenada, Guyana, Hawaii, Hong Kong, Indonesia, Jamaica, Japan, Kiribati, Liberia, Malaysia, Mauritius, Montserrat, Newfoundland, New Zealand, Panama, St Kitts-Nevis, St Lucia, St Vincent, Scotland, Sierra Leone, Singapore, Solomin Islands, Straits Settlements, Trinidad and Tobago, Tuvalu, USA, Virgin Islands, Western Samoa, Zimbabwe

Dolya Russia

Dong Annam, Vietnam

Doppia Italian States

Doppietta Sardinia

Double Guernsey

Dou Dou French Indochina

Douzain France

Drachma Crete, Greece

Dram Armenia

Dreibatzner Austria, German States

Dreigroscher Lithuania, Prussia

Dreiling German States

Dub Hyderabad, India

Dubbeltje Holland

Ducat Austria, Austrian States, Courland, Czechoslovakia, Denmark, German States, Hungary, Italian States, Liechtenstein, Liege, Netherlands,Poland, Roumania, Sweden, Swiss Cantons, Russia, Yugoslavia

Ducaton Belgium, Netherlands

Ducatone Italian States

Dudu India

Duetto Italian States

Duit Ceylon, German States, Netherlands, Netherlands Indies

Dukat Czechoslovakia, German States, Hungary, Poland, Sweden, Yugoslavia

Duplone Swiss Cantons

Duro Spain

Dyak Nepal

Ecu Belgium, Bosnia, France, Gibraltar

Ekuele Equatorial Guinea

Elisabeth d'Or Russia

Emalangeni (plural of **Lilangeni**) Swaziland

Escalin Belgium, Guadeloupe, Haiti, Liege, Martinique

Escudillo Spain

Escudo Angola, Argentina, Azores, Bolivia, Cape Verde Islands, Central American Republic, Chile, Colombia, Costa Rica, Ecuador, Guadeloupe, Guatemala, Guinea-Bissau, Madeira, Mexico, Mozambique, Peru, Portugal, Portuguese Guinea/India, St Thomas and Prince Islands, Spain, Timor

Espadin Portugal

Esphera Goa

Euro Austria, Belgium, Finland, France, Germany, Greece, Ireland, Italy, Luxembourg, Monaco, The Netherlands, Portugal, San Marino, Slovenia, Spain, The Vatican

Excelente Spain

Eyrir (singular **Aurar**) Iceland

Fals Iraq

Faluce Ceylon

Falus Afghanistan, China, India, Iran, Morocco, Turkestan

Fanam Ceylon, Dutch East Indies, Travancore

Fano Tranquebar (Danish Indian Settlements)

Fanon French Indian Settlements

Farthing Antigua, Ceylon, Great Britain, Isle of Man, Jamaica, Malta, Scotland, South Africa

Fels Algeria

Fen People's Republic of China, Manchukuo

Fenig (ow) Poland

Feoirling Eire

Ferding Courland, Livonia

Filiberto Savoy

Filippo Italian States

Filler Hungary

Fils Bahrain, Iraq, Jordan, Kuwait, South Arabia, United Arab Emirates, Yemen

Fiorino Italian States

Flitter South German States

Floirin Eire

Florin Australia, Austria, East Africa, Fiji, Great Britain, Hungary, Ireland, Malawi, New Zealand, Rhodesia and Nyasaland, South Africa, Swiss Cantons

Follis Rome, Byzantine Empire

Forint Hungary

Franc Algeria, Belgian Congo, Belgium, Burundi, Cambodia, Cameroon,

Central African Republic, Chad, Comoro Islands, Congo, Danish West Indies, Djibouti, Dominican Republic, Ecuador, France, French colonies, Gabon, Guadeloupe, Guinea, Ivory Coast, Katanga, Luxembourg, Madagascar, Malagasy Republic, Mali, Martinique, Mauretania, Monaco, Morocco, New Caledonia, New Hebrides, Reunion, Ruanda-Urundi, Rwanda, St Pierre and Miquelon, Senegal, Switzerland, Togo, Tunisia, West African States

Francescone Italian States
Franchi Switzerland
Franco Dominican Republic, Ecuador, Italian States, Swiss Cantons
Frang Luxembourg
Frank(en) Belgium, Liechtenstein, Saar, Switzerland, Westphalia
Franka Ara Albania
Frederik d'Or Denmark
Friedrich d'Or German States
Fyrk Sweden
Gabellone Papal States

Gayah Sumatra
Gazetta Venice
Genovino Genoa, Florence, Venice
Genevoise Geneva
George Noble England
Georgstaler German States
Gersh Ethiopia
Gigliato Hungary, Naples, Rhodes
Gigot Brabant, Flanders
Gin Japan
Giorgino Ferrara, Modena
Giovannino Genoa
Girsh Hejaz, Nejd, Saudi Arabia, Sudan
Giulio Italian States
Golde Sierra Leone
Goldgulden German States, Swiss Cantons
Goldpfennig German States
Goryoban Japan
Gourde Haiti
Gourmier Morocco
Gram Afghanistan
Gramme Burma
Gramo Bolivia, Tierra del Fuego
Grana Italian States
Grano Italian States, Mexico, Sovereign Order of Malta
Grenadino Colombia, New Granada
Greschl Roumania, Transylvania
Grivenka Russia
Grivennik Russia
Grivna (plural **Grivny**) Ukraine
Groat Great Britain
Groeschl Bohemia
Groot Netherlands
Gros France
Groschel German States
Groschen Austria, German States, Poland, Swiss Cantons
Groshen Austria, German States
Grossetto Dalmatia, Illyria, Venice
Grosso Italian States
Grossone Italian States
Grosspfennig Pomerania, Rhineland
Grossus Courland, Poland
Grosz (plural **Grosze** or **Groszy**) Poland
Grote German States
Grush Albania
Guarani Paraguay
Guerche Egypt, Saudi Arabia
Guinea Great Britain, Saudi Arabia
Gulden Austria, Curacao, German States, Netherlands, Netherlands Indies, Swiss Cantons
Guldiner Austria, South German States, Swiss Cantons
Gutegroschen North and Central German States
Guterpfennig German States
Habibi Afghanistan
Halala Saudi Arabia, Yemen
Halbag Frankfurt
Haler (plural **Halere, Haleru**) Czechoslovakia, Czech Republic
Halierov Slovakia
Haller Swiss Cantons

Hao China, Vietnam
Hapalua Hawaii
Hardhead Scotland
Hardi France, Turin
Hau Tonga
Hayrir Altin Iraq, Turkey
Hekte Lesbos, Mytilene
Heller Austria, German States, German East Africa
Helm England
Henri d'Or France
Hryvnia Ukraine
Hsien China
Hvid Denmark
Hwan Korea
Hyperpyron Byzantine Empire
Ichibu-gin Japan
Ikilik Russia
Imadi Yemen
Imami Mysore

Imperial	Russia
Isabella	Spain
Ischal	Russia
Ishu Gin	Japan
Jacondale	France
Jawa	Nepal
Jeon	Korea
Jerome d'Or	Westphalia
Jiao	People's Republic of China
Jedid	Egypt
Jefimok (plural **Jefimki**)	Russia
Joachimico	Italy
Joachimik	Poland
Joachimstaler	Bohemia
Joao	Portugal
Johanna	Portugal
Johannes	Portugal
Jokoh	Kelantan, Malaysia
Judenpfennig	Frankfurt
Justo	Portugal
Kapang	Sarawak
Kapeikas	Latvia, Belarus
Karolin	German States
Kas	Danish Indian Settlements
Kasu	Mysore
Kazbeg	Caucasia, Safavid Persia
Khayriya	Egypt
Khoum	Mauretania
Kin	Japan
Kina	Papua New Guinea
Kip	Laos
Koban	Japan
Kobo	Nigeria
Kopec	Poland
Kopejek	Outer Mongolia (Tannu Tuva)
Kopek	Russia
Kori	KutchKorona Bohemia and Moravia, Hungary, Slovakia
Kortling	German States
Korun(a) (plural **Koruny** or **Koruncic**)	Czechoslo-vakia
Koula	Tonga
Krajczar	Hungary
Kran	Iran, Persia
Kreu(t)zer	Austria, Austrian States, Czechoslovakia, German States, Hungary, Liechtenstein, Poland, Roumania, Swiss Cantons
Krona (plural **Kronor** or **Kronur**)	Iceland, Sweden
Krona (plural **Kroner** or **Kronen**)	Austria, Denmark, German States, Greenland, Liechtenstein, Norway
Kroon(i)	Estonia
Krugerrand	South Africa
Kuna (plural **Kune**)	Croatia
Kupang	Malaysia, Thailand
Kurus	Turkey
Kuta	Congo-Kinshasa, Zaire
Kwacha	Malawi, Zambia
Kwanza	Angola
Kwartnik	Poland
Kyat	Burma, Myanmar
Kyrmis	Russia
Lang	Annam
Laree, Lari, Lariat or Larin	Maldive Islands
Lati, Lats	Latvia
Laurel	England
Lei	Roumania
Lek (plural **Leke** or **Leku**)	Albania
Lempira	Honduras
Leone	Sierra Leone
Leopard	England
Lepton (plural **Lepta**)	Crete, Greece, Ionian Islands
Leu (plural **Lei**)	Roumania
Lev(a)	Bulgaria
Li	Manchukuo
Liang	China, Laos
Liard	Belgium, France, Luxembourg
Libra	Peru
Licente	Lesotho
Likuta	Zaire

Lilangeni	(plural Emalangeni) Swaziland
Lion	Scotland
Lion d'Or	Austrian Netherlands
Lira (plural **Lire**)	Eritrea, Italian East Africa, Italy, San Marino, Syria, Turkey, Vatican
Lira (plural **Lirot**)	Israel
Lisente	Lesotho
Litas (plural **Litai** or **Litu**)	Lithuania
Litra	Sicily, Syracuse
Livre	France, Guadeloupe, Lebanon, Martinique, Mauritius, Reunion
Louis d'Argent	France
Louis d'Or	France
Luhlanga	Swaziland
Lumma	Armenia
Lweis	Angola
Mace	China
Macuta	Angola
Magdalon d'Or	Aix-en-Provence, Tarascon
Mahalek	Ethiopia
Mahallak	Harar
Mahbub	Egypt, Ottoman Empire
Mahmudi	Saudi Arabia
Makuta	Zaire
Maloti	Lesotho
Manat	Azerbaijan

Manghir Crimea
Marabotin Moorish kingdoms, Southern Spain
Maravedi Spain
Marchetto Italian States
Marck German States
Marengo France
Mariengroschen German States
Mark Germany, German States, German New Guinea, Norway, Poland, Sweden
Marka Estonia
Markka(a) Finland
Mas Malaysia
Masriya Egypt
Masson Lorraine and Bar
Mat Burma
Matapan Venice
Mathbu Morocco
Maticaes Mozambique
Matona Ethiopia
Mattier German States
Maximilian d'Or German States
Mazuna Morocco
Medin Egypt
Mehmudiye Altin Ottoman Empire
Meinhard Austria, German States
Melgarejo Bosnia

Merk Scotland
Metica Mozambique
Meung Japan
Mil Cyprus, Hong Kong, Israel, Malta, Palestine
Milan d'Or Serbia
Miliarense Byzantine Empire
Milesima Spain
Millieme Egypt, Libya
Millime Tunisia
Milreis Brazil
Miscals China
Mohar Nepal
Mohur Afghanistan, Bikanir, Cooch Behar, Gwalior, Hyderabad, India (Mughal Empire), Maldive Islands, etherlands Indies, Rajkot
Moidore (**Moeda de ouro**) Portugal
Momme Japan
Mon Japan, Ryukyu Islands
Mongo Mongolia
Mouton d'Or France
MuBurma
Mun Korea
Mung Mongolia
Munzgulden Swiss Cantons
Muzuna Algeria
Naira Nigeria
Nami-sen Japan
Napoleon France
Naya Paisa Bhutan, India
Negotiepenning Netherlands
Neugroschen German States
New Pence Gibraltar, Great Britain, Guernsey, Isle of Man, Jersey
Ngultrum Bhutan
Ngwee Zambia
Nisar Afghanistan, India
Nisfiya Egypt
Noble Austria,England, Scotland, Isle of Man
Nomisma Byzantine Empire
Nonsunt Scotland
Nummion (plural **Nummia**) Byzantine Empire
Oban Japan
Obol Greece, Ionian Islands
Ochavo Spain
Octavo Mexico, Philippines
Omani Oman
Onca Mozambique
Oncia Italian States
Onlik Crimea
Onluk Turkey
Onza Bolivia, Chile, Costa Rica, Mexico Or Sweden
Ore Denmark, Faroe Islands, Greenland, Norway, Sweden
Ort(e) Poland, Prussia
Ortug (plural **Ortugar**) Sweden
Ouguiya Mauretania
Pa'anga Tonga
Pagoda India (Madras)
Pahlavi Iran
Pai India, Siam (Thailand)
Paisa Afghanistan, Bhutan, India, Nepal, Pakistan
Panchia India
Pano Portuguese Africa
Paoli Italian States
Papetto Papal States
Para (plural **Paras** or **Parades**) Crimea, Egypt, Greece, Iraq, Libya, Nejd, Roumania, Saudi Arabia, Serbia, Sudan, Syria, Turkey, Walachia, Yugoslavia
Pardao Portuguese India
Parisis d'Or France
Pataca Macau
Pataco Portugal
Patagon Belgium
Patrick Ireland
Pavillon d'Or France
Pe Burma, Cambodia
Peca Portugal
Pengo Hungary

Penni(a) Finland
Penning(ar) Denmark, Sweden
Penny (plural **Pence**) Australia, Bahamas, Barbados, Bermuda, Biafra, British Guiana, British East Africa British West Africa, Canada, Ceylon, Falkland Islands, Fiji, Gambia, Ghana, Gibraltar, Gold Coast, Great Britain, Guernsey, Ireland, Isle of Man, Jamaica, Jersey, Malawi, Montserrat, New Guinea, New Zealand, Nigeria, Rhodesia and Nyasaland, St Helena, St Kitts-Nevis, South Africa, Southern Rhodesia, Trinidad & Tobago, Tristan da Cunha, Zambia
Pentekontalitron Sicily
Pentekontedrachm Hellenistic kingdoms
Pentenummion Byzantine Empire
Perper(a) Montenegro
Pesa German East Africa
Peseta Andorra, Equatorial Guinea, Peru, Spain
Pesewa Ghana
Peso Argentina, Bolivia, Cambodia, Chile, Colombia, Costa Rica, Cuba, Dominican Republic, El Salvador, Guatemala, Guinea-Bissau, Honduras, Mexico, Netherlands Antilles, Nicaragua, Paraguay, Peru, Philippines, Puerto Rico, Uruguay, Venezuela
Pessa Yemen (Lahej), Zanzibar
Petermannchen Trier
Pfennig(e) Austria, Bohemia, Germany, German States, Poland, Swiss Cantons

Pfenning Austrian States, German States
Philippeioi Macedon
Phoenix Greece
Piastra Italian States
Piastre Annam, Cambodia, Cochin China, Cyprus, Denmark, Egypt, French Indochina, Hejaz, Iraq, Khmer, Lebanon, Libya, Nejd, Saudi Arabia, Syria, Sudan, Tonkin, Tunisia, Turkey, Vietnam, Yemen
Piataltynny Russia
Picciolo Sovereign Order of Malta
Piccolo Italian States
Pice Bhutan, Ceylon, East Africa, India, Kenya, Malaysia
Pinto Portugal
Piso Philippines
Pistole France, German States, Ireland, Scotland, Swiss Cantons
Pitis Brunei, Java, Sumatra, Siam
Plack Scotland
Plappart Switzerland
Poisha Bangladesh
Poltina Russia
Poltura Hungary, Roumania
Poludenga Russia
Polupoltinnik Russia
Polushka Russia
Pond Transvaal
Pound Ascension, Australia, Biafra, Cyprus, Egypt, Falkland Islands, Ghana, Gibraltar, Great Britain, Guernsey, Iran, Isle of Man, Israel, Jersey, Malta, Nigeria, Rhodesia, St Helena, South Arabia, South Africa, Sudan, Syria
Protea South Africa
Pruta(ot) Israel
Puffin Lundy
Pul Afghanistan, China, Turkestan
Pula Botswana
Puli Caucasia
Pultorak Poland
Pya(t) Burma
Pysa Zanzibar
Qindar(ka) Albania
Qiran Afghanistan
Qirsh Egypt
Quadrans Roman Republic
Quan Annam
Quart Gibraltar, Swiss Cantons
Quart d'Ecu France
Quartenses Silesia
Quartillo Spain
Quartinho Portugal
Quarto Ecuador, Mexico, Philippines, Spain
Quartuncia Rome
Quaternio Rome
Quattrino Italian States
Qepiq Azerbaijan
Quetzal Guatemala
Quinarius Rome
Quint USA
Quinto di Scudo Papal States
Rand South Africa
Rappen Switzerland
Rasi Netherlands Indies
Real(es) Argentina, Bolivia, Central American Republic, Chile, Colombia, Costa Rica, Dominican Republic, Ecuador, El Salvador, Venezuela
Real Batu Indonesia
Reichsmark Germany
Reichspfennig Germany
Reichsthaler Germany

Reis Angola, Azores, Brazil, Madeira, Mozambique, Portugal, Portuguese India
Reisedaler Denmark
Rentenmark Germany
Rentenpfennig Germany
Reul Eire
Rial Iran, Morocco, Muscat and Oman, Oman, Persia, Yemen Arab Republic
Rider Scotland
Riel Kampuchea
Rigsbankdaler Denmark
Rigsbankskilling Denmark
Rigsdaler Denmark, Norway
Rigsmontskilling Denmark
Rijder Friesland, Guelderland, United Provinces
Rijksdaalder Netherlands
Riksdaler Sweden
Riksdaler Riksmynt Sweden
Riksdaler Specie Sweden
Rin Japan
Ringgit Malaysia
Rio Japan
Rixdollar Ceylon
Riyal Iran, Iraq, Saudi Arabia, United Arab Emirates, Yemen Arab Republic
Rose Noble England
Rouble Russia, USSR
Royal d'Or France
Royalin(er) Tranquebar, Danish Indian Settlements
Rub Ethiopia
Rubel German occupation of Russia
Rubiya Egypt
Ruble Poland, Transnistria
Rublis Latvia
Rufiyaa Maldive Islands
Rumi Altin Ottoman Empire
Rupee Afghanistan, Andaman Islands, Bhutan, Burma, China, Cocos Keeling Islands, India, Iran, Kenya, Mauritius, Nepal, Pakistan, Saudi Arabia, Seychelles, Sri Lanka, Tanzania, Tibet, United Arab Emirates, Yemen
Rupia Portuguese India, Somalia
Rupiah Indonesia
Rupie German East Africa
Ruspone Italian States
Ryal England, Hejaz, Iran, Muscat and Oman, Nejd, Oman, Persia, Quaiti State, Saudi Arabia, Yemen, Zanzibar
Ryo Japan
Rytterpenning Denmark, Hanseatic League
Saidi Oman
Saiga Merovingian Empire
Salung Siam (Thailand)
Salut d'Or France
Sampietrino Papal States
Sanar Afghanistan
Sanese Siena
Santa Croce Italian States
Santim(at) Morocco
Santims (plural **Santimi** or **Santimu**) Latvia
Sapeque Annam, Cochin China, French Indochina
Sar Sinkiang
Sarrazzino Crusader kingdoms
Satang Siam (Thailand)
Sceat Anglo-Saxon England
Scellino Somalia
Schilling Austria, German States, Poland, Swiss Cantons
Schoter Breslau, Silesia
Schwaren German States
Scilling Eire
Scudo Bolivia, Italian States, Mexico, Malta, Papal States, Peru, San Marino
Sechsling German States
Semis Rome
Semuncia Rome
Sen Brunei, Cambodia, Indonesia, Irian Barat, Japan, Kampuchea, Malaysia, Riau Lingga, West New Guinea
Sene Samoa
Sengi Zaire
Seniti Tonga
Sent Estonia
Sente Lesotho
Senti Estonia, Somalia, Tanzania
Sentimo Philippines
Serebrnik Bulgaria

Sertum Bhutan
Sesena Spain
Sesino Italian States
Sestertius Rome
Sestino Italian States
Shahi Afghanistan, Iran, Turkestan
Sheqal(im) Israel
Shilingi Tanzania
Shilling Australia, Biafra, British West Africa, Canada, Cyprus, East Africa, Fiji, Gambia, Ghana, Great Britain, Grenada, Guernsey, Ireland, Isle of Man, Jamaica, Jersey, Kenya, Malawi, Malta, New Guinea, New

Zealand, Nigeria, Scotland, Somalia, South Africa, Trinidad and Tobago, Uganda, Zambia
Sho Nepal, Tibet
Shokang Tibet
Shu Japan
Siglos Achaemenid Empire
Sik Siam (Thailand)
Silbergroschen German States, Luxembourg
Silbergulden South Germany
Skar Tibet
Skilling Danish West Indies, Denmark, Norway, Sweden
Skillingrigsmont Denmark
Skot Prussia, Silesia
Sol(es) Argentina, Belgium, Bolivia, France, Haiti, Luxembourg, Mauritius, Peru, Reunion, Switzerland, Windward Islands
Soldo (plural Soldi) Italian States, Swiss Cantons, Papal States, Yugoslavia
Solidus Argentina, Bolivia, Peru, Rome
Solot Siam
Som Kyrgyzstan
Somalo Somalia
Sosling Denmark
Sou Canada, French colonies, Guadeloupe, Mauritius, Reunion, Spain
Souverain d'Or Austrian Netherlands
Sovereign Australia, Canada, England, Falkland Islands, India, Isle of Man, Saudi Arabia, South Africa, United Kingdom
Sovrano Italian States
Speciedaler Denmark, Norway
Species Ducat Denmark
Srang Tibet
Stater Greece
Stella USA
Stiver British Guiana, Ceylon, Demerara and Essequibo, Dutch East Indies, Netherlands
Stotinka Bulgaria
Stuber German States
Stuiver Curacao, Dutch East Indies, Netherlands, Netherlands Antilles
Styca Northumbria
Styver Sweden
Su South Vietnam
Sucre Ecuador, Galapagos
Sueldo Bolivia, Spain
Sukus Indonesia
Sultani Algeria, Libya, Tunisia
Surre Altin Ottoman Empire
Syli Guinea
Tackoe Gold Coast
Tael China, Laos
Taka Bangladesh
Tala Samoa, Tokelau
Talar(a) Poland
Talaro Ethiopia
Taler German States, Poland, Swiss Cantons
Talirion Greece
Tallero Ethiopia, Italian States, Ragusa
Tambac-tron Annam
Tambala Malawi
Tamlung Siam
Tanga Portuguese India

Tangka Tibet
Tanka Nepal
Tankah Burma
Tarin Naples, Sicily
Taro (plural **Tari**) Italian States, Malta
Tek Altin Ottoman Empire
Tenga China, Bokhara, Turkestan
Ternar Poland
Tester England
Testern British East Indies
Testone Italian States
Testoon England
Tetartemorion Greece
Tetarteron Byzantine Empire
Tetradrachm Greece
Tetrobol Greece
Thaler Austria, Austrian States, Courland, Czechoslovakia, German States, Hungary, Liechtenstein, Poland, Roumania, Switzerland
Thebe Botswana
Theler Frankfurt
Thistle Crown England
Thistle Merk Scotland
Thistle Noble Scotland
Thrymsa Anglo-Saxon England
Tical Cambodia, Thailand
Tien Annam, Vietnam
Tilla Afghanistan, Sinkiang, Turkestan
Timasha Afghanistan
Tostao Portugal
Toea Papua New Guinea
Tola India, Nepal
Tolar Slovenia
Toman Iran, Persia, Azerbaijan
Tornese Italian States
Tournois France
Trade Dollar Great Britain, Japan, USA
Trah Malaysia
Tremissis Rome, Byzantine Empire, Franks, Lombards, Visigoths

Tressis	Rome
Triens	Rome
Trihemiobol	Greece
Triobol	Greece
Tritartemorion	Greece
Tughrik	Mongolia
Turner	Scotland
Tympf	Poland
Tyyn	Kyrgyzstan
Unghero	Italian States
Unicorn	Scotland
Unit	Scotland, French West Africa
Unite	England
Van	Vietnam
Vatu	Vanuatu
Veld Pond	South African Republic
Venezolano	Venezuela
Vereinstaler	Austria-Hungary, German States
Victoriate	Rome
Vierer	Swiss Cantons
Vintem	Portugal
Wan	Korea
Wark	Ethiopia
Warn	Korean
Wen	China
Whan	Korea
Won	South Korea
Xerafim	Portuguese India
Xu	Vietnam
Yang	Korea
Yarim	Turkey
Yen	Japan
Yirmilik	Ottoman Empire
Yuan	China
Yuzluk	Ottoman Empire
Zaire	Zaire
Zalat	Yemen Arab Republic
Zecchino	Italian States, Malta
Zelagh	Morocco
Zeri Mahbub	Egypt, Libya, Turkey
Zloty (plural **Zlote** or **Zlotych**)	Poland
Zolota	Turkey
Zolotnik	Russia
Zolotoj	Russia
Zweidritteltaler	German States
Zyfert	East Friesland

glossary of Coin terms

In this section we list all the terms commonly encountered in numismatics or in the production of coins.

Abbey Coins Medieval coins struck in the abbeys, convents and other great religious houses which were granted coinage rights. These coins were often used also by pilgrims journeying from one monastery to another.

Abschlag (German for "discount") A *restrike* from an original die.

Accolated Synonym for *conjoined* or *jugate* and signifying two or more profiles overlapping.

Acmonital Acronym from *Aciaio Monetario Italiano*, a stainless steel alloy used for Italian coins since 1939.

Adjustment Reduction of metal in a *flan* or *blank* to the specified weight prior to striking, accomplished by filing down the face. Such file marks often survived the coining process and are occasionally met with in coins, especially of the 18th century.

Ae Abbreviation for the Latin *Aes* (bronze), used for coins made of brass, bronze or other copper alloys.

Aes Grave (Latin for heavy bronze) Heavy circular coins first minted at Rome in 269 BC.

Aes Rude (Latin for rough bronze) Irregular lumps of bronze which gradually developed into ingots of uniform shape and were the precursors of coins in Rome.

Aes Signatum (Latin for signed bronze) Bronze ingots of regular size and weight, bearing marks of authority to guarantee their weight (289–269 BC).

Agonistic (Greek) Term for coins issued to commemorate, or pertaining to, sporting events.

Alliance Coinage struck by two or more states acting together and having common features of design or inscription.

Alloy Coinage metal composed of two or more metallic elements.

Altered Deliberately changed, usually unofficially, with the aim of increasing the numismatic value of a coin, medal or note. This applies particularly to dates, where a common date may be altered to a rare date by filing or re-engraving one of the digits.

Aluminium (American *Aluminum*) Silvery lightweight metal, developed commercially in the late 19th century for commemorative medals, but used for tokens and emergency money during the First World War and since 1940 widely used in subsidiary coinage.

Aluminium-bronze Alloy of aluminium and copper. Hard-wearing and gold-coloured, it is now widely used in tokens and subsidiary coinage.

Amulet Coin or medal believed to have talismanic qualities, such as warding off disease and bad luck. Many Chinese and Korean pieces come into this category. See also *Touchpiece*.

Androcephalous Heraldic term for creatures with a human head.

Anepigraphic Coins or medals without a legend.

Annealing Process of heating and cooling applied to metal to relieve stresses and prepare it for striking into coins.

Annulet Small circle often used as an ornament or spacing device in coin inscriptions.

Antimony Brittle white metal, chemical symbol *Sb*, virtually impractical as a coinage metal but used for the Chinese 10 cents of Kweichow, 1931. Alloyed with tin, copper or lead, it produces the white metal popular as a medallic medium.

Antoniniani Silver coins minted in Imperial Rome. The name derives from the Emperor Caracalla (Marcus Aurelius Antoninus) in whose reign they were first struck. The silver content was progressively reduced and by the last issue (AD 295) they were reduced to *billon*.

Ar Abbreviation for Latin *Argentum* (silver), used for coins struck in this metal.

Assay Mark Mark applied to a medal struck in precious metal by an assayer or assay office as a guarantee of the fineness of the metal.

Assignat Type of paper money used in France 1789–96, representing the land assigned to the holders.

Attribution Identification of a coin by characteristics such as issuing authority, date or reign, mint, denomination, metal, and by a standard reference.

Au Abbreviation for *aurum* (Latin for gold), denoting coins of this metal.

AU Abbreviation for "About Uncirculated", often found in catalogues and dealers' lists to describe the condition of a numismatic piece.

Autodollar Name given to the silver yuan issued by Kweichow, 1928, and having a contemporary motor car as the obverse motif.

Auxiliary Payment Certificate Form of paper money intended for use by American military personnel stationed in overseas countries. See also *Baf* and *Scrip*.

Babel Note Nickname given to the paper money of the Russian Socialist Federated Soviet Republic (1919) because it bore the slogan "workers of the world unite" in seven languages, a reference to the biblical tower of Babel.

Baf Acronym from British Armed Forces, the popular name for the vouchers which could only be exchanged for goods in service canteens from 1945 onwards.

Bag Mark Minor scratch or abrasion on an otherwise uncirculated coin, caused by coins in mint bags knocking together.

Banknote Form of paper money issued by banks and usually promising to pay the bearer on demand in coin of the realm.

Barbarous Imitation of Greek or Roman coins by the Celtic and Germanic tribes who lived beyond the frontiers of the civilised world.

Base Non-precious metals or alloys.

Bath Metal Inferior bronze alloy, named after the English city where it was used for casting cannon. Used by William Wood of Bristol for Irish and American tokens and by Amos Topping for Manx coins of 1733/4.

Beading Ornamental border found on the raised rim of a coin.

Behalfszahlungsmittel German term for auxiliary payment certificates used in occupied Europe from 1939 to 1945.

Bell Metal Alloy of copper and tin normally used for casting bells, but employed for the subsidiary coinage of the French Revolutionary period.

Billon Silver alloy containing less than 50 per cent fine silver, usually mixed with copper. In Spain this alloy was known as *vellon*.

Bi-metallic Coins struck in two separate metals or alloys. Patterns for such coins exist from the 19th century but actual coins with a centre of one metal surrounded by a ring of another did not appear till 1982 (Italy, San Marino and Vatican). Canada introduced coins with a tiny plaque inset in a second metal (1990). See also *Clad, Plugged* and *Sandwich*.

Bi-metallism Monetary system in which two metals are in simultaneous use and equally available as legal tender, implying a definite ratio between the two. A double standard of gold and silver, with a ratio of 16:1, existed till the mid-19th century.

Bingle American term for a trade token, more specifically the US government issue of tokens for the Matacuska, Alaska colonization project, 1935.

Birthday Coins Coins celebrating the birthday of a ruler originated in Roman Imperial times, notably the reigns of Maximianus (286–305) and Constantinus I (307–37). Birthday talers were issued by many German states, and among recent examples may be cited coins marking the 70th, 80th and 90th birthdays of Gustaf Adolf VI of Sweden, 80th and 90th birthday coins from the British Commonwealth for the Queen Mother, and coins honouring Queen Elizabeth, the Duke of Edinburgh and the Prince of Wales.

Bit Term denoting fragments of large silver coins, cut up and circulating as fractional values. Spanish dollars were frequently broken up for circulation in the American colonies and the West indies. Long bits and short bits circulated at 15 and 10 cents respectively, but the term came to be equated with the Spanish real or eighth peso, hence the American colloquialism "two-bit" signifying a quarter dollar.

Black Money English term for the debased silver deniers minted in France which circulated freely in England until they were banned by government decree in 1351.

Blank Piece of metal, cut or punched out of a roller bar or strip, and prepared for striking to produce coins. Alternate terms are *flan* and *planchet*.

Blundered Inscription Legend in which the lettering is jumbled or meaningless, indicating the illiteracy of the tribes who copied Greek and Roman coins.

Canada's "Bi-metallic" Lunar Cameo Coin for the Year of the Rat

Bonnet Piece Scottish gold coin, minted in 1539–40. The name is derived from the obverse portraying King James V in a large, flat bonnet.

Bon Pour French for "good for", inscribed on Chamber of Commerce brass tokens issued in 1920–7 during a shortage of legal tender coinage.

Bouquet Sou Canadian copper token halfpenny of 1837 deriving its name from the nosegay of heraldic flowers on the obverse.

Box Coin Small container formed by *obverse* and *reverse* of two coins, hollowed out and screwed together.

Bracteate (Latin *bractea*, a thin piece of metal) Coins struck on blanks so thin that the image applied to one side appears in reverse on the other. First minted in Erfurt and Thuringia in the 12th century, and later produced elsewhere in Germany, Switzerland and Poland till the 14th century.

Brass Alloy of copper and zinc, widely used for subsidiary coinage. The term was also formerly used for bronze Roman coins, known numismatically as first, second or third brass.

Breeches Money Derisive term given by the Royalists to the coinage of the Commonwealth, 1651, the conjoined elongated oval shields on the reverse resembling a pair of breeches.

Brockage Mis-struck coin with only one design, normal on one side and *incuse* on the other. This occurs when a coin previously struck adheres to the die and strikes the next blank to pass through the press.

Broken Bank-note Note issued by a bank which has failed, but often applied more generally to banknotes which have been demonetised.

Bronze Alloy of copper and tin, first used as a coinage metal by the Chinese c. 1000 BC. Often used synonymously with copper, though it should be noted that bronze only superseded copper as the constituent of the base metal British coins in 1860.

George III Bull Neck Coin

Bull Neck Popular term for the coins of King George III, 1816–17.

Bullet Money Pieces of silver, *globular* in shape, bearing various *countermarks* and used as coins in Siam (Thailand) in the 18th and 19th centuries.

Bullion Precious metal in bars, ingots, strip or scrap (i.e. broken jewellery mounts, watch-cases and plate), its weight reckoned solely by weight and fineness, before being converted into coin.

Bullion Coin A coin struck in platinum, gold or silver, whose value is determined solely by the prevailing market price for the metal as a commodity. Such coins do not generally have a nominal face value, but include in their inscriptions their weight and fineness. Good examples of recent times include the Krugerrand (South Africa), the Britannia (UK), the Maple Leaf (Canada), Libertad (Mexico), the Nugget (Australia) and the Eagle (USA).

Victoria Bun Penny

Bun Coinage British coins of 1860–94 showing Queen Victoria with her hair in a bun.

Bungtown Coppers Derisive term (from Anglo-American slang *bung*, to swindle or bribe) for halfpence of English or Irish origin, often counterfeit, which circulated in North America towards the end of the colonial period.

Carat (American *Karat*) Originally a unit of weight for precious stones, based on carob seeds (ceratia), it also denotes the fineness or purity of gold, being 1/24th part of the whole. Thus 9 carat gold is .375 fine and 22 carat, the English sovereign standard, is .916 fine. Abbreviated as ct or kt.

Cartwheel Popular term for the large and cumbersome penny and twopenny pieces of 1797 weighing one and two ounces, struck by Matthew Boulton at the Soho Mint, Birmingham.

Cased Set Set of coins in mint condition, housed in the official case issued by the mint. Formerly leather cases with blue plush or velvet lining were used, but nowadays many sets are encapsulated in plastic to facilitate handling.

Brass "Cash" coin.

Cash (from Portuguese *caixa*, Hindi *kasu*). Round piece of bronze or brass with a square hole in the centre, used as subsidiary coinage in China for almost 2000 years, till the early 12th century. In Chinese these pieces were known as *Ch'ien* or *Li* and strung together in groups of 1000 were equivalent to a silver tael.

Cast Coins Coins cast from molten metals in moulds. This technique, widespread in the case of early commemorative medals, has been used infrequently in coins, the vast majority of which are struck from *dies*. Examples of cast coins include the Chinese cash and the Manx coins of 1709.

Check A form of *token* given as a means of identification, or issued for small amounts of money or for services of a specific nature.

Cheque (American *Check*) A written order directing a bank to pay money.

Chop (Hindi, to seal). Countermark, usually consisting of a single character, applied by Chinese merchants to precious metal coins and ingots as a guarantee of their weight and fineness. Coins may be found with a wide variety of chop marks and the presence of several different marks on the same coin considerably enhances its interest and value. See also *Shroff mark*.

Christmas Coins issued as Christmas gifts date from the Middle Ages when the Venetian Doges struck *Osselle* as presents for their courtiers. In modern times, however, the custom has developed only since the late 1970s, several countries having issued attractive coins at Christmas since then.

Cistophori (Greek for chest bearing) a generic term for the coins of Pergamum with an obverse motif of a chest showing a serpent crawling out of the half-opened lid. Cistophori became very popular all over Asia Minor in the 3rd and 2nd centuries BC and were struck also at mints in Ionia, Phrygia, Lydia and Mysia.

Clad Coins Coins with a core of one alloy, covered with a layer or coating of another. US half dollars from 1965 to 1970, for example, had a core of 21 per cent silver and 79 per cent copper, bonded to outer layers of 80 per cent silver and 20 per cent copper. More recently, however, coins usually have a body in a cheap alloy, with only a thin cladding of a more expensive material, such as the British 1p and 2p coins of stainless steel with a copper cladding, introduced late in 1992.

Clash Marks Mirror image traces found on a coin which has been struck from a pair of dies, themselves damaged by having been struck together without a blank between.

Clipped Coins Precious metal coins from which small amounts have been removed by clipping the edges. It was to prevent this that *graining* and *edge inscriptions* were adopted.

Cob Crude, irregularly shaped silver piece, often with little more than a vestige of die impressions, produced in the Spanish American mints in the 16th–18th centuries.

Coin Piece of metal, marked with a device, issued by government authority and intended for use as money.

Collar Retaining ring within which the *dies* for the *obverse* and *reverse* operate. When the *blank* is struck under high pressure between the dies the metal flows sideways and is formed by the collar, taking up the impression of *reeding* or *edge inscription* from it.

Commemorative Coin, medal, token or paper note issued to celebrate a current event or the anniversary of a historic event or personality.

Communion Token Token, cast in lead, but later struck in pewter, brass, bronze or white metal, issued to members of a congregation to permit them to partake of the annual communion service in the Calvinist and Presbyterian churches. John Calvin himself is said to have invented the communion token in 1561 but they were actually referred to in the minutes of the Scottish General Assembly in 1560. Later they were adopted by the Reformed churches in many parts of Europe. They survived in Scotland till the early years of this century. Each parish had its own tokens, often bearing the names or initials of individual ministers, with dates, symbols and biblical texts.

"Conjoined" portraits of Prince Charles and Lady Diana.

Conjoined Term denoting overlapped profiles of two or more rulers (e.g. William and Mary).

Contorniate (from Italian *contorno*, edge). Late 4th and 5th century Roman bronze piece whose name alludes to the characteristic grooving on the edges.

Contribution Coins Coins struck by Bamberg, Eichstatt, Fulda and other German cities in the 1790s during the First Coalition War against the French Republic. The name alludes to the fact that the bullion used to produce the coins necessary to pay troops was raised by contribution from the Church and the public.

Convention Money Any system of coinage agreed by neighbouring countries for mutual acceptance and interchange. Examples include the Amphictyonic coins of ancient Greece, and the Austrian and Bavarian talers and gulden of 1753–1857 which were copied by other south German states and paved the way for the German Monetary union.

Copper Metallic element, chemical symbol *Cu*, widely used as a coinage medium for 2,500 years. Pure or almost pure copper was used for subsidiary coinage in many countries till the mid-19th century, but has since been superseded by copper alloys which are cheaper and more durable: *bronze* (copper and tin), *brass* (copper and zinc), *Bath metal* or *bell metal* (low-grade copper and tin), *aluminium-bronze* (copper and aluminium), *potin* (copper, tin, lead and silver) or *cupro-nickel* (copper and nickel). Copper is also alloyed with gold to give it its reddish hue, and is normally alloyed with silver in coinage metals. When the copper exceeds the silver content the alloy is known as *billon*.

Copperhead Popular term for a copper *token* about the size and weight of an American cent which circulated in the USA during the Civil War (1861–65) during a shortage of subsidiary coinage. Many different types were produced, often of a political or patriotic nature.

Coppernose Popular name for the debased silver shillings of Henry VIII. Many of them were struck in copper with little more than a silver wash which tended to wear off at the highest point of the obverse, the nose on the full-face portrait of the king.

Counter A piece resembling a coin but intended for use on a medieval accountancy board or in gambling. See also *jeton*.

Counterfeit Imitation of a coin, token or banknote intended for circulation to deceive the public and defraud the state.

Countermark Punch mark applied to a coin some time after its original issue, either to alter its nominal value, or to authorise its circulation in some other country.

Cowrie Small shell (*Cypraea moneta*) circulating as a form of primitive currency from 1000 BC (China) to the present century (East and West Africa) and also used in the islands of the Indian and Pacific Oceans.

Crockard Debased silver imitation of English pennies produced in the Netherlands and imported into England in the late 13th century. Edward I tried to prevent their import then, in 1299, allowed them to pass current as halfpennies. As they contained more than a halfpennyworth of silver this encouraged their trading in to be melted down and they disappeared from circulation within a year. Sometimes known as *pollards*. See also *Lushbourne*.

Crown Gold Gold of 22 carat (.916) fineness, so called on account of its adoption in 1526 for the English gold crown. It has remained the British standard gold fineness ever since.

Cumberland Jack Popular name for a counter or medalet of sovereign size, struck unofficially in 1837 in brass. The figure of St George was replaced by the Duke of Cumberland on horseback with the inscription "To Hanover" a reference to the unpopular Duke of Cumberland, uncle of Queen Victoria, who succeeded to the Hanoverian throne since Victoria, as a female, was debarred by Salic law from inheritance.

Cupellation (Latin *cupella*, a little cup). Process by which gold and silver were separated from lead and other impurities in their ores. A cupel is a shallow cup of bone-ash or other absorbent material which, when hot, absorbs any molten material that wets its surface. Lead melts and oxidises with impurities into the cupel, whereas gold and silver remain on the cupel. Cupellation is also used in assaying the fineness of these precious metals.

Cupro-nickel Coinage alloy of 75 per cent copper and 25 per cent nickel, now widely used as a base metal substitute for silver. A small amount of zinc is added to the alloy in modern Russian coins.

Currency Coins, tokens, paper notes and other articles intended to pass current in general circulation as money.

Current Coins and paper money still in circulation.

Cut Money Coins cut into smaller pieces to provide correspondingly smaller denominations. The cross on many medieval coins assisted the division of silver pennies into halfpence and farthings. Spanish dollars were frequently divided into *bits* which themselves became units of currency in America and the West Indies.

Darlehnskassen (German for "state loan notes"). Paper money issued during the First World War in an abortive bid to fill the shortage of coinage in circulation. These low-denomination notes failed to meet demand and were superseded by local issues of small *Notgeld* in 1916.

Debasement The reduction in the precious metal content of the coinage, widely practised since time immemorial by governments for economic reasons. British coins, for example, were debased from sterling (.925 fine) silver to .500 in 1920 and from silver to cupro-nickel in 1947.

Decimalisation A currency system in which the principal unit is subdivided into ten, a hundred, or a thousand fractions. Russia was the first country to decimalise, in 1534 when the rouble of 100 kopeks was introduced, but it was not till 1792 that France adopted the franc of 100 centimes and 1793 when the USA introduced the dollar of 100 cents. Most European countries decimalised their currency in the 19th century. Britain toyed with the idea, introducing the florin or tenth of a pound in 1849 as the first step, but did not complete the process till 1971. The last countries to decimalise were Malta and Nigeria, in 1972 and 1973 respectively.

Demidiated Heraldic term to describe the junction of two armorial devices, in which only half of each is shown.

Demonetisation The withdrawal of coins or paper money from circulation and declaring them to be worthless.

Device Heraldic term for the pattern or emblem on coins or paper notes.

Die Hardened piece of metal bearing a mirror image of the device to be struck on one side of a coin or medal.

Die Proof An impression, usually pulled on soft carton or India paper, of an *intaglio* engraving of a banknote, usually taken during the progress of the engraving to check the detail. Banknote proofs of this nature usually consist of the portrait or some detail of the design, such as the border, rather than the complete motif.

Dodecagonal Twelve-sided, a term applied to the nickel-brass threepence of Great Britain, 1937–67.

Dump Any primitive coin struck on a very thick *flan*, but more specifically applied to the circular pieces cut from the centre of Spanish dollars, countermarked with the name of the colony, a crown and the value, and circulated in New South Wales at 15 pence in 1813. See *Holey Dollar*.

Duodecimal Currency system based on units of twelve, i.e. medieval money of account (12 denarii = 1 soldo) which survived in Britain as 12 pence to the shilling as late as 1971.

Ecclesiastical Coins Coins struck by a religious authority, such as an archbishop, bishop, abbot, prior or the canons of a religious order. Such coins were common in medieval times but survived as late as the early 19th century, the bishops of Breslau (1817) and Gurk (1823) being the last prelates to exercise coinage rights. Coins were struck by authority of the Pope at Rome till 1870 but since 1929 coinage has been struck at the Italian state mint on behalf of the Vatican.

Edge Inscription Lettering on the edge of a coin or medal to prevent clipping. Alluding to this, the Latin motto *Decus et Tutamen* (an ornament and a safeguard) was applied to the edge of English milled coins in the reign of Charles II.

Edge Ornament An elaboration of the *graining* found on many milled coins to prevent clipping, taking the form of tiny leaves, florets, interlocking rings, pellets and zigzag patterns. In some cases the ornament appears between layers of more conventional reeding.

EF Abbreviation for Extremely Fine.

Effigy An image or representation of a person, normally the head of state, a historical personage, or an allegorical figure, usually on the *obverse* or "heads" side of a coin or medal.

Electrotype A reproduction of a coin or medal made by an electrolytic process.

Electrum Alloy of gold and silver, sometimes called white gold, used for minting the staters of Lydia, 7th century BC, and other early European coins.

Elongated Coin An oval *medalet* created by passing a coin, such as an American cent, between rollers under pressure with the effect of squeezing it out and impressing on it a souvenir or commemorative motif.

Emergency Money Any form of money used intimes of economic and political upheaval, when traditional kinds of currency are not available. Examples include the comparatively crude silver coins issued by the Royalists during the *Civil War* (1642–49), *obsidional* money, issued in time of siege, from Tyre (1122) to Mafeking (1900), the *Notgeld* issued by many German towns (1916–23), *encased money*, *fractional currency, guerrilla notes, invasion, liberation* and *occupation money* from the two World Wars and minor campaigns. Among the more recent examples may be cited the use of sweets and cheques in Italy (1976–77) and the issue of coupons and vouchers in many of the countries of the former Soviet Union pending the introduction of their own distinctive coins and notes.

Enamelled Coins Coins decorated by enamelling the obverse and reverse motifs in contrasting colours was an art practised by many jewellers

Enamelled halfcrown of 1671.

in Birmingham and Paris in the 19th century, and revived in Europe and America in the 1970s.

Encased Money Postage and revenue stamps enclosed in small metal and mica-faced discs, circulated as small change in times of emergency. The practice was invented by John Gault, a Boston sewing-machine salesman, during the American Civil War (1862). The face of the stamp was visible through the transparent window, while the back of the disc was embossed with firms' advertisements. This practice was revived during and after the First World War when there was again a shortage of small coins. Encased stamps have also been recorded from France, Austria, Norway, Germany and Monaco. See also under *Stamp Money*.

Engrailing Technical term for the close serrations or vertical bars round the edge of a coin, applied as a security device.

Engraving The art of cutting lines or grooves in plates, blocks or dies. Numismatically this takes the form of engraving images into the face of the dies used in striking coins, a process which has now been almost completely superseded by *hubbing* and the use of *reducing machinery*. In the production of paper money, *intaglio* engraving is still commonly practised. In this process the engraver cuts the design into a steel die and the printing ink lies in the grooves. The paper is forced under great pressure into the grooves and picks up the ink, and this gives banknotes their characteristic ridged feeling to the touch. Nowadays many banknotes combine traditional intaglio engraving with multicolour lithography or photogravure to defeat the would-be counterfeiter.

Epigraphy The study of inscriptions, involving the classification and interpretation of coin legends, an invaluable adjunct to the study of a coin series, particularly the classical and medieval coins which, in the absence of dates and mintmarks, would otherwise be difficult to arrange in chronological sequence.

Erasion The removal of the title or effigy of a ruler from the coinage issued after his or her death. This process was practised in imperial Rome, and applied to the coins of Caligula, Nero and Geta, as part of the more general practice of *damnatio memoriae* (damnation of the memory) ordered by the Senate.

Error Mistakes on coins and paper money may be either caused at the design or engraving stage, or as a result of a fault in the production processes. In the first category come mis-spellings in legends causing, in extreme cases, *blundered inscriptions*, or anachronisms or inaccuracies in details of the design. In the second, the most glaring error is the mule caused by marrying the wrong dies. Faulty alignment of dies can cause obverse and reverse to be out of true. Although many coins are issued with obverse and reverse upside down in relation to each other, this can also occur as an error in coins where both sides should normally be facing the same way up. Other errors caused at the production stage include striking coins in the wrong metal or with the wrong *collar* thus creating a different edge from the normal.

Essay (From the French *essai*, a trial piece). The term is applied to any piece struck for the purposes of examination, by parliamentary or financial bodies, prior to the authorisation of an issue of coins or paper money. The official nature of these items distinguishes them from *patterns*, which denote trial pieces often produced by mints or even private individuals bidding for coinage contracts.

Evasion Close copy or imitation of a coin, with sufficient deliberate differences in the design or inscription to avoid infringing counterfeit legislation. A good example is the imitation of Sumatran coins by European merchants, inscribed SULTANA instead of SUMATRA.

Exergue Lower segment of a coin or medal, usually divided from the rest of the *field* by a horizontal line, and often containing the date, value, ornament or identification symbols.

Exonumia Generic term for numismatic items not authorised by a government, e.g. *patterns*, *tokens*, *medalets* or *model coins*.

F Fine

Face The surface of a coin, medal or token, referred to as the *obverse* or the *reverse*. The corresponding faces of a paper note are more correctly termed *verso* and *recto*, but the coin terms are often used instead.

Facing Term for the portrait, usually on the obverse, which faces to the front instead of to the side (profile).

Fantasy Piece of metal purporting to be the coinage of a country which does not exist. Recent examples include the money of Atlantis and the Hutt River Province which declared its independence of Western Australia.

FDC Abbreviation for *Fleur de Coin*, a term denoting the finest possible condition of a coin.

Fiat Money Paper notes issued by a government but not redeemable in coin or bullion.

Field Flat part of the surface of a coin or medal, between the *legend*, the *effigy* and other raised parts of the design.

Fillet Heraldic term for the ribbon or headband on the effigy of a ruler or allegorical figure.

Find Term applied to an archaeological discovery of one or more coins. A large quantity of such material is described as a *hoard*.

Flan Alternative name for *blank* or *planchet*, the piece of metal struck between dies to produce a coin or medal.

Forgery An unauthorised copy or imitation, made with the intention of deceiving collectors. Forgeries intended to pass current for real coins or notes are more properly called *counterfeits*.

Fractional Currency Emergency issue of small-denomonation notes by the USA in 1863–5, following a shortage of coins caused by the Civil War. This issue superseded the *Postage Currency* notes, but bore the inscription "Receivable for all US stamps", alluding to the most popular medium of small change at that time. Denominations ranged from 3c to 50c.

Franklinium Cupro-nickel alloy developed by the Franklin Mint of Philadelphia and used for coins, medals and gaming tokens since 1967.

Freak An *error* or *variety* of a non-recurring type, usually caused accidentally during production.

Frosting Matt surface used for the high relief areas of many proof coins and medals, for greater contrast with the mirrored surface of the field.

Funeral Money Imitations of banknotes, used in China and Latin America in funeral ceremonies.

Geat (Git) Channel through which molten metal is ducted to the mould. Cast coins and medals often show tiny protrusions known as geat marks.

Ghost Faint image of the design on one side of a coin visible on the other. Good examples were the British penny and halfpenny of George V, 1911–27, the ghosting being eliminated by the introduction of a smaller effigy in 1928.

Globular Coins struck on very thick *dumps* with convex faces. The term is applied to some Byzantine coins, and also the *bullet money* of Siam (Thailand).

Godless (or *Graceless*) Epithet applied to any coin which omits the traditional reference to the deity, e.g. the British florin of 1849 which omitted D.G. (*Dei Gratia*, "by the Grace of God").

Gold Precious metal, chemical symbol and numismatic abbreviation *Au*, from the *Latin Aurum*, used as a coinage medium from the 7th century BC till the present day. The purity of gold is reckoned in *carats* or a decimal system. Thus British gold sovereigns are 22 carat or .916 fine. Medieval coins were 23.5 carat or .995 fine, and some modern bullion coins are virtually pure gold, denoted by the inscription .999. Canadian maple leaves are now struck in "four nines" gold and bear the inscription .9999.

Goodfor Popular name for token coins and *emergency money* made of paper or card, from the inscription "Good for" or its equivalent in other languages (e.g. French *Bon pour* or Dutch *Goed voor*) followed by a monetary value. They have been recorded from Europe, Africa and America during times of economic crises or shortage of more traditional coinage.

Gothic Crown Popular name for the silver crown issued by the United Kingdom (1847–53), so-called on account of its script (more properly Old English, rather than Gothic).

Grain The weight of a single grain of wheat was taken as the smallest unit of weight in England. The troy grain was 1/5760 of a pound, while the avoirdupois grain was 1/7000 pound, the former being used in the weighing of precious metals and thus employed by numismatists in weighing coins. A grain is 1/480 troy ounce or 0.066 gram in the metric system.

Graining Term sometimes used as a synonym for the *reeding* on the edge of milled coins.

Gripped Edge Pattern of indentations found on the majority of American cents of 1797, caused by the milling process. Coins of the same date with a plain edge are rather scarcer.

Guerrilla Money Money issued in areas under the control of guerrillas and partisans during wartime range from the *veld ponds* of the Boers (1900–2) to the notes issued by the Garibaldi Brigade in Italy and the anti-fascist notes of Tito's forces in Yugoslavia. The most prolific issues were those produced in Luzon, Mindanao and Negros Occidental by the Filipino resistance during the Japanese occupation (1942–5).

Guilloche French term signifying the intricate pattern of curved lines produced by the rose engine and used as a security feature in the production of banknote, cheques, stocks and share certificates.

Gun Money Emergency coinage of Ireland (1689–91) minted from gunmetal, a type of bronze used in the casting of cannon. All

"Gun Money" Halfcrown of James II..

denominations of James II, from the sixpence to the crown, normally struck in silver, were produced in this base metal.

Gutschein German word for voucher or coupon, denoting the paper money used aboard ships of the Imperial Navy during the First World War. The last issue was made at Scapa Flow, 1918–19, during the internment of the High Seas Fleet.

Hammered Term denoting coins produce by the traditional method of striking a *flan* laid on an anvil with a hammer. A characteristic of hammered coins is their uneven shape which tended to encourage *clipping*. This abuse was gradually eliminated by the introduction of the screw press in the 15th century and the mechanisation of coining processes in the course of the 16th and 17th centuries.

"Hard Times" tokens issued by the New York and Harlem Railroad Company.

Hard Times Token Copper piece the size of the large cent, issued in the USA, 1834–44, during a shortage of coins caused by the collapse of the Bank of the United States, the panic of 1837 and the economic crisis of 1839, the landmarks in the period known as the Hard Times. Banks suspended *specie* payments and the shortage of coinage was filled by tradesmen's tokens. Many of these were more in the nature of satirical *medalets* than circulating pieces.

Hat Piece Alternative name for the *bonnet piece* of James VI of Scotland, 1591.

Hell Notes Imitation paper money used in Chinese funeral ceremonies and buried with the dead to pay for services in the next world.

Hoard Accumulation of coins concealed in times of economic or political upheaval and discovered, often centuries later. Under English common law, such hoards are subject to th law of *treasure trove* if they contain precious metal.

Hog Money Popular name for the early coinage of Bermuda, issued about 1616. The coins were minted in brass with a silver wash and circulated at various values from twopence to a shilling. They derived their name from the hog depicted on the obverse, an allusion to the pigs introduced to the island in 1515 by Juan Bermudez.

Holed Term denoting two different categories: (a) coins which have been pierced for suspension as a form of jewellery or talisman, and (b) coins which have a hole as part of their design. In the latter category come the Chinese *cash* with a square hole, and numerous issues of the 19th and 20th centuries from many countries, with the object of reducing weight and metal without sacrificing overall diameter.

Holey Dollar Spanish silver peso of 8 reales with the centre removed. The resultant ring was counter-marked "New South Wales" and dated 1813, with "Five Shillings" on the reverse, and placed into circulation during a shortage of British coin. The centre, known as a *dump*, was circulated at 15 pence.

Hub Heavy circular piece of steel on which the *die* for a coin or medal is engraved. The process of cutting the die and transferring the master die, by means of intermediary *punches*, to the die from which the coins will be struck, is known as hubbing. Soft steel is used in the preliminary process, and after the design has been transferred, the hub is hardened by chemical action.

Hybrid Alternative name for a *mule*.

Imitation Money Also known as play money or toy money, it consists of coins and notes produced for games of chance (like Monopoly), children's toy shops and post offices, as tourist souvenirs, or for political satire (e.g. the shrinking pound or dollar). See also *funeral money*, *hell notes*, *model coins* and *skit notes*.

Imprint Inscription on a paper note giving the name of the printer.

American $2.5 Eagle designed by Bela Pratt.

Incuse Impression which cuts into the surface of a coin or medal, as opposed to the more usual raised relief. Many of the earliest coins, especially those with a device on one side only, bear an incuse impression often in a geometric pattern. An incuse impression appears on one side of the coins, reflecting the image on the other side. Few modern coins have had an incuse design, notable examples being the American half and quarter eagle gold coins of 1908–29 designed by Bela Pratt. Incuse inscriptions on a raised rim, however, are more common, and include the British *Cartwheel* coins of 1797 and the 20p coins since 1982.

Inflation Money Coins produced as a result of inflation date back to Roman times when bronze minimi, little bigger than a pinhead, circulated as denarii. Nearer the present day inflation has had devastating effects on the coinge and banknotes of Germany (1921–3), Austria (1923), Poland (1923), Hungary (1945–6), Greece (1946) and many Latin American countries since the 1980s. Hungary holds the record for the highest value of any note ever issued — one thousand million adopengos, which is written as 20,000,000,000,000,000,000,000,000,000 pengos.

Ingot Piece of precious metal, usually cast in a mould, and stamped with the weight and fineness. though mainly used as a convenient method of storing bullion, ingots have been used as currency in many countries, notably Russia and Japan.

Inlay Insertion into the surface of a coin or medal of another substance for decorative effect. e.g. Poland Amber Trade Routes 20zl (amber), Isle of Man Queen Mother centenery (pearl) and various coins incorporating rubies or diamonds.

Intaglio Form of *engraving* in which lines are cut into a steel die for the recess-printing of banknotes.

Intrinsic The net metallic value of a coin, as distinguished from the nominal or face value.

Iron Metal, chemical symbol *Fe* (from Latin *Ferrum*), used as a primitive form of currency from classical times onwards. Iron spits (obeliskoi) preceded the obol as the lowest unit of Greek coinage, a handful of six spits being worth a drachma (from *drassomai*, "I grasp"). Cast iron coins were issued in China as a substitute for copper *cash*. Many of the emergency token issues of Germany during the First World War were struck in iron. Iron coins were issued by Bulgaria in 1943. See also *Steel*.

Ithyphallic (Greek for "erect penis"). Term descriptive of coins of classical Greece showing a satyr.

Janiform Double profiles back to back, after the Roman god Janus.

Jeton (From French *jeter*, to throw). Alternative term for *counter*, and used originally on the chequerboard employed by medieval accountants. Nuremberg was the most important centre for the production of medieval jetons, often issued in lengthy portrait series. In modern parlance the term is often synonymous with *token*, though more specifically confined to pieces used in vending equipment, parking meters, laundromats, telephones and urban transport systems in many European countries. Apart from security, removing the temptation of vandals to break into the receptacles, the main advantage of such pieces is that they can be retariffed as charges increase, without any alteration in their design or composition, a method that is far cheaper than altering costly equipment to take larger coins.

Jubilee Head The effigy of Queen Victoria by Joseph Boehm adopted for British coinage after the 1887 Golden Jubilee.

Jugate (From Latin *jugum*, a yoke). Alternative to *accolated* or *conjoined* to denote overlapping profiles of rulers.

Key Date Term describing the rarest in a long-running series of coins with the dates changed at annual intervals.

Kipperzeit German term meaning the time of clipped money, denoting the period during and after the Thirty Years War (1618–48) in which debased and clipped money was in circulation.

Klippe Rectangular or square pieces of metal bearing the impression of a coin. Coins of this type were first struck in Sweden in the 16th century and were subsequently produced in many of the German states. The idea has been revived in recent years as a medium for striking commemorative pieces.

Knife Money Cast bronze pieces, with an elongated blade and a ring at one end to facilitate stringing together in bunches, were used as currency in China from the 9th century BC until the 19th century.

Kreditivsedlar (Swedish for "credit notes"). The name given to the first issue of paper money made in the western world. Paper money of this type was the brainchild of Johan Palmstruch at Riga in 1652, but nine years elapsed before it was implemented by the Stockholm Bank. The notes were redeemable in copper *platmynt*.

Laureate Heraldic term for a laurel wreath, often framing a state emblem or shown, in the Roman fashion, as a crown on the ruler's forehead.

Leather Money Pieces of leather embossed with an official device have been used as money on various occasions, including the sieges of Faenza and Leiden and in the Isle of Man in the 15th and 16th centuries. Several towns in Austria and Germany produced leather tokens during and after the First World War.

Legal Tender Coins or paper money which are declared by law to be current money and which tradesmen and shopkeers are obliged to accept in payment for goods or services. (See *Money and the Law*).

Legend The inscription on a coin or medal.

Liberation Money Paper money prepared for use in parts of Europe and Asia, formerly under Axis occupation. Liberation notes were used in France, Belgium and the Netherlands in 1944–5, while various Japanese and Chinese notes were overprinted for use in Hong Kong when it was liberated in 1945. Indian notes overprinted for use in Burma were issued in 1945–6 when that country was freed from Japanese occupation.

Ligature (From Latin *ligatus*, bound together). Term denoting the linking of two letters in a *legend*, e.g. Æ and Œ.

Long Cross Coinage Type of coinage introduced by King Henry III in 1247, deriving its name from the reverse which bore a cross whose arms extended right to the edge to help safeguard the coins against *clipping*. This remained the style of the silver penny, its fractions and multiples, till the reign of Henry VII, and vestiges of the long cross theme is seen in the silver coins throughout the remaining years of the Tudor period.

Love Token A coin which has been altered by smoothing one or both surfaces and engraving initials, dates, scenes, symbols of affection and messages thereon.

Lushbourne English word for base pennies of inferior silver, said to have emanated from Luxembourg, from which the name derived. These coins were first minted under John the Blind who adopted the curious spelling of his name EIWANES in the hope that illiterate English merchants might confuse it with EDWARDVS and thus be accepted as coin issued in the name of Edward III. Lushbournes were also minted by Robert of Bethune, William I of Namur and the bishops of Toul during the mid-14th century.

Lustre The sheen or bloom on the surface of an uncirculated coin resulting from the centrifugal flow of metal caused by striking.

Magnimat Trade name used by VDM (*Verein Deutscher Metallwerke*) for a high-security alloy containing copper, nickel and magnetised steel. First used for the 5 deutschemark coin of 1975, it has since been adopted for other high-value coins in Germany and other countries.

Manilla Copper, bronze or brass rings, sometimes shaped like horseshoes and sometimes open, with flattened terminals, used as currency in West Africa until recent years.

Matrix Secondary die for a coin or medal, produced from the master die by means of an intermediate punch. In this way dies can be duplicated from the original cut on the reducing machine.

Matt or Matte Finely granulated surface or overall satin finish to proof coins, a style which was briefly fashionable at the turn of the century. The Edward VII proof set of 1902 is a notable example. In more recent years many issues produced by the Franklin Mint have been issued with this finish.

Maundy coins of Queen Anne and William & Mary.

Maundy Money Set of small silver coins, in denominations of 1, 2, 3 and 4 pence, distributed by the reigning British monarch to the poor and needy on Maundy Thursday. The custom dates back to the Middle Ages, but in its present form, of distributing pence to as many men and women as the years in the monarch's age, it dates from 1666. At first ordinary silver pennies and multiples were used but after they went out of everyday use distinctive silver coins were produced specifically for the purpose from the reign of George II (1727–60) onwards. For centuries the ceremony took place in Westminster Abbey but since 1955 other venues have been used in alternate years.

Medal (French *medaille*, Italian *medaglia*, from Latin *metallum*). A piece of metal bearing devices and legends commemorating an event or person, or given as an award. Military medals date from the 16th and 17th centuries, but were not generally awarded to all ranks till the 19th century. Commemora-tive medals can be traced back to Roman times, but in their present form they date from the Italian Renaissance when there was a fashion for large cast portrait medals.

Medalet A small medal, generally 25mm or less in diameter.

Medallion Synonym for medal, but usually confined to those with a diameter of 50mm or more.

Milling Process denoting the mechanical production of coins, as opposed to the handmade technique implied in *hammering*. It alludes to the use of watermills to drive the machinery of the screw presses and blank rollers developed in the 16th century. As the even thickness and diameter of milled coins permitted a security edge, the term milling is popularly, though erroneously, used as a synonym for *graining* or *reeding*.

Mint The place in which coins and medals are produced. Mint condition is a term sometimes used to denote pieces in an uncirculated state.

Mint Set A set of coins or medals in the package or case issued by the mint. See also *year set*.

Mintmark A device appearing on a coin to denote the place of minting. Athenian coins of classical times have been recorded with up to 40 different marks, denoting individual workshops. In the 4th century AD the Romans adopted this system to identify coins struck in provincial mints. This system was widely used in the Middle Ages and survives in France and Germany to this day. Initials and symbols are also used to identify mints, especially where the production of a coin is shared between several different mints. From 1351 onwards symbols were adopted in England to denote periods between trials of the *Pyx*, and thus assist the proper chronological sequence of coins, in an era prior to the adoption of dating. These mintmarks continued into the 17th century, but gradually died out as the use of dates became more widespread. See also *countermark* and *privy mark*.

Mionnet Scale Scale of nineteen diameters covering all sizes of coins belonging to the classical period, devised by the French numismatist, Theodore-Edme Mionnet (1770–1842) during the compilation of his fifteen-volume catalogue of the numismatic collection in the Bibliotheque Nationale in Paris.

Mirror Finish The highly polished surface of proof coins.

Misstrike A coin or medal on which the impression has been struck off-centre.

Model Coin Tiny pieces of metal, either reproducing the designs of existing coins (used as play money by children) or, more specifically, denoting patterns produced by Joseph Moore and Hyam Hyams in their attempts to promote an improved subsidiary coinage in 19th century Britain. These small coins were struck in bronze with a brass or silver centre and were designed to reduce the size of the existing cumbersome range of pence, halfpence and farthings.

Modified Effigy Any coin in which the profile on the obverse has been subtly altered. Examples include minor changes in the Victorian Young Head and Old Head effigies and the George V profile by Sir Bertram Mackennal.

Money Order Certificate for a specified amount of money, which may be transmitted by post and encashed at a money order office or post office. This system was pioneered by Britain and the United States in the early 19th century and is now virtually worldwide. The term is now confined to certificates above a certain value, the terms *postal order* and *postal note* being used for similar certificates covering small amounts.

Mule Coin whose obverse is not matched with its official or regular reverse. Mules include the erroneous combination of dies from different reigns, but in recent years such hybrids have arisen in mints where coins for several countries are struck. Examples include the Coronation Anniversary crowns combining Ascension and Isle of Man dies and the 2 cent coins with Bahamas and New Zealand dies. *Restrikes* of rare American coins have been detected in which the dated die has been paired with the wrong reverse die, e.g. the 1860 restrike of the rare 1804 large cent.

Mute An *anepigraphic* coin, identifiable only by the devices struck on it.

Nail Mark Small indentation on ancient coins. The earliest coins of Asia Minor developed from the electrum *dumps* which merchants marked with a broken nail as their personal guarantee of value, the ancient counterpart of the *chop* marks used in China and Japan.

NCLT Coins Abbreviation for "Non Circulating Legal Tender", a term devised by modern coin catalogues to denote coins which, though declared *legal tender*, are not intended for general circulation on account of their precious metal content or superior finish.

Nicked Coin Coin bearing a tiny cut or nick in its edge. Silver coins were tested by this method, especially in the reign of Henry I (1100–35) when so many base silver pennies were in circulation. Eventually people refused to accept these nicked coins a problem which was only overcome when the state decreed that all coins should have a nick in them.

Nickel Metallic element, chemical symbol *Ni*, a hard white metal relatively resistant to tarnish, and extensively used as a cheap substitute for silver. It was first used for the American 5 cent coin in 1866, hence its popular name which has stuck ever since, although nowadays the higher denominations are minted in an alloy of copper and nickel. Although best known as a silver substitute, nickel was widely used in Jamaica (1869–1969) for halfpence and pennies and in British West Africa for the tiny 1/10th pennies (1908–57). Pure nickel was used for French francs and German marks, but usually it is alloyed with copper or zinc to produce *cupro-nickel* or nickel brass.

Notaphily Hybrid word from Latin *nota* (note) and Greek philos (love), coined about 1970 to denote the branch of numismatics devoted to the study of paper money.

Notgeld German word meaning emergency money, applied to the *tokens*, in metals, wood, leather and even ceramic materials, issued during the First World War when coinage disappeared from circulation. These tokens were soon superseded by low-denomination paper money issued by shops and businessmen in denominations from 10 to 50 pfennige and known as *kleine Notgeld* (small emergency money). These notes were prohibited in September 1922 but by that time some 50,000 varieties are thought to have been issued. Inflation raced out of control and the government permitted a second issue of local notes, known as *large Notgeld*, as the denomi-nations were in thousands, and latterly millions, of marks. Some 3,600 types appeared in 1922 and over 60,000 in 1923 alone. These mementoes of the German hyperinflation ceased to circulate in 1924 when the currency was reformed.

Numismatics The study of coins, medals and other related fields, a term derived from the Latin *numisma* and Greek *nomisma* (money).

Obsidional Currency (From Latin *obsidium*, a siege). Term for *emergency money* produced by the defenders of besieged towns and cities. These usually took the form of pieces of silver plate, commandeered for the purpose, crudely marked with an official device and the value. Instances of such seige coinage have been recorded from the 12th to the 19th centuries.

Obverse The "heads" side of a coin or medal, generally bearing the effigy of the head of state or an allegorical figure.

Off Metal Term denoting a piece struck in a metal other than the officially authorisied or issued alloy. This originally applied to *patterns* which were often struck in lead or copper instead of gold and silver as trial pieces or to test the dies; but in recent years it has applied to collectors' versions, e.g. proofs in platinum, gold or silver of coins normally issued in bronze or cupro-nickel.

Overdate One or more digits in a date altered by superimposing another figure. Alterations of this kind, by means of small hand punches, were made to dated dies so that they could be used in years other than that of the original manufacture. Coins with overdates invariably show traces of the original digit.

Overstrike Coin, token or medal produced by using a previously struck pieces as a flan. The Bank of England dollar of 1804 was overstruck on Spanish pieces of eight, and examples showing traces of the original coins are worth a good premium.

Paduan Name given to imitations of medals and bogus coins produced in Italy in the 16th century, and deriving from the city of Padua where forgeries of bronze sculpture were produced for the antique market.

Patina Oxidation forming on the surface of metallic objects. So far as coins and medals are concerned, this applies mainly to silver, brass, bronze and copper pieces which may acquire oxidation from the atmosphere, or spectacular patination from salts in the ground in which they have been buried. In extreme forms patina leads to verdigris and other forms of rust which corrode the surface, but in uncirculated coins it may be little more than a mellowing of the original *lustre*. Coins preserved in blue velvet presentation cases often acquire a subtle toning from the dyes in the material.

"Pattern" Halfcrown of Charles I.

Pattern Piece resembling a coin or medal, prepared by the mint to the specifications or on the authorisation of the coin-issuing authority, but also applied to pieces produced by mints when tendering for coinage or medal contracts. Patterns may differ from the final coins as issued in the type of alloy used (*off metal*) but more often they differ in details of the design.

Pellet Raised circular ornament used as a spacing device between words and abbreviations in the *legend* of coins and medals. Groups of pellets were also used as ornaments in the angles of the cross on the reverse of English silver pennies.

Piece de Plaisir (French for "fancy piece"). Term given to coins struck in a superior precious metal, or to a superior finish, or on a much thicker flan than usual. See *off metal*, *piedfort* and *proof*.

Piedfort (Piefort) Piece struck with coinage dies on a *flan* of much more than normal thickness. This practice originated in France in the late 16th century and continues to the present day. In recent years it has been adopted by mints in Britain and other countries as a medium for collectors' pieces.

Pile Lower die incorporating the obverse motif, used in striking coins and medals. See also *trussel*.

Planchet French term used as an alternative for *blank* or *flan*.

Plaque or **Plaquette** Terms sometimes used for medals struck on a square or rectangular flan.

Plaster Cast taken from the original model for a coin or medal sculpted by an artist, and used in modern reducing machines in the manufacture of the master *die*.

Plated Coins Coins stuck in base metal but given a wash of silver or some other precious metal. This expedient was adopted in inflationary times, from the Roman Republic (91 BC) till the Tudor period. American cents of 1943 were struck in steel with a zinc coating, and more recently *clad* coins have produced similar results.

Platinum The noblest of all precious metals, platinum has a higher specific gravity than gold and a harder, brighter surface than silver. Until an industrial application was discovered in the mid-19th century, it was regarded as of little value, and was popular with counterfeiters as a cheap substitute for gold in their forgeries which, with a light gold wash, could be passed off as genuine. It was first used for circulating coins in Russia (the chief source of the metal since 1819) and 3, 6 and 12 rouble coins were mined at various times between 1828 and 1845. In recent years platinum has been a popular metal for limited-edition proof coins.

Platmynt (Swedish for "plate money"). Large copper plates bearing royal cyphers and values from half to ten dalers produced in Sweden between 1643 and 1768. They represented laudable attempts by a country rich in copper to produce a coinage in terms of its silver value, but the net result was far too cumbersome to be practical. The weight of the daler plate, for example, ranged from 766 grams to 1.1kg, and special carts had to be devised to transport them!

Plugged Coins Coins struck predominantly in one metal, but containing a small plug of another. This curious practice may be found in the farthings of Charles II (1684–85) and the halfpence or farthings of James II (1685–87), which were struck in tin, with a copper plug, to defeat forgers.

Porcelain Money Tokens made of porcelain circulated in Thailand from the late 18th century till 1868. The Meissen pottery struck tokens in 1920–22 as a form of small *Notgeld*, using reddish-brown Bottger stoneware and white *bisque* porcelain. These ceramic tokens circulated in various towns of Saxony.

Postage Currency Small paper notes in denominations of 5, 10, 25 and 50 cents, issued by the US federal government in 1862–63, were thus inscribed and had reproductions of postage stamps engraved on them — five 5c stamps on the 25c and five 10c stamps on the 50c notes. The earliest issue even had perforations in the manner of stamps, but this unnecessary device was soon done away with. See also *stamp money*.

Postal Notes or Orders Low-value notes intended for transmission by post and encashable at post offices. Introduced by Britain in 1883, they were an extension of the earlier *money order* system, and are now issued by virtually every country.

Potin (French for pewter). Alloy of copper, tin, lead and silver used as a coinage metal by the Celtic tribes of eastern Gaul at the beginning of the Christian era.

Privy Mark Secret mark incorporated in the design of a coin or medal to identify the minter, or even the particular die used. The term is also used more loosely to denote any small symbol or initials appearing on a coin other than a *mint mark*, and is sometimes applied to the symbols associated with the trial of the *Pyx* found on English coins.

Prize Coins Coins of large size and value struck primarily as prizes in sporting contests. this principle dates from the late 5th century BC when Syracuse minted decadrachms as prizes in the Demareteian Games. The most notable example in modern times is the lengthy series of talers and five-franc coins issued by the Swiss cantons since 1842 as prizes in the annual shooting festivals, the last of which honoured the Lucerne contest of 1939.

Profile A side view of the human face, widely used as a coinage effigy.

Proof Originally a trial strike testing the *dies*, but now denoting a special collectors' version struck with dies that have been specially polished on *flans* with a mirror finish. Presses operating at a very slow speed, or multi-striking processes, are also used.

Propaganda Notes Paper money containing a

political slogan or a didactic element. During the Second World War forgeries of German and Japanese notes were produced by the Allies and additionally inscribed or overprinted with slogans such as "Co-Prosperity Sphere—What is it worth?" (a reference to the Japanese occupied areas of SE Asia). Forged dollars with anti-American propaganda were airdropped over Sicily by the Germans in 1943 and counterfeit pounds with Arabic propaganda over Egypt in 1942–43. Various anti-communist organisations liberated propaganda forgeries of paper money by balloon over Eastern Europe during the Cold War period.

Provenance Mark Form of *privy mark* denoting the source of the metal used in coins. Examples include the plumes or roses on English coins denoting silver from Welsh or West of England mines, and the elephant or elephant and castle on gold coins denoting bullion imported by the African Company. Coins inscribed VIGO (1702-03) or LIMA (1745–46) denote bullion seized from the Spaniards by Anglo-Dutch privateers and Admiral Anson respectively. Other provenance marks on English coins include the letters EIC and SSC, denoting bullion imported by the East India Company or the South Sea Company.

Pseudo Coins Derisory term coined in recent years to signify pieces of precious metal, often struck in *proof* versions only, aimed at the international investment market. Many of these pieces, though bearing a nominal face value, are not *legal tender* in the countries purporting to issue them and in many cases they go straight from the overseas mint where they are produced to coin dealers in America and western Europe, without ever appearing in the so-called country of origin. See also *NCLT coins*.

Punch or Puncheon Intermediate *die* whereby working dies can be duplicated from the master die, prior to the striking of coins and medals.

Pyx Box in which a specimen from every 15 pounds troy weight of gold and every 60 pounds of silver minted in England is kept for annual trial by weight and assay. Many of the *mintmarks* on English coins of the 14th–17th centuries were in use from one trial to the next and still exist today and can therefore be used to date them.

Reducing Machinery Equipment designed on the pantographic principle for transferring the image from a *plaster* to a *hub* and reducing it to the size of the actual coin or medal. The image is transferred by means of a stylus operating rather like a gramophone needle, but working from the centre to the outer edge.

Reeding Security edging on coins, consisting of close vertical ridges. As a rule, this appears all round the edge but some coins, e.g. New Zealand's 50c (1967) and the Isle of Man's £1 (1978) have segments of reeding alternating with a plain edge, to help blind and partially sighted persons to identify these coins.

Re-issue A coin or note issued again after an extended lapse of time.

Relief Raised parts of the *obverse* and *reverse* of coins and medals, the opposite of *incuse*.

Remainder A note from a bank or issuing authority which has never been circulated, due to inflation, political changes or bank failure. Such notes, some-times in partial or unfinished state (e.g. missing serial numbers or signatures), are generally unloaded on to the numismatic market at a nominal sum and provide a good source of inexpensive material for the beginner.

Restrike Coin, medal or token produced from *dies* subsequent to the original use. Usually restrikes are made long after the original and can often be identified by marks caused by damage, pitting or corrosion of the dies after they were taken out of service.

Retrograde Term describing inscriptions running from right to left, or with the letters in a mirror image, thought to arise from unskilled die-cutters failing to realise that inscriptions have to be engraved in negative form to achieve a positive impression. Retrograde inscriptions are common on ancient Greek coins, but also found on Roman and Byzantine coins.

Reverse The side of a coin or medal regarded as of lesser importance; in colloquial parlance, the "tails" side.

Saltire Heraldic term for a cross in the shape of an X.

Sandwich Coin *blank* consisting of thin outer layers in one alloy bonded to a core in another. See *clad coins*.

Sceat (Anglo-Saxon for "treasure", or German *Schatz*). Money of account in Kent early in the 7th century as the twelfth part of a shilling or Merovingian gold tremissis. As a silver coin, it dates from about AD 680–700 and weighed about 20 grains, putting it on par with the Merovingian denier or penny. Sceats spread to other parts of England in the 8th century but tended to decline in weight and value, but from about 760 it was gradually superseded by the silver penny minted under Offa and his successors.

Scissel The clippings of metal left after a *blank* has been cut. Occasionally one of these clippings accidentally adheres to the blank during the striking process, producing characteristic crescent-shaped flaws on the finished coin.

Scrip Paper money of restricted validity or circulation, e.g.*Bafs* and other military scrip used in canteens and post exchanges.

Scyphate (Greek *scypha*, a skiff or small boat). Byzantine coin with a concave *flan*.

Sede Vacante (Latin for "Vacant See"). Coins struck at *ecclesiastical mints* between the death of a prelate and the election of his successor are often thus inscribed. This practice originated at Rome in the 13th century.

Seignorage or Seigneurage Royalty or percentage paid by persons bringing *bullion* to a mint for conversion into coin, but nowadays synonymous with the royalty paid by mints in respect of the precious metal versions of coins sold direct to collectors. It arises from the medieval right of the king to a small portion of the proceeds of a mint, and amounted to a tax on moneying. It has also been applied to the money accruing to the state when the coinage is re-issued in an alloy of lesser fineness, as, for example, the debased sovereigns of Henry VIII in 20 instead of 23 carat gold, the king's treasury collecting the difference.

Series Term applied to sets of medals of a thematic character, which first became fashionable in the early 18th century. Jean Dassier pioneered the medallic series in the 1720s with his set of 72 medals portraying the rulers of France till Louis XV. The idea was developed by J. Kirk, Sir Edward Thomason, J. Mudie and A. J. Stothard in Britain, and by Moritz Fuerst and Amedee Durand in Europe. The fashion died out in the 19th century, but has been revived in America and Europe since 1964.

Serrated Having a notched or toothed edge, rather like a cogwheel. Coins of this type, struck in *electrum,* an alloy of silver and gold, are known from Carthage in the 2nd century BC, and some silver denarii of Rome in the 2nd century AD also come into this category.

Sexagesimal System Monetary system in which the principal unit is divided into 60 parts. The oldest system in the Western world was based on the gold talent of 60 minae and the mina of 60 shekels. In medieval Europe 60 groschen were worth a fine mark; in England from 1551, the silver coinage was based on the crown of 60 pence, and in the south German states till 1873 the gulden was worth 60 kreuzers.

Shin Plasters Derisory term originally applied to the Continental currency notes issued during the American War of Independence, the fractional currency of the Civil War period and also the low-denomination notes of Canada between 1870 and 1935, but often applied indiscriminately to any other low-denomination, small-format notes.

Short Cross Coinage Term for the silver coinage introduced by Henry II in 1180 and minted till 1247 at which time it was replaced by the *Long Cross* type. The termination of the arms of the cross on the reverse well within the circumference encouraged the dishonest practice of *clipping*.

Shroff Mark A *countermark* applied by Indian bankers or merchants to attest the full weight and purity of coins. See also *chop*.

Siege Money See *Obsidional Currency*

Silver Precious metal, chemical symbol *Ag*, numismatic abbreviation *Ar*, from Latin *Argentum*, widely used as a coinage metal from the 6th century BC to the present day.

Sterling silver denotes an alloy of .925 fine silver with .075 copper. Fine silver alloys used over the past 2,500 years have ranged from .880 to .960 fine, but base silver has also been all too common. British coins from 1920 to 1946 were struck in .500 fine silver, while alloys of lesser fineness are known as *billon* or *vellon*. Silver alloyed with gold produces a metal called *electrum*, used for the earliest coinage of the western world, the staters of Lydia in the 7th century BC. Since 1970 silver as a medium for circulating coinage has almost virtually disappeared, yet the volume of silver coins for sale to collectors has risen considerably in recent years.

Skit Note Piece of paper masquerading as a banknote. It differs from a *counterfeit* in that its design parodies that of a genuine note, often for political, satirical or advertising reasons. Others were produced as April Fools' Day jokes or a form of Valentine (e.g. the Bank of Lovers). In recent years they have been produced as advertising gimmicks, or as coupons permitting a discount off the list price of goods.

Slug Popular name for the $50 gold pieces produced by private mints in California in the mid-19th century. The term is also applied nowadays to *tokens* intended for use in gaming machines.

Spade Guinea Name given to the guineas of George III issued between 1787 and 1799 because the shield on the reverse design resembled the shape of a spade. In Victorian times the spade guinea was extensively copied in brass for gaming counters.

Spade Money Cast bronze pieces resembling miniature spades and other agricultural implements, used as money and derived from the actual implements which had previously been used in barter. Often referred to as *Pu* or *Boo* money.

Specie Financial term denoting money in the form of precious metals (silver and gold), usually struck as coin, as opposed to money in the form of paper notes and bills of exchange. It occurs in the name of some European coins (e.g. *speciedaler*, *speciestaler* and *speciesducat*) to denote the use of fine silver or gold.

Specimen Generally used to denote a single piece, but more specifically applying to a coin in a special finish, less than *proof* in quality but superior to the general circulating version. It also denotes paper notes intended for circulation between banks or for press publicity and distinguished from the generally issued version by zero serial numbers, punch holes or a security endorsement.

Spintriae Metal tokens produced in Roman imperial times, with erotic motifs, thought to have been tickets of admission to brothels.

Spit Copper or iron rod used as a primitive form of currency in the Mediterranean area. The Greek word *belos* meant a spit, dart or bolt, and from this came the word *obolos* used for a coin worth a 6th of a drachma.

Stamp Money Both postage and revenue (fiscal) stamps have circulated as money during shortages of coins, from the American Civil War onwards. *Encased postage stamps* were used in the USA, 1861–62, before they were superseded by *Postage Currency* notes, but the same expedient was adopted by many countries during and immediately after the First World War. Stamps affixed to special cards have circulated as money in Rhodesia (now Zimbabwe) in 1900, the French colonies and Turkey during the First World War, in Spain during the Civil War (1936–39) and the Philippines during the Second World War. Stamps printed on thick card, with an inscription on the reverse signifying their parity with silver coins, were issued in Russia (1917–18) and also in Armenia, the Crimea and the Ukraine (1918–20). During the Second World War Ceylon (now Sri Lanka) and several Indian states issued small money cards with contemporary stamps printed on them.

Steel Refined and tempered from *iron*, and used in chromed or stainless versions as a coinage metal in the 20th century. Zinc-coated steel cents were issued by the USA (1943) but in the form known as *acmonital* (nickel steel) it has been extensively used by Italy since 1939. Other alloys of nickel and steel have been used for coins of the Philippines (1944–45) and Roumania since 1963. Chrome steel was used by France for 5 centime coins in 1961–64. Copper-clad steel is now extensively used for subsidiary coins formerly struck in bronze.

Sterling Word of uncertain origin denoting money of a standard weight and fineness, and hence the more general meaning of recognised worth. The traditionally accepted derivation from the Easterlings, north German merchants who settled in London in the 13th century and produced silver pennies of uniform fineness, is unlikely as the term has been found in documents a century earlier. A more plausible explanation is from Old English *steorling* ("little coin with a star"), alluding to Viking pennies with this device, or even as a diminutive of *stater*. Sterling silver denotes silver of .925 fineness.

Stone Money Primitive currency in the form of large stone discs, used in West Africa in the pre-colonial period, and in the Pacific island of Yap (now Micronesia) as recently as 1940.

Striation A pattern of alternate light and dark parallel marks or minute grooves on the surface of a coin or medal. In the latter case it is sometimes done for textural effect, but in coins it may result from faulty *annealing*. Deliberate ridging of the surface, however, was a distinctive feature of Japanese *koban* and *goryoban* coins of 1736–1862.

Styca Name given to the debased silver *sceats* of Northumbria in the 8th century.

Tael Chinese unit of weight corresponding to the European ounce and sometimes referred to as a liang. It was a measure of silver varying between 32 and 39 grams. In the 19th century it served as *money of account*, 100 British or Mexican trade dollars being worth 72 tael. The term has also been loosely applied to the Chinese silver yuan, although this was worth only .72 tael, or 7 mace and 2 candareens (10 candareens = 1 mace; 10 mace = 1 tael).

Thrymsa Early Anglo-Saxon gold coin based on the Merovingian tremissis or third-solidus, current in Kent, London and York about AD 63–75.

Tical Unit of weight in Thailand, first appearing as coins in the form of crudely shaped *bullet money* current from the 14th till the late 19th centuries. When European-style coins were introduced in 1860 the word was retained as a denomination (32 solot = 16 atts = 8 peinung or sio = 4 songpy or sik = 2 fuang= 1 salung or quarter-tical. The currency was decimalised in 1909 (100 satangs = 1 tical), and the tical was superseded by the baht about 1950.

Tin Metallic element, chemical symbol *Sn* (from Latin *Stannum*). Because of its unstable nature and tendency to oxidise badly when exposed to the atmosphere, it is unsatisfactory as a coinage metal, but has been used on several occasions, notably in Malaya, Thailand and the East Indies. In was also used for British halfpence and farthings, 1672–92.

Whitchurch & Dore of Bath 4 shilling token of 1811

Token Any piece of money whose nominal value is greater than its intrinsic value is, strictly speaking, a token or promise. Thus most of the coins issued since 1964 can be regarded in this light, but numismatists reserve the term for a piece of limited validity and circulation, produced by tradesmen, chambers of commerce and other organisations during times of a shortage of government coinage. The term is also loosely applied to metal tickets of admission, such as *communion tokens*, or *jetons* and *counters* intended for games of chance. Tokens with a nominal value may be produced for security reasons to lessen the possibility of theft from milk bottles, vending machines, telephones, parking meters and transport facilities. Tokens exchangeable for goods have been issued by co-operative societies and used in prisons and internment camps in wartime. In addition to the traditional coinage alloys, tokens have been produced in ceramics, plastics, wood, stout card, leather and even rubber, in circular, square or polygonal shapes.

Tombac Type of brass alloy with a high copper content, used in coinage requiring a rich golden colour. It is, in fact, a modern version of the *aurichalcum* used by the Romans. It was used for the Canadian 5-cent coins of 1942–43, while 5- and 10-pfennig coins of Germany have a tombac cladding on a steel core.

Touchpiece Coin kept as a lucky charm, but more specifically the medieval gold angel of England which was worn round the neck as an antidote to scrofula, otherwise known as king's evil, from the belief that the reigning monarch possessed the power of healing by touch. The ceremony of touching for king's evil involved the suspension of an angel round the victim's neck, hence the prevalence of these coins pierced for suspension.

Trade Coins Coins widely used as a medium of international trade, often far beyond the boundaries of the country issuing them. The earliest examples were the Aiginetan turtles and Athenian tetrdrachms of the classical period. In the Middle Ages the English *sterling* was widely prized on account of its silver purity. Arab dinars and Italian florins were popular as gold coins in late-medieval times, while the British gold sovereign has been the preferred gold coin of modern times. The Maria Theresa silver thaler of Austria, with its date frozen at 1782, has been minted widely down to the present time for circulation in the Near and Middle East as a trade coin. Trade dollars were minted by Britain, the USA, the Netherlands and Japan to compete with the Spanish, and later the Mexican, peso or 8-reales coins as a trading medium in the Far East.

Transport Tokens Coin-like pieces of metal, plastic or card, issued by companies and corporations to employees and exchangeable for rides on municipal transport systems, date from the mid-19th century. In more recent times similar tokens have been used in many countries to activate turnstiles in buses, trams and rapid-transit railway systems.

Treasury Note Paper money worth 10 shillings or one pound, issued by the British Treasury on the outbreak of the First World War when *specie* payments were suspended, and continuing till 1928 when the Bank of England took over responsibility for note-issuing.

Treasure Trove Articles of precious metal concealed in times of economic or political upheaval and discovered years (often centuries) later are deemed by law to be treasure trove (from the French word *trouve*, found). For further details see *Money and the Law.*

Henry VIII Silver Trial Plate from The Royal Mint Collection

Trial Plate Plate of the same metal as the current coinage against which the fineness and quality of the coins produced are compared and tested.

Troy Weight System of weights derived from the French town of Troyes whose standard pound was adopted in England in 1526. It continued in Britain till 1879 when it was abolished, with the exception of the troy ounce and its decimal parts and multiples, which were retained for gold, silver, platinum and precious stones. The troy ounce of 480 grains is used by numismatists for weighing coins.

Truncation Stylised cut at the base of a coinage effigy, sometimes containing a die number, engraver's initials or *mintmark*.

Trussel Reverse die in *hammered* coinage, the opposite of the *pile*.

Type Principal motif on a coin or medal, enabling numismatists to identify the issue.

Type Set A set of coins comprising one of each coin in a particular series, regardless of the actual date of issue.

Uncirculated Term used in grading coins to denote specimens in perfect condition, with original mint lustre. In recent years the term "Brilliant Uncirculated" has been adopted (abbreviated as BUnc or BU) both to indicate the condition of a coin, and, by The Royal Mint, to indicate the standard to which some coins are minted, being a standard between Circulation and Proof.

Uniface Coin with a device on one side only.

Vecture Term (mainly US) for a *transport token*.

Veiled Head The effigy of Queen Victoria by Thomas Brock adopted for British coinage after 1893—often referred to as the "Old Head" coinage.

Veld Pond (Dutch for "field pound"). Gold coin struck by the Boer guerrillas at Pilgrims Rest in 1902, in imitation of the British sovereign.

VF Abbreviation for Very Fine, used to describe the state of a coin or medal.

VG Abbreviation for Very Good.

Vignette Strictly speaking the pictorial element of a paper note shading off into the surrounding unprinted paper rather than having a clearly defined border or frame; but nowadays applied generally to the picture portion of a banknote, as opposed to portrait, armorial or numeral elements.

Vis-à-Vis (French for "face to face"). Term describing coins with double portraits of rulers, their profiles or busts facing each other. A good example is the English coinage of Philip and Mary, 1554–58.

Wampum Barter currency of the North American Indians, composed of shells of *Venus mercenaria* strung together to form belts or "fathoms" worth 5 shillings. Wampum were tariffed variously from three to six to the English penny in the American colonies till 1704.

Wire Money Primitive currency of the Maldive Islands in the form of lengths of silver wire known as lari, from which the modern currency unit *laree* is derived. The term was also applied to English coins of the 18th century in which the numerals of value were exceptionally thin, resembling wire.

Wooden Coins Thin pieces of wood used as tokens are known from many parts of China and Africa, and as small *Notgeld* from Austria and Germany during World War I. Wooden nickels is the name given to tokens of a commemorative nature, widely popular in the USA since 1930.

Copper Victoria Young Head Farthing

Young Head Profile of Queen Victoria sculpted by William Wyon for the Guildhall Medal of 1837 and subsequently utilised for British coins struck from 1837 to 1860 (copper) and 1887 (silver and gold).

Zinc Metallic element, chemical symbol *Zn*, widely used, with copper, as a constituent of brass. Alloyed with copper to form *tombac*, it was used for Canadian 5-cent coins (1942–43) and, coated on steel, it was used for American cents (1943). Zinc was used for *emergency coinage* in Austria, Belgium, Luxembourg and Germany (1915–18) and in Germany and German-occupied countries during World War II. Since then alloys of copper, nickel and zinc have been used for coinage in Eastern Europe.

Mintmarks
of the world

The following is a list of the initials and symbols denoting mints. In many cases, notably the Royal Mint, no mintmark was used on either British coins or those struck on behalf of other countries. Conversely many countries have only used one mintmark, that of one or other of the leading private mints.

It should be noted that the mintmarks of the main private mints have been recorded on the coins of the following countries:

H (Heaton, later the Birmingham Mint): Australia, Bolivia, British Honduras, British North Borneo, British West Africa, Bulgaria, Canada, Ceylon, Chile, Colombia, Costa Rica, Cyprus, Dominican Republic, East Africa, Ecuador, Egypt, El Salvador, Finland, French Indochina, Great Britain, Greece, Guatemala, Guernsey, Haiti, Hong Kong, Iran, Israel, Italy, Jamaica, Jersey, Liberia, Malaya and British Borneo, Mauritius, Mombasa, Mozambique, Newfoundland, Nicaragua, Poland, Roumania, Sarawak, Serbia, Siam, Straits Settlements, Uruguay and Venezuela.

FM (Franklin Mint, Philadelphia): Bahamas, Belize, British Virgin Islands, Cayman Islands, Cook Islands, Guyana, Jamaica, Liberia, Malaysia, Malta, Panama, Papua New Guinea, Philippines, Solomon Islands, Trinidad and Tobago.

PM (Pobjoy Mint, Sutton, Surrey): Ascension, Bosnia, Cook Islands, Gibraltar, Isle of Man, Liberia, Macau, Niue, Philippines, St Helena, Senegal, Seychelles, Tonga and Tristan da Cunha.

ALBANIA

L	London
R	Rome
V	Valona

ARGENTINA

BA	Buenos Aires
Bs	Buenos Aires
B.AS	Buenos Aires
JPP	Jose Policarpo Patino
M	Mendoza
PNP	Pedro Nolasco Pizarro
PP	Pedro Nolasco Pizarro
PTS	Potosi
R	Rioja
RA	Rioja
SE	Santiago del Estero
SoEo	Santiago del Estero
TN	Tucuman

AUSTRALIA

A	Perth
D	Denver
H	Heaton (1912–16)
I	Bombay (1942–43)
I	Calcutta (1916–18)
M	Melbourne
P	Perth
PL	Royal Mint, London
S	Sydney
S	San Francisco (1942–43)
Dot before and after PENNY and I on obverse	Bombay (1942–43)
Dot before and after HALFPENNY and I on obverse	Bombay (1942–43)
Dot before and after PENNY	Bombay (1942–43)
Dot after HALFPENNY	Perth
Dot before SHILLING	Perth (1946)
Dot above scroll on reverse	Sydney (1920)
Dot below scroll on reverse	Melbourne (1919–20)
Dot between designer's initials KG	Perth (1940–41)
Dot after AUSTRALIA	Perth (1952–53)

AUSTRIA

A	Vienna (1765–1872)
AH–AG	Carlsburg, Transylvania (1765–76)
AH–GS	Carlsburg (1776–80)
A–S	Hall, Tyrol (1765–74)
AS–IE	Vienna (1745)
AW	Vienna (1764, 1768)
B	Kremnitz (1765–1857)
B–L	Nagybanya (1765–71)
B–V	Nagybanya (1772–80)
C	Carlsburg (1762–64)

C	Prague (1766–1855)
C–A	Carlsburg (1746–66)
C–A	Vienna (1774–80)
CG–AK	Graz (1767–72)
CG–AR	Graz (1767)
C–K	Vienna (1765–73)
CM	Kremnitz (1779)
CVG–AK	Graz (1767–72)
CVG–AR	Graz (1767)
D	Graz (1765–72), Salzburg (1800–09)
E	Carlsburg (1765–1867)
EC–SK	Vienna (1766)
EvM–D	Kremnitz (1765–74)
EvS–AS	Prague (1765–73)
EvS–IK	Prague (1774–80)
F	Hall (1765–1807)
FH	Hall
G	Graz (1761–63)
G	Gunzburg (1764–79)
G	Nagybanya (1766–1851)
G–K	Graz (1767–72)
G–R	Graz (1746–67)
GTK	Vienna (1761)
H	Hall (1760–80)
H	Gunzburg (1765–1805)
H–A	Hall (1746–65)
H–G	Carlsburg (1765–77)
H–S	Carlsburg (1777–80)
IB–FL	Nagybanya (1765–71)
IB–IV	Nagybanya (1772–80)
IC–FA	Vienna (1774–80)
IC–IA	Vienna (1780)
IC–SK	Vienna (1765–73)
I–K	Graz (1765-67)
I–K	Vienna (1767)
IZV	Vienna (1763–65)
K	Kremnitz (1760–63)
K–B	Kremnitz (1619–1765)
K–D	Kremnitz (1765)
K–M	Kremnitz (1763–65)
M	Milan (1780–1859)
N	Nagybanya (1780)
N–B	Nagybanya (1630–1777, 1849)
O	Oravicza (1783–1816)
P	Prague (1760–63)
P–R	Prague (1746–67)
PS–IK	Prague (1774–80)
S	Hall (1765–80), Schmollnitz (1763–1816)
S–C	Gunzburg (1765–74)
SC–G	Gunzburg (1765)
S–F	Gunzburg (1775–80)
S–G	Gunzburg (1764–65)
S–IE	Vienna (1745)
SK–PD	Kremnitz (1774–80)
TS	Gunzburg (1762–88)
V	Venice (1805–66)
VC–S	Hall (1774–80)
VS–K	Prague (1774–80)
VS–S	Prague (1765–73)
W	Vienna (1748–63)
W–I	Vienna (1746–71)

BAHAMAS

FM	Franklin Mint
JP	John Pinches

BELGIUM

A	Vienna
B	Kremnitz
C	Prague
E	Carlsburg
F	Hall
G	Nagybanya
H	Gunzburg
hand	Antwerp
lion	Bruges

BELIZE (British Honduras)

FM	Franklin Mint
H	Heaton (1912–16)

BOLIVIA

H	Heaton (1892–1953)
P, PTR, PTS	Potosi

BRAZIL

A	Berlin (1913)
B	Bahia (1714–1831)
C	Cuiaba (1823–33)
G	Goias (1823–33)
M	Minas Gerais (1823–28)
P	Pernambuco
R	Rio de Janeiro (1703–1834)
RS	Rio de Janeiro (1869)
SP	Sao Paulo (1825–32)

BRITISH NORTH BORNEO (Sabah)

H	Heaton (1882–1941)

BRITISH WEST AFRICA

G	JR Gaunt, Birmingham
H	Heaton, Birmingham (1911–57)
K	King's Norton
KN	King's Norton
SA	Pretoria

BULGARIA

A	Berlin
BP	Budapest
Heaton	Heaton, Birmingham (1881–1923)
KB	Kormoczbanya
cornucopia	Paris
thunderbolt	Poissy

CANADA

C	Ottawa
H	Heaton (1871–1907)
maple leaf	Ottawa (on coins struck after the year inscribed on them)

CENTRAL AMERICAN REPUBLIC

CR	San Jose (Costa Rica)
G	Guatemala

NG	Guatemala
T	Tegucigalpa (Honduras)

CEYLON

H	Heaton (1912)

CHILE

A	Agustin de Infante y Prado (1768–72)
AJ	The above and Jose Maria de Bobadilla (1800–01)
D	Domingo Eizaguirre
DA	Domingo Eizaguirre and Agustin de Infante (1772–99)
BFF	Francisco Rodriguez Brochero
FJJF	Brochero and Jose Maria de Bobadilla (1803–17)
H	Heaton (1851)
J	Jose Larraneta (1749–67)
So	Santiago
VA	Val Distra

COLOMBIA

A	Paris
B	Bogota
BA	Bogota
B.B	Bogota
H	Heaton (1912)
M	Medellin
NR	Nuevo Reino
NoRo	Nuevo Reino
P	Popayan
PN, Pn	Popayan
SM	Santa Marta

COSTA RICA

CR	San Jose (1825–1947)
HBM	Heaton (1889–93)
S	San Domingo
SD	San Domingo

COURLAND

ICS	Justin Carl Schroder
IFS	Johan Friedrich Schmickert

CYPRUS

H	Heaton (1881–2)

DENMARK

FF	Altona
KM	Copenhagen Altona (1842)
crown	Copenhagen
heart	Copenhagen
orb	Altona (1839–48)

Other letters are the initials of mintmasters and moneyers

DOMINICAN REPUBLIC

HH	Heaton (1888–1919)

EAST AFRICA

A	Ackroyd & Best, Morley
H	Heaton (1910–64)
I	Bombay
K	Kynoch (IMI)
KN	King's Norton
SA	Pretoria

ECUADOR

BIRM^{M}H	Heaton (1915)
BIRMING-HAM	Heaton (1899–1900, 1928)
D	Denver
H	Heaton (1890, 1909, 1924–5)
HEATON BIRMING-HAM	Heaton (1872–95)
HF	Le Locle
LIMA	Lima
Mo	Mexico
PHILA	Philadelphia
QUITO	Quito
SANTIAGO	Santiago de Chile

EGYPT

H	Heaton (1904–37)

EL SALVADOR

CAM	Central American Mint, San Salvador
H	Heaton (1889–1913)
Mo	Mexico
S	San Francisco

FIJI

S	San Francisco

FINLAND

H	Heaton (1921)
heart	Copenhagen (1922). Since then coins have been struck at Helsinki without a mintmark.

Initials of mintmasters:

S	August Soldan (1864–85)
L	Johan Lihr (1885–1912)
S	Isaac Sundell (1915–47)
L	V. U. Liuhto (1948)
H	Uolevi Helle (1948–58)
S	Allan Soiniemi (1958–75)
SH	Soiniemi & Heikki Halvaoja (1967–71)
K	Timo Koivuranta (1977, 1979)
KN	Koivuranta and Antti Neuvonen (1978)
KT	Koivuranta and Erja Tielinen (1982)
KM	Koivuranta and Pertti Makinen (1983)
N	Reino Nevalainen (1983)

FRANCE

A	Paris (1768)
AA	Metz (1775–98)
B	Rouen (1786–1857)
B	Beaumont le Roger (1943–58)
BB	Strasbourg (1743–1870)
C	Castelsarrasin (1914, 1942–46)

CC	Genoa (1805)
CL	Genoa (1813–14)
D	Lyons (1771–1857)
G	Geneva (1796–1805)
H	La Rochelle (1770–1837)
L	Limoges (1766–1837)
K	Bordeaux (1759–1878)
L	Bayonne (1761–1837)
M	Toulouse (1766–1837)
MA	Marseilles (1787–1857)
N	Montpellier (1766–93)
O	Riom
P	Dijon
Q	Perpignan (1777–1837)
R	Royal Mint, London (1815)
R	Orleans (1780–92)
T	Nantes (1739–1835)
U	Turin (1814)
V	Troyes
W	Lille (1759–1857)
X	Amiens (1740)
&	Aix en Provence (1775)
9	Rennes
cow	Pau (1746–93)
flag	Utrecht (1811–14)
crowned R	Rome (1811–14)
thunderbolt	Poissy (1922-24)
star	Madrid (1916)

In addition, French coins include symbols denoting the privy marks of Engravers General (Chief Engravers since 1880) and Mint Directors.

GERMANY

The first name gives the location of the mint, and the second the name of the country or state issuing the coins.

A	Amberg, Bavaria (1763–94)
A	Berlin (1850)
A	Clausthal, Hannover (1832–49)
AE	Breslau, Silesia (1743–51)
AGP	Cleve, Rhineland (1742–43)
AK	Dusseldorf, Julich-Berg (1749–66)
ALS	Berlin (1749)
B	Bayreuth, Franconia (1796–1804)
B	Breslau, Silesia (1750–1826)
B	Brunswick, Brunswick (1850–60)
B	Brunswick, Westphalia (1809–13)
B	Dresden, Saxony (1861–72)
B	Hannover, Brunswick (1860–71)
B	Hannover, East Friesland (1823–25)
B	Hannover, Hannover (1821–66)
B	Hannover, Germany (1866-78)
B	Regensburg, Regensburg (1809)
B	Vienna, Germany (1938–45)
BH	Frankfurt (1808)
B–H	Regensburg, Rhenish Confederation (1802–12)
C	Cassel, Westphalia (1810–13)
C	Clausthal, Brunswick
C	Clausthal, Westphalia (1810–11)
C	Dresden, Saxony (1779–1804)
C	Frankfurt, Germany (1866–79)
CHI	Berlin (1749–63)
CLS	Dusseldorf, Julich-Berg (1767–70)
D	Aurich, East Friesland (1750–1806)
D	Dusseldorf, Rhineland (1816–48)
D	Munich, Germany (1872)
E	Dresden, Germany (1872–87)
E	Koenigberg, East Prussia (1750–98)
E	Muldenhutte, Germany (1887–1953)
EC	Leipzig, Saxony (1753–63)
EGN	Berlin (1725–49)
F	Dresden, Saxony (1845–58)
F	Magdeburg, Lower Saxony (1740–1806)
F	Cassel, Hesse-Cassel (1803–07)
F	Stuttgart, Germany (1872)
FW	Dresden, Saxony (1734–63)
G	Dresden, Saxony (1833–44, 1850–54)
G	Glatz, Silesia (1807–09)
G	Karlsruhe, Germany (1872)
G	Stettin, Pomerania (1750–1806)
GK	Cleve (1740–55)
GN	Bamberg, Bamberg
H	Darmstadt, Germany (1872–82)
H	Dresden, Saxony (1804–12)
HK	Rostock, Rostock (1862–64)
I	Hamburg, Germany (1872)
IDB	Dresden, Prussian occupation (1756–59)
IEC	Dresden, Saxony (1779–1804)
IF	Leipzig, Saxony (1763–65)
IGG	Leipzig, Saxony (1716–34, 1813–32)
J	Hamburg, Germany (1873)
J	Paris, Westphalia (1808–09)
L	Leipzig, Saxony (1761–62)
MC	Brunswick, Brunswick (1813–14, 1820)
PM	Dusseldorf, Julich-Berg (1771–83)
PR	Dusseldorf, Julich-Berg (1783–1804)
S	Dresden, Saxony (1813–32)
S	Hannover, Hannover (1839–44)
S	Schwabach, Franconia (1792–94)
SGH	Dresden, Saxony (1804–12)
ST	Strickling, Blomberg (1820–40)

GREAT BRITAIN

A	Ashby (1645)
B	Nicolas Briot (1631–39)
B	Bridgnorth (1646)
B	Bristol (1696)
Br	Bristol (1643–45)
C	Chester (1696)
CARL	Carlisle (1644–45)
CC	Corfe Castle (1644)
CHST	Chester (1644)
CR	Chester (1644)
E	Southwark (1547–49)
E	Exeter (1696)
E	Edinburgh (1707–13)
E*	Edinburgh (1707–09)
H	Heaton, Birmingham (1874–1919)
HC	Hartlebury Castle (1646)
K	London (1547–49)
KN	King's Norton

N	Norwich (1696)
OX	Oxford (1644–45)
OXON	Oxford (1644)
PC	Pontefract (1648–49)
SC	Scarborough (1644–45)
SOHO	Birmingham (1797–1806)
T	Canterbury (1549)
TC	Bristol (1549)
WS	Bristol (1547–49)
Y	Southwark (1551)
boar	Shrewsbury (1643–44)
book	Aberystwyth (1638–42)
bow	Durham House (1548–49)
castle	Exeter (1644–45)
crown	Aberystwyth Furnace (1648–49)
plume	Shrewsbury (1642)
plume	Oxford (1642–46)
plume	Bristol (1643–46)

Other symbols and marks on the hammered coins of Great Britain are usually referred to as Initial Marks. Complete listings of these marks appear in a number of specialist publications.

GREECE

A	Paris
B	Vienna
BB	Strasbourg
H	Heaton (1921)
K	Bordeaux
KN	King's Norton
owl	Aegina (1828–32)
owl	Athens (1838-55)
thunderbolt	Poissy

GUATEMALA

CG	Guatemala City (1733-76)
G	Guatemala City (1776)
H	Heaton (1894–1901)
NG	Nueva Guatemala (1777)

GUERNSEY

H	Heaton (1855–1949)

HAITI

A	Paris
HEATON	Heaton (1863)

HONDURAS

A	Paris (1869–71)
T	Tegucigalpa (1825–62)

HONG KONG

H	Heaton (1872–1971)
KN	King's Norton

HUNGARY

A	Vienna
B	Kremnitz
BP	Budapest
CA	Vienna
G	Nagybanya
GN	Nagybanya
GYF	Carlsburg
HA	Hall
K	Kremnitz
KB	Kremnitz
NB	Nagybanya
S	Schmollnitz
WI	Vienna

INDIA

B	Bombay (1835-1947)
C	Calcutta (1835-1947)
I	Bombay (1918)
L	Lahore (1943-45)
M	Madras (1869)
P	Pretoria (1943-44)
diamond	Bombay
dot in diamond	Hyderabad
split diamond	Hyderabad
star	Hyderabad

IRAN

H	Heaton (1928–29)

IRAQ

I	Bombay

ISRAEL

H	Heaton (1951–52)
star of David	Jerusalem

ITALY AND STATES

B	Bologna
B/I	Birmingham (1893–4)
FIRENZE	Florence
H	Heaton (1866–67)
KB	Berlin
M	Milan
N	Naples
OM	Strasbourg
R	Rome
T	Turin
V	Venice
ZV	Venice
anchor	Genoa
eagle head	Turin

JAMAICA

C	Ottawa
FM	Franklin Mint
H	Heaton (1882–1916)

JERSEY

H	Heaton (1877)

KENYA

C/M	Calcutta
H	Heaton (1911–64)

LIBERIA

B	Berne
FM	Franklin Mint
H	Heaton (1896–1906)
PM	Pobjoy Mint

LIECHTENSTEIN

A Vienna
B Berne
M Munich

LUXEMBOURG

A Paris
H Gunzburg
anchor Paris
angel Brussels
caduceus Utrecht
double eagle Brussels
sword Utrecht

MALAYSIA

B Bombay
FM Franklin Mint
H Heaton (1955–61)
I Calcutta (1941)
I Bombay (1945)
KN King's Norton
W James Watt, Birmingham

MAURITIUS

H Heaton (1877–90)
SA Pretoria

MEXICO

A, As Alamos
C, CN Culiacan
CA, CH Chihuahua
Ce Real del Catorce
D, Do Durango
Eo Tlalpam
GA Guadalajara
GC Guadelupe y Calvo
Go Guanajuato
Ho Hermosillo
M, Mo Mexico City
Mo Morelos
MX Mexico City
O, OA, OKA Oaxaca
Pi San Luis Potosi
SLPi San Luis Potosi
TC Tierra Caliente
Z, Zs Zacatecas

MONACO

A Paris
M Monte Carlo
clasped hands Cabanis
thunderbolt Poissy

MOZAMBIQUE

H Heaton (1894)
R Rio

NETHERLANDS AND COLONIES

Austrian Netherlands (1700-93)
H Amsterdam
S Utrecht
W Vienna
hand Antwerp
head Brussels
lion Bruges

Kingdom of the Netherlands
B Brussels (1821–30)
D Denver (1943–45)
P Philadelphia (1941–45)
S Utrecht (1816–36)
S San Francisco (1944–45)
Sa Surabaya
caduceus Utrecht

NICARAGUA

H Heaton (1880–1916)
NR Leon de Nicaragua

NORWAY

hammers Kongsberg

PANAMA

CHI Valcambi
FM Franklin Mint

PERU

AREQ, AREQUIPA Arequipa
AYACUCHO Ayacucho
CUZCO, CoCuzco
L, LM, LR Lima
LIMAE Lima
PASCO Pasco
Paz, Po Pasco
P Lima (1568-70)
P Philadelphia
S San Francisco

PHILIPPINES

BSP Bangko Sentral Pilipinas
D Denver (1944–45)
FM Franklin Mint
M, MA Manila
PM Pobjoy Mint
S San Francisco (1903–47)
5 point star Manila

POLAND

AP Warsaw (1772–74)
CI Cracow (1765–68)
EB Warsaw (1774–92)
EC Leipzig (1758–63)
FF Stuttgart (1916–17)
FH Warsaw (1815–27)
FS Warsaw (1765–68)
FWoF Dresden (1734–64)
G Cracow (1765–72)
H Heaton (1924)
IB Warsaw (1811–27)
IGS Dresden (1716–34)
IP Warsaw (1834–43)
IS Warsaw (1768–74)
JGG Leipzig (1750–53)

JS	Warsaw (1810–11)
KG	Warsaw (1829–34)
MV, MW	Warsaw
arrow	Warsaw (1925–39)
Dot after date	Royal Mint (1925)
8 *torches*	Paris (1924)

ROUMANIA

B	Bucharest (1879–85)
C	Bucharest (1886)
H	Heaton (1867–1930)
HUGUENIN	Le Locle
J	Hamburg
KN	King's Norton
V	Vienna
W	Watt, Birmingham
thunderbolt	Poissy

RUSSIA

AM	Annensk (1762–96)
BM	Warsaw (1825–55)
bM	St Petersburg (1796)
C–M	Sestroretsk (1762–96)
CM	Souzan (1825–55)
E–M	Ekaterinburg (1762–1810)
KM	Kolpina (1810)
K–M	Kolyvan (1762–1810)
MM, M–M	Moscow (1730–96)
MMD	Moscow (1730–96)
MW	Warsaw (1842–54)
NM	Izhorsk (1811–21)
SP	St Petersburg (1798–1800)
SPB	St Petersburg (1724–1915)
SPM	St Petersburg (1825–55)
T–M	Feodosia (1762–96)

SAN MARINO

M	Milan
R	Rome
SIAM (Thailand)	H Heaton (1898)

SOUTH AFRICA

SA	Pretoria

SPAIN

B	Burgos
B, BA	Barcelona
Bo	Bilbao
C	Catalonia
C	Cuenca
C	Reus
CA	Zaragoza
G	Granada
GNA	Gerona
LD	Lerida
J, JA	Jubia
M, MD	Madrid
P	Palma de Majorca
PpP, PL, PA	Pamplona
S, S/L	Seville
Sr	Santander
T, To, Tole	Toledo
TOR:SA	Tortosa
V, VA, VAL	Valencia
crowned C	Cadiz
crowned M	Madrid
aqueduct	Segovia
crowned shield	Tarragona
pomegranate	Granada
quartered shield	Palma
scallop	Coruna
stars:	
3 points	Segovia
4 points	Jubia
5 points	Manila
6 points	Madrid
7 points	Seville (1833)
8 points	Barcelona (1838)
wavy lines	Valladolid

SURINAM

P	Philadelphia
S	Sydney
caduceus	Utrecht

SWITZERLAND

A	Paris
AB	Strasbourg
B	Berne
B	Brussels (1874)
BA	Basle
BB	Strasbourg
S	Solothurn

URUGUAY

H	Heaton (1869)

UNITED STATES OF AMERICA

C	Charlotte, North Carolina
Cc	Carson City, Nevada
D	Dahlonega, Georgia (1838–61)
D	Denver, Colorado (1906)
O	New Orleans
P	Philadelphia
S	San Francisco
W	West Point

VENEZUELA

A	Paris
H	Heaton (1852)
HEATON	Heaton (1852–63)

YUGOSLAVIA (including former Serbia)

A	Paris
H	Heaton (1883–84)
KOBHNUA, A.D.	Kovnica
V	Vienna
thunderbolt	Poissy

PETER MORRIS

Coins • Banknotes • Antiquities • Tokens • Medals

Dealer in Coins & Medals

Ask for our latest Coin, Token or Banknote List via our **FREE POST** Service or visit our web-site:

www.petermorris.co.uk

or e-mail: **info@petermorris.co.uk**

Retail: **1 STATION CONCOURSE, BROMLEY NORTH, BR STATION, KENT**

Monday - Friday 10am - 1pm, 2pm - 6pm

Closed Wednesdays, Saturdays 9am - 2pm

Tel: 020 8313 3410 Fax: 020 8466 8502

Postal: **P.O. BOX 223, BROMLEY, KENT BR1 4EQ**

BNTA

GLENN OGDEN COINS

www.glennogdencoins.com

British coins
Crowns to Farthings
Bought and Sold

- Please ask for our list -

BNTA

53 Chestnut Crescent,
Culver Green,
Chudleigh TQ13 0PT
Tel: 01626 859350 Mobile: 07971 709427
Email: glenn@gillianogden.wanadoo.co.uk

Weighton Coin Wonders

Tel: 01430 879740 / 07905 467650

e-mail: **sales@weightoncoin.co.uk**

We specialise in British & Colonial Gold & Silver coins & sets of the modern age. Sovereigns of different Monarchs, dates & Mint Marks also available.

BNTA BNTA

Always in stock are:

- **Gold Proof Coins & Sets**
- **Silver Proof Coins & Sets**
- **Gold & Silver Bullion Coins**
- **Royal Mint Collectors Pieces**
- **Gold Sovereigns**

Visit our e-shop and order on line at

www.weightoncoin.co.uk

18 High Street, Market Weighton, York, YO43 3AH

We also buy single coins or whole collections.

Coin inscriptions

This alphabetical listing is confined to inscriptions found on coins, mainly in the form of mottoes or of a commemorative nature. Names of rulers are, for the most part, excluded. Where the inscription is in a language other than English a translation is given, followed by the name of the issuing country or authority in parentheses.

A Deo et Caesare From God and the Emperor (Frankfurt).

A Domino Factum est Istud et est Mirabile in Oculis Nostris This is the Lord's doing and it is marvellous in our eyes (England, Mary).

A Solo Iehova Sapientia From God alone comes true wisdom (Wittgenstein).

Ab Inimicis Meis Libera Me Deus Free me from enemies (Burgundy).

Ad Legem Conventionis According to the law of the Convention (Furstenberg).

Ad Normam Conventionis According to the standard of the Convention (Prussia).

Ad Palmam Pressa Laeturo Resurgo Pressed to the palm I rise more joyfully (Wittgenstein).

Ad Usam Luxemburgi CC Vallati For the use of the besieged Luxembourgers (Luxembourg siege coins).

Adiuva Nos Deus Salutaris Noster Help us, O God, our Saviour (Lorraine).

Adventus Optimi Principis The coming of the noblest prince (Papacy).

Aes Usibus Aptius Auro Bronze in its uses is more suitable than gold (Brazil).

Aeternum Meditans Decus An ornament intended for all time (Alencon).

Aliis Inserviendo Consumor I spend my life devoted to others (Brunswick-Wolfenbuttel).

Alles Mit Bedacht All with reflection (Brunswick).

Amor Populi Praesidium Regis The love of the people is the king's protection (England, Charles I).

Ang Fra Dom Hib & Aquit (King) of England and France, Lord of Ireland and Aquitaine (England, Edward III).

Anno Regni Primo In the first year of the reign (Britain, edge inscription on crowns).

Apres les Tenebres la Lumiere After the shadows, the light (Geneva).

Archangelus Michael Archangel Michael (Italy, Grimoald IV).

Ardua ad Gloriam Via Struggles are the way to glory (Waldeck).

Arte Mea Bis Iustus Moneta Lud Iust By my art I am twice the just coin of King Louis (France, 1641).

Aspera Oblectant Wild places delight (Nassau-Weilburg).

Aspice Pisas Sup Omnes Specio Behold the coin of Pisa, superior to all (Pisa).

Audiatur Altera Pars Let the other part be heard (Stavelot).

Auf Gott Trawe Ich In God I trust (Brunswick).

Ausen Gefaesen der Kirchen und Burger From the vessels of the Church and citizens (Frankfurt siege, 1796).

Auspicio Regis et Senatus Angliae By authority of the king and parliament of England (East India Company).

Auxilio fortissimo Dei With the strongest help of God (Mecklenburg).

Auxilium de Sanctio Aid from the sanctuary (Papacy).

Auxilium Meum a Dno Qui Fecit Celum e Terram My help comes from God who made heaven and earth (Portugal).

Beata Tranquillatis Blessed tranquillity (Rome, Licinius II).

Beatus Qui Speravit in dom Blessed is he who has hoped in the Lord (Mansfeld).

Benedic Haereditati Tuae Blessings on your inheritance (Savoy).

Benedicta Sit Sancta Trinitas Blessed be the Holy Trinity (Albon).

Benedictio Domini Divites Facit The blessing of the Lord makes the rich (Teschen).

Benedictus Qui Venit in Nomine Domini Blessed is he who comes in the name of the Lord (Flanders).

Beschaw das Ziel Sage Nicht Viel Consider the matter but say little (Quedlinburg).

Besser Land und Lud Verloren als ein Falscher Aid Geschworn Better to lose land and wealth than swear a false oath (Hesse).
Bey Gott ist Rath und That With God is counsel and deed (Mansfeld).
Britanniarum Regina Queen of the Britains (Britain, Victoria).
Britt Omn Rex King of all the Britains (i.e. Britain and the overseas dominions) (Britain, 1902–52).
Cal et Car Com de Fugger in Zin et Norn Sen & Adm Fam Cajetan and Carl, Counts of Fugger in Zinnenberg and Nordendorf, Lords and Administrators of the Family (Empire, Fugger).
Candide et Constanter Sincerely and steadfastly (Hesse-Cassel).
Candide sed Provide Clearly but cautiously (Osterwitz).
Candore et Amore With sincerity and love (Fulda).
Candore et Constantia With sincerity and constancy (Bavaria).
Capit Cath Ecclesia Monasteriensis Chapter of the Cathedral Church of Munster (Munster).
Capit Eccle Metropolit Colon Chapter of the Metropolitan Church of Cologne (Cologne).
Capitulum Regnans Sede Vacante Chapter governing, the See being vacant (Eichstadt).
Carola Magna Ducissa Feliciter Regnante Grand Duchess Charlotte, happily reigning (Luxembourg).
Carolus a Carolo Charles (I) to Charles (II) (England).
Cedunt Prementi Fata The fates yield to him who presses (Ploen, Hese-Cassel).
Charitate et Candore With charity and sincerity (East Frisia).
Charta Magna Bavariae The Great Charter of Bavaria (Bavaria).
Christo Auspice Regno I reign under the auspices of Christ (England, Charles I).
Christus Spes Una Salutis Christ is our one hope of salvation (Cleve).
Chur Mainz Electoral Principality of Mainz (Mainz).
Circumeundo Servat et Ornat It serves and decorates by going around (Sweden).
Civibus Quorum Pietas Coniuratione Die III Mai MDCCXCI Obrutam et Deletam Libertate Polona Tueri Conabatur Respublica Resurgens To the citizens whose piety the resurgent commonwealth tried to protect Poland overturned and deprived of liberty by the conspiracy of the third day of May 1791 (Poland).
Civitas Lucemborgiensis Millesimum Ovans Expletannum Completing the celebration of a thousand years of the city of Luxembourg (Luxembourg).
Civium Industria Floret Civitas By the industry of its people the state flourishes (Festival of Britain crown, 1951).
Cluniaco Cenobio Petrus et Paulus Peter and Paul from the Abbey of Cluny (Cluny).
Comes Provincie Fili Regis Francie Court of Provence and son of the King of France (Provence).
Communitas et Senatus Bonon City and senate of Bologna (Bologna).
Concordia Fratrum The harmony of the brothers (Iever).
Concordia Patriae Nutrix Peace, the nurse of the fatherland (Waldeck).
Concordia Res Parvae Crescunt Little things increase through harmony (Batavian Republic).
Concordia Res Parvae Crescunt, Discordia Dilabuntur By harmony little things increase, by discord they fall apart (Lowenstein-Wertheim-Virneburg).
Concordia Stabili With lasting peace (Hildesheim).
Confidens Dno Non Movetur He who trusts in God is unmoved (Spanish Netherlands).
Confidentia in Deo et Vigilantia Trust in God and vigilance (Prussian Asiatic Company).
Confoederato Helvetica Swiss Confederation (Switzerland)
Conjuncto Felix Fortunate in his connections (Solms).
Conservator Urbis Suae Saviour of his city (Rome, 4th century).
Consilio et Aequitate With deliberation and justice (Fulda).
Consilio et Virtutis With deliberation and valour (Hesse-Cassel).
Constanter et Sincere Steadfastly and sincerely (Lautern).
Crescite et Multiplicamini Increase and multiply (Maryland).
Cristiana Religio Christian religion (Germany, 11th century).
Crux Benedicat May the cross bless you (Oldenburg).
Cuius Cruore Sanati Sumus By His sacrifice are we healed (Reggio).
Cultores Sui Deus Protegit God protects His followers (England, Charles I).
Cum Deo et Die (Jure) With God and the day (Wurttemberg).
Cum Deo et Jure With God and the law (Wurttemberg).
Cum Deo et Labore With God and work (Wittgenstein).
Cum His Qui Orderant Pacem Eram Pacificus With those who order peace I was peaceful (Zug).
Curie Bonthon to so Doulo Protect his servant, o Lord (Byzantine Empire).
Custos Regni Deus God is the guardian of the kingdom (Naples and Sicily).
Da Gloriam Deo et Eius Genitrici Marie Give glory to God and His mother Mary (Wurttemberg).
Da Mihi Virtutem Contra Hostes Tuos Give me valour against mine enemies (Netherlands, Charles V).

Dat Wort is Fleis Gworden The word is made flesh (Muster).
Date Caesaris Caesari et Quae Sunt Dei Deo Render unto Caesar the things that are Caesar's and unto God the things that are God's (Stralsund).
De Oficina . . . From the mint of . . . (France, medieval).
Decreto Reipublicae Nexu Confoederationis lunctae Die V Xbris MDCCXCII Stanislao Augusto Regnante By decree of the state in conjunction with the joint federation on the fifth day of December 1792, Stanislaus Augustus ruling (Poland).
Decus et Tutamen An ornament and a safeguard (Britain, pound).
Deducet Nos Mirabiliter Dextera Tua Thy right hand will guide us miraculously (Savoy).
Denarium Terrae Mariae Penny of Maryland (Maryland).
Deo Conservatori Pacis To God, preserver of peace (Brandenburg-Ansbach).
Deo OM Auspice Suaviter et Fortiter sed Luste nec Sibi sed Suis Under the auspices of God, greatest and best, pleasantly and bravely but justly, not for himself but for his people (Speyer).
Deo Patriae et Subditio For God, fatherland and neighbourhood (Mainz).
Der Recht Glaubt In Ewig Lebt Who believes in right will live in eternity (Linange-Westerburg).
Der Rhein ist Deutschlands Strom Nicht Deutschlands Grenze The Rhine is Germany's River not Germany's Frontier.
Deum Solum Adorabis You will venerate God alone (Hesse).
Deus Constituit Regna God establishes kingdoms (Ni jmegen).
Deus Dat Qui Vult God gives to him who wishes (Hanau-Munzenberg).
Deus et Dominus God and Lord (Rome, 3rd century).
Deus in Adiutorium Meum Intende God stretch out in my assistance (France).
Deus Providebit God will provide (Lowenstein-Wertheim-Virneburg).
Deus Refugium Meum God is my refuge (Cleve).
Deus Solatium Meum God is my comfort (Sweden).
Dextera Domini Exaltavit Me The right hand of God has raised me up (Modena, Spain).
Dextra Dei Exalta Me The right hand of God exalts me (Denmark).
Dieu et Mon Droit God and my right (Britain, George IV).
Dilexit Dns Andream The Lord delights in St Andrew (Holstein).
Dilexit Dominus Decorem lustitiae The Lord is pleased with the beauty of justice (Unterwalden).
Dirige Deus Gressus Meos O God, direct my steps (Tuscany, Britain, Una £5).
Discerne Causam Meam Distinguish my cause (Savoy).
Divina Benedictiae et Caesarea lustitia Sacrifice of blessings and imperial justice (Coblenz).
Dn Ihs Chs Rex Regnantium Lord Jesus Christ, King of Kings (Rome, Justinian II).
Dns Ptetor Ms Z Lib'ator Ms The Lord is my protector and liberator (Scotland, David II).
Dominabitur Gentium et Ipse He himself will also be lord of the nations (Austrian Netherlands).
Domine Conserva Nos in Pace O Lord preserve us in peace (Basle, Mulhausen).
Domine Elegisti Lilium Tibi O Lord Thou hast chosen the lily for Thyself (France, Louis XIV).
Domine ne in Furore Tuo Arguas Me O Lord rebuke me not in Thine anger (England, Edward III).
Domine Probasti Me et Congnovisti Me O Lord Thou hast tested me and recognised me (Mantua).
Domini est Regnum The Kingdom is the Lord's (Austrian Netherlands).
Dominus Deus Omnipotens Rex Lord God, almighty King (Viking coins).
Dominus Mihi Adiutor The Lord is my helper (Spanish Netherlands).
Dominus Providebit The Lord will provide (Berne).
Dominus Spes Populi Sui The Lord is the hope of his people (Lucerne).
Donum Dei ex Fodinis Vilmariens A gift of God from the Vilmar mines (Coblenz).
Duce Deo Fide et Justicia By faith and justice lead us to God (Ragusa).
Dum Praemor Amplior I increase while I die prematurely (Savoy).
Dum Spiro Spero While I live, I hope (Pontefract siege coins).
Dum Totum Compleat Orbem Until it fills the world (France, Henri II).
Dura Pati Virtus Valour endures hardships (Saxe-Lauenburg).
Durae Necessitatis Through force of necessity (Bommel siege, 1599).
Durum Telum Necessitas Hardship is a weapon of necessity (Minden).
Dux et Gubernatores Reip Genu Duke and governors of the republic of Genoa (Genoa).
E Pluribus Unum One out of more (USA).
Eccl S. Barbarae Patronae Fodin Kuttenbergensium Duo Flor Arg Puri The church of St Barbara, patron of the Kuttensberg mines, two florins of pure silver (Hungary).
Een en Ondelbaer Sterk One and indivisible (Batavian Republic).
Eendracht Mag Macht Unity makes strength (Belgium, South African Republic).
Einigkeit Recht und Freiheit Union, right and freedom (Germany).
Electorus Saxoniae Administrator Elector and administrator of Saxony (Saxony).

Elimosina Alms (France, Pepin).
Ep Fris & Ratisb Ad Prum Pp Coad Aug Bishop of Freising and Regensburg, administrator of Pruem, prince-provost, co-adjutant bishop of Augsburg (Trier).
Equa Libertas Deo Gratia Frat Pax in Virtute Tua et in Domino Confido I believe in equal liberty by the grace of God, brotherly love in Thy valour and in the Lord (Burgundy).
Equitas Iudicia Tua Dom Equity and Thy judgments O Lord (Gelderland).
Espoir Me Conforte Hope comforts me (Mansfeld).
Espreuve Faicto Par Lexpres Commandement du Roy Proof made by the express commandment of the King (France, piedforts).
Et in Minimis Integer Faithful even in the smallest things (Olmutz).
Ex Auro Argentes Resurgit From gold it arises, silver again (Sicily).
Ex Auro Sinico From Chinese gold (Denmark).
Ex Flammis Orior I arise from the flames (Hohenlohe-Neuenstein-Ohringen).
Ex Fodinis Bipontio Seelbergensibus From the Seelberg mines of Zweibrucken (Pfalz-Birkenfeld).
Ex Metallo Novo From new metal (Spain).
Ex Uno Omnis Nostra Salus From one is all our salvation (Eichstadt, Mulhouse).
Ex Vasis Argent Cleri Mogunt Pro Aris et Focis From the silver vessels of the clergy of Mainz for altars and for hearths (Mainz).
Ex Visceribus Fodinse Bieber From the bowels of the Bieber mine (Hanau-Munzenberg).
Exaltabitur in Gloria He shall be exalted in glory (England, quarter nobles).
Exemplum Probati Numismatis An example of a proof coin (France, Louis XIII piedforts).
Exemtae Eccle Passau Episc et SRI Princ Prince Bishop of the freed church of Passau, prince of the Holy Roman Empire (Passau).
Expectate Veni Come, o expected one (Roman Britain, Carausius).
Extremum Subidium Campen Kampen under extreme siege (Kampen, 1578).
Exurgat Deus et Dissipentur Inimici Eius Let God arise and let His enemies be scattered (England, James I).
Faciam Eos in Gentem Unam I will make them one nation (England, unites and laurels).
Faith and Truth I will Bear unto You (UK £5, 1993).
Fata Consiliis Potiora The fates are more powerful than councils (Hesse-Cassel).
Fata Viam Invenient The fates will find a way (Gelderland).
Fecit Potentiam in Brachio Suo He put power in your forearm (Lorraine).
Fecunditas Fertility (Naples and Sicily).
Fel Temp Reparatio The restoration of lucky times (Rome, AD 348).
Felicitas Perpetua Everlasting good fortune (Rome, Constantius II).
Felix coniunctio Happy Union (Brandenburg-Ansbach).
Fiat Misericordia Tua Dne Let Thy mercy be O Lord (Gelderland).
Fiat Voluntas Domini Perpetuo Let the goodwill of the Lord last for ever (Fulda).
Fidei Defensor Defender of the Faith (Britain).
Fidelitate et Fortitudine With fidelity and fortitude (Batthanyi).
Fideliter et Constanter Faithfully and steadfastly (Saxe-Coburg-Gotha).
Fidem Servando Patriam Tuendo By keeping faith and protecting the fatherland (Savoy).
Filius Augustorum Son of emperors (Rome, 4th century).
Fisci Iudaici Calumnia Sublata The false accusation of the Jewish tax lifted (Rome, Nerva).
Florent Concordia Regna Through harmony kingdoms flourish (England, Charles I and II).
Fortitudo et Laus Mea Dominu Fortitude and my praise in the Lord (Sardinia).
Free Trade to Africa by Act of Parliment *(Sic)* (Gold Coast).
Friedt Ernehrt Unfriedt Verzehrt Peace nourishes, unrest wastes (Brunswick).
Fulgent Sic Littora Rheni Thus shine the banks of the Rhine (Mannheim).
Fundator Pacis Founder of peace (Rome, Severus).
Gaudium Populi Romani The joy of the Roman people (Rome, 4th century).
Gen C Mar VI Dim Col USC & RAMAI Cons & S Conf M General field marshal, colonel of the only dragoon regiment, present privy councillor of both their sacred imperial and royal apostolic majesties, and state conference minister (Batthanyi).
Gerecht und Beharrlich Just and steadfast (Bavaria).
Germ Hun Boh Rex AAD Loth Ven Sal King of Germany, Hungary and Bohemia, Archduke of Austria, Duke of Lorraine, Venice and Salzburg (Austria).
Germ Jero Rex Loth Bar Mag Het Dux King of Germany, Jerusalem, Lorraine and Bar, Grand Duke of Tuscany (Austrian Netherlands).
Germania Voti Compos Germany sharing the vows (Brandenburg-Ansbach).
Gloria ex Amore Patriae Glory from love of country (Denmark).
Gloria in Excelsis Deo Glory to God in the highest (France, Sweden).
Gloria Novi Saeculi The glory of a new century (Rome, Gratian).
God With Us (England, Commonwealth).
Godt Met Ons God with us (Oudewater).
Gottes Freundt der Pfaffen Feindt God's friend, the Pope's enemy (Brunswick, Christian).

Gratia Dei Sum Id Quod Sum By the grace of God, I am what I am (Navarre).
Gratia Di Rex By the grace of God, king (France, 8th century).
Gratitudo Concivibus Exemplum Posteritati Gratitude to fellow Citizens, an example to posterity (Poland).
Gud och Folket God and the people (Sweden).
Hac Nitimur Hanc Tuemur With this we strive, this we shall defend (Batavian Republic).
Hac Sub Tutela Under this protection (Eichstadt).
Haec Sunt Munera Minerae S Antony Eremitae These are the rewards of the mine of St Antony the hermit (Hildesheim).
Hanc Deus Dedit God has given this (Pontefract siege coins).
Hanc Tuemur Hac Nitimur This we defend, by this we strive (Batavian Republic).
Has Nisi Periturus Mihi Adimat Nemo Let no one remove these (Letters) from me under penalty of death (Commonwealth, edge inscription).
Henricus Rosas Regna Jacobus Henry (united) the roses, James the kingdoms (England and Scotland, James VI and I).
Herculeo Vincta Nodo Bound by a Herculean fetter (Savoy).
Herr Nach Deinem Willen O Lord Thy will be done (Palatinate, Erbach).
Herre Gott Verleich Uns Gnade Lord God grant us grace (Brunswick).
Hic Est Qui Multum Orat Pro Populo Here is he who prays a lot for the people (Paderborn).
Hir Steid te Biscop Here is represented the bishop (Gittelde).
His Ventis Vela Levantur By these winds the sails are raised up (Hesse-Cassel).
Hispaniarum Infans Infante of Spain and its dominions (Spain).
Hispaniarum et Ind Rex King of Spain and the Indies.
Hispaniarum Rex King of Spain (Spain).
Hoc Signo Victor Eris With this sign you will be victor (Rome, Vetranio).
Honeste et Decenter Honestly and decently (Nassau-Idstein).
Honi Soit Qui Mal y Pense Evil to him who evil thinks (Britain, George III).
Honni Soit Qui Mal y Pense (Hesse-Cassel).
Hospitalis et S Sepul Hierusal Hospital and Holy Sepulchre of Jerusalem (Malta).
Hun Boh Gal Rex AA Lo Wi et in Fr Dux King of Hungary, Bohemia and Galicia, Archduke of Austria, Dalmatia, Lodomeria, Wurzburg and Duke in Franconia (Austria).
Hung Boh Lomb et Ven Gal Lod Ill Rex Aa King of Hungary, Bohemia, Lombardo-Venezia, Galicia, Lodomeria and Illyria, Archduke of Austria (Austria).
Ich Dien I serve (Aberystwyth 2d, UK 2p).
Ich Getrawe Got in Aller Noth I trust in God in all my needs (Hesse-Marburg).
Ich Habe Nur Ein Vaterland und das Heisst Deutschland I have only one fatherland and that is called Germany (Germany).
Ielithes Penniae Penny of Gittelde (Gittelde, 11th century).
Iesus Autem Transiens Per Medium Illorum Ibat But Jesus, passing through the midst of them, went His way (England, Scotland, Anglo-Gallic).
Iesus Rex Noster et Deus Noster Jesus is our king and our God (Florence).
Ihs Xs Rex Regnantium Jesus Christ, King of Kings (Byzantine Empire).
Ihsus Xristus Basileu Baslie Jesus Christ, King of Kings (Byzantine Empire).
Imago Sanch Regis Illustris Castelle Legionis e Toleto The image of Sancho the illustrious king of Castile, Leon and Toledo.
In Casus Per Vigil Omnes In all seasons through vigil (Wertheim).
In Deo Meo Transgrediar Murum In my God I shall pass through walls (Teschen).
In Deo Spes Mea In God is my hope (Gelderland).
In Domino Fiducia Nostra In the Lord is our trust (Iever).
In Equitate Tua Vivificasti Me In thy equity Thou hast vivified me (Gelderland).
In God We Trust (USA).
In Hoc Signo Vinces In this sign shalt thou conquer (Portugal).
In Honore Sci Mavrici Marti In honour of the martyr St Maurice (St Maurice, 8th century).
In Manibus Domini sortes Meae In the hands of the Lord are my fates (Mainz siege, 1688–9).
In Memor Vindicatae Libere ac Relig In memory of the establishment of freedom and religion (Sweden).
In Memoriam Conjunctionis Utriusque Burgraviatus Norice In memory of the union of both burgraviates in peace (Brandenburg-Ansbach).
In Memorian Connub Feliciaes Inter Princ Her Frider Carol et Dub Sax August Louis Frider Rodas D 28 Nov 1780 Celebrati In memory of the most happy marriage between the hereditary prince Friedrich Karl and the Duchess of Saxony Augusta Louisa Frederika, celebrated on 28 Nov 1780 (Schwarzburg-Rudolstadt).
In Memorian Felicisssimi Matrimonii In memory of the most happy marriage (Wied).
In Memoriam Pacis Teschinensis Commem orating the Treaty of Teschen (Brandenburg-Ansbach).
In Nomine Domini Amen In the name of the Lord amen (Zaltbommel).
In Omnem Terram Sonus Eorum In to all the land their shall go sound (Chateau Renault, Papal States).
In Silencio et Spe Fortitudo Mea In silence and hope is my fortitude (Brandenburg-Kustrin).

In Spe et Silentio Fortitudo Mea In hope and silence is my fortitude (Vianen).
In Te Domine Confido In you O Lord I place my trust (Hesse).
In Te Domine Speravi In You, O Lord, I have hoped (Gurk).
In Terra Pax Peace in the land (Papacy).
In Via Virtuti Nulla Via There is no way for virtue on the way. (Veldenz).
Ind Imp, Indiae Imperator, Imperatrix Emperor (Empress) of India (Britain).
India Tibi Cessit India has yielded to thee (Portuguese India).
Infestus Infestis Hostile to the troublesome (Savoy).
Inimicos Eius Induam Confusione As for his enemies, I shall clothe them in shame (Sardinia, England, Edward VI).
Insignia Capituli Brixensis The badge of the chapter of Brixen (Brixen).
Isti Sunt Patres Tui Verique Pastores These are your fathers and true shepherds (Papacy).
Iudicium Melius Posteritatis Erit Posterity's judgment will be better (Paderborn).
Iure et Tempore By right and time (Groningen).
Iusques a Sa Plenitude As far as your plenitude (France, Henri II).
Iuste et Constanter Justly and constantly (Paderborn).
Iustirt Adjusted (Hesse-Cassel).
Iustitia et Concordia Justice and harmony (Zurich).
Iustitia et Mansuetudine By justice and mildness (Bavaria, Cologne).
Iustitia Regnorum Fundamentum Justice is the foundation of kingdoms (Austria).
Iustitia Thronum Firmat Justice strengthens the throne (England, Charles I).
Iustus Non Derelinquitur The just person is not deserted (Brandenburg-Calenberg).
Iustus Ut Palma Florebit The just will flourish like the palm (Portugal).
L Mun Planco Rauracorum Illustratori Vetustissimo To L Municius Plancus the most ancient and celebrated of the Rauraci (Basle).
Landgr in Cleggov Com in Sulz Dux Crum Landgrave of Klettgau, count of Sulz, duke of Krumlau (Schwarzburg-Sonderhausen).
Latina Emeri Munita Latin money of Merida (Suevi).
Lege et Fide By law and faith (Austria).
Lex Tua Veritas Thy law is the truth (Tuscany).
Liberta Eguaglianza Freedom and equality (Venice)
Libertad en la Ley Freedom within the law (Mexico).
Libertas Carior Auro Freedom is dearer than gold (St Gall).
Libertas Vita Carior Freedom is dearer than life (Kulenberg).
Libertas Xpo Firmata Freedom strengthened by Christ (Genoa).
Liberte, Egalite, Fraternite Liberty, equality, fraternity (France).
Lucerna Pedibus Meis Verbum Est Thy word is a lamp unto mine feet (England, Edward VI).
Lumen ad Revelationem Gentium Light to enlighten the nations (Papacy).
L'Union Fait la Force The union makes strength (Belgium)
Macula Non Est in Te There is no sin in Thee (Essen).
Magnus ab Integro Saeculorum Nascitur Ordo The great order of the centuries is born anew (Bavaria).
Mandavit Dominus Palatie hanc Monetam Fiert The lord of the Palatine ordained this coin to be made (Balath).
Manibus Ne Laedar Avaris Lest I be injured by greedy hands (Sweden).
Mar Bran Sac Rom Imp Arcam et Elec Sup Dux Siles Margrave of Brandenburg, archchamberlain of the Holy Roman Empire and elector, senior duke of Silesia (Prussia).
Maria Mater Domini Xpi Mary mother of Christ the Lord (Teutonic Knights).
Maria Unxit Pedes Xpisti Mary washes the feet of Christ (France, Rene d'Anjou).
Mater Castrorum Mother of fortresses (Rome, Marcus Aurelius).
Matrimonio Conjuncti Joined in wedlock (Austria).
Me Coniunctio Servat Dum Scinditur Frangor The relationship serves me while I am being torn to pieces (Lowenstein-Wertheim).
Mediolani Dux Duke of Milan (Milan).
Mediolani et Man Duke of Mantua and Milan (Milan).
Memor Ero Tui Iustina Virgo I shall remember you, o maiden Justina (Venice).
Merces Laborum Wages of work (Wurzburg).
Mirabilia Fecit He wrought marvels (Viking coinage).
Misericordia Di Rex King by the mercy of God (France, Louis II).
Mo Arg Ord Foe Belg D Gel & CZ Silver coin of the order of the Belgian Federation, duchy of Guelder-land, county of Zutphen (Guelderland).
Moneta Abbatis Coin of the abbey (German ecclesiastical coins, 13th–14th centuries).
Moneta Argentiae Ord Foed Belgii Holl Silver coin of the federated union of Belgium and Holland (Batavian Republic).
Mo No Arg Con Foe Belg Pro Hol New silver coin of the Belgian Federation, province of Holland (Holland).
Mo No Arg Pro Confoe Belg Trai Holl New silver coin of the confederated Belgian provinces, Utrecht and Holland (Batavian Republic).
Mon Lib Reip Bremens Coin of the free state of Bremen (Bremen).

Mon Nova Arg Duc Curl Ad Norma Tal Alb New silver coin of the duchy of Courland, according to the standard of the Albert thaler (Courland).
Mon Nov Castri Imp New coin of the Imperial free city of . . . (Friedberg).
Moneta Bipont Coin of Zweibrucken (Pfalz-Birkenfeld-Zweibrucken).
Monet Capit Cathedr Fuld Sede Vacante Coin of the cathedral chapter of Fulda, the see being vacant (Fulda).
Moneta in Obsidione Tornacensi Cusa Coin struck during the siege of Tournai (Tournai, 1709).
Moneta Livosesthonica Coin of Livonia (Estonia).
Moneta Nov Arg Regis Daniae New silver coin of the king of Denmark (Denmark).
Moneta Nova Ad Norman Conventionis New coin according to the Convention standard (Orsini-Rosenberg).
Moneta Nova Domini Imperatoris New coin of the lord emperor (Brunswick, 13th century).
Moneta Nova Lubecensis New coin of Lubeck.
Moneta Nova Reipublicae Halae Suevicae New coin of the republic of Hall in Swabia.
Moneta Reipublicae Ratisbonensis Coin of the republic of Regensburg.
Nach Alt Reichs Schrot und Korn According to the old empire's grits and grain (Hesse).
Nach dem Conventions Fusse According to the Convention's basis (German Conventionsthalers).
Nach dem Frankf Schlus According to the Frankfurt standard (Solms).
Nach dem Schlus der V Staend According to the standard of the union (Hesse).
Navigare Necesse Est It is necessary to navigate (Germany).
Nec Aspera Terrent Nor do difficulties terrify (Brunswick).
Nec Cito Nec Temere Neither hastily nor rashlly (Cambrai).
Nec Numina Desunt Nor is the divine will absent (Savoy).
Nec Temere Nec Timide Neither rashly nor timidly (Danzig, Lippe).
Necessitas Legem Non Habet Necessity has no law (Magdeburg).
Nemo Me Impune Lacessit No one touches me with impunity (UK, Scottish pound edge inscription).
Nihil Restat Reliqui No relic remains (Ypres).
Nil Ultra Aras Nothing beyond the rocks (Franque-mont).
No Nobis Dne Sed Noi Tuo Da Gloriam Not to us, o Lord but to Thy name be glory given (France, Francis I).
Nobilissimum Dom Ac Com in Lipp & St Most noble lord and count in Lippe and Sternberg (Schaumburg-Lippe).
Nomen Domini Turris Fortissima The name of the Lord is the strongest tower (Frankfurt).
Non Aes Sed Fides Not bronze but trust (Malta).
Non Est Mortale Quod Opto What I desire is not mortal. (Mecklenburg).
Non Mihi Sed Populo Not to me but to the people (Bavaria).
Non Relinquam Vos Orphanos I shall not leave you as orphans (Papacy).
Non Surrexit Major None greater has arisen (Genoa, Malta).
Nullum Simulatum Diuturnum Tandem Nothing that is feigned lasts long (Wittgenstein).
Nummorum Famulus The servant of the coinage (England, tin halfpence and farthings).
Nunquam Retrorsum Never backwards (Brunswick-Wolfenbuttel).
O Crux Ave Spes Unica Hail, o Cross, our only hope (England half-angels, France, Rene d'Anjou).
O Maria Ora Pro Me O Mary pray for me (Bavaria).
Ob Cives Servatos On account of the rescued citizens (Rome, Augustus).
Oculi Domini Super Iustos The eyes of the Lord look down on the just (Neuchatel).
Omnia Auxiliante Maria Mary helping everything (Schwyz).
Omnia Cum Deo Everything with God (Reuss-Greiz).
Omnia cum Deo et Nihil Sine Eo Everthing with God and nothing without Him (Erbach).
Omnis Potestas a Deo Est All power comes from God (Sweden).
Opp & Carn Dux Comm Rittb SCM Cons Int & Compi Mareschal Duke of Troppau and Carniola, count of Rietberg, privy councillor of his sacred imperial majesty, field marshal (Liechtenstein).
Opp & Carn . . . Aur Velleris Eques Duke of Troppau . . . knight of the Golden Fleece (Liechtenstein).
Opportune Conveniently (Savoy).
Optimus Princeps Best prince (Rome, Trajan).
Opulentia Salerno Wealthy Salerno (Siculo-Norman kingdom).
Pace et Iustitia With peace and justice (Spanish Netherlands).
Pacator Orbis Pacifier of the world (Rome, Aurelian).
Palma Sub Pondere Crescit The palm grows under its weight (Waldeck).
Pater Noster Our Father (Flanders, 14th century).
Pater Patriae Farther of his country (Rome, Caligula).
Patria Si Dreptul Meu The country and my right (Roumania).
Patrimon Henr Frid Sorte Divisum The heritage of Heinrich Friedrich divided by lot (Hohenlohe-Langenberg).
Patrimonia Beati Petri The inheritance of the blessed Peter (Papacy).

Patrona Franconiae Patron of Franconia (Wurzburg).
Pax Aeterna Eternal peace (Rome, Marcus Aurelius).
Pax et Abundantia Peace and plenty (Burgundy, Gelderland).
Pax Missa Per Orbem Peace sent throughout the world (England, Anne).
Pax Petrus Peace Peter (Trier, 10th century).
Pax Praevalet Armis May peace prevail by force of arms (Mainz).
Pax Quaeritur Bello Peace is sought by war (Commonwealth, Cromwell).
Pecunia Totum Circumit Orbem Money goes round the whole world (Brazil).
Per Aspera Ad Astra Through difficulties to the stars (Mecklenburg-Schwerin).
Per Angusta ad Augusta Through precarious times to the majestic (Solms-Roedelheim, a pun on the name of the ruler Johan August).
Per Crucem Tuam Salva Nos Christe Redemptor By Thy cross save us, O Christ our Redeemer (England, angels).
Per Crucem Tuam Salva Nos Xpe Redemt By Thy cross save us, O Christ our Redeemer (Portugal, 15th century).
Perdam Babillonis Nomen May the name of Babylon perish (Naples).
Perennitati Iustissimi Regis For the duration of the most just king (France, Louis XIII).
Perennitati Principis Galliae Restitutionis For the duration of the restoration of the prince of the Gauls (France, Henri IV).
Perfer et Obdura Bruxella Carry on and stick it out, Brussels (Brussels siege, 1579–80).
Perpetuus in Nemet Vivar Hereditary count in Nemt-Ujvar (Batthanyi).
Pietate et Constantia By piety and constancy (Fulda).
Pietate et Iustitia By piety and justice (Denmark).
Plebei Urbanae Frumento Constituto Free distribu-tion of grain to the urban working-class established (Rome, Nerva).
Pleidio Wyf Im Gwlad True am I to my country (UK, Welsh pound edge inscription).
Plus Ultra Beyond (the Pillars of Hercules) (Spanish America).
Point du Couronne sans Peine Point of the crown without penalty (Coburg).
Pons Civit Castellana The bridge of the town of Castellana (Papacy).
Populus et Senatus Bonon The people and senate of Bologna (Bologna).
Post Mortem Patris Pro Filio For the son after his father's death (Pontefract siege coins).
Post Tenebras Lux After darkness light (Geneva).
Post Tenebras Spero Lucem After darkness I hope for light (Geneva).
Posui Deum Adiutorem Meum I have made God my helper (England, Ireland, 1351–1603).
Praesidium et Decus Protection and ornament (Bologna).
Prima Sedes Galliarum First see of the Gauls (Lyon).
Primitiae Fodin Kuttenb ab Aerari Iterum Susceptarum First results dug from the Kuttenberg mines in a renewed undertaking (Austria).
Princps Iuventutis Prince of youth (Roman Empire).
Pro Defensione Urbis et Patriae For the defence of city and country (France, Louis XIV).
Pro Deo et Patria For God and the fatherland (Fulda).
Pro Deo et Populo For God and the people (Bavaria).
Pro Ecclesia et Pro Patria For the church and the fatherland (Constance).
Pro Fausio PP Reitur VS For happy returns of the princes of the Two Sicilies (Naples and Sicily).
Pro Lege et Grege For law and the flock (Fulda).
Pro maximo Dei Gloria et Bono Publico For the greatest glory of God and the good of the people (Wurttemberg).
Pro Patria For the fatherland (Wurzburg).
Propitio Deo Secura Ago With God's favour I lead a secure life. (Saxe-Lauenburg).
Protector Literis Literae Nummis Corona et Salus A protection to the letters (on the face of the coin), the letters (on the edge) are a garland and a safeguard to the coinage (Commonwealth, Cromwell broad).
Protege Virgo Pisas Protect Pisa, O Virgin (Pisa).
Provide et Constanter Wisely and firmly (Wurttem-berg).
Providentia et Pactis Through foresight and pacts (Brandenburg-Ansbach).
Providentia Optimi Principis With the foresight of the best prince (Naples and Sicily).
Proxima Fisica Finis Nearest to natural end (Orciano).
Proxima Soli Nearest to the sun (Modena).
Pulcra Virtutis Imago The beautiful image of virtue (Genoa).
Pupillum et Viduam Suscipiat May he support the orphan and the widow (Savoy).
Quae Deus Conjunxit Nemo Separet What God hath joined let no man put asunder (England, James I).
Quem Quadragesies et Semel Patriae Natum Esse Gratulamur Whom we congratulate for the forty-first time for being born for the fatherland (Lippe-Detmold).
Qui Dat Pauperi Non Indigebit Who gives to the poor will never be in need (Munster).
Quid Non Cogit Necessitas To what does Necessity not drive. (Ypres).
Quin Matrimonii Lustrum Celebrant They celebrate their silver wedding (Austria, 1879).
Quocunque Gesseris (Jeceris) Stabit Whichever way you throw it it will stand (Isle of Man).

Quod Deus Vult Hoc Semper Fit What God wishes always occurs. (Saxe-Weimar).
Reconduntur non Retonduntur They are laid up in store, not thundered back (Savoy).
Recta Tueri Defend the right (Austria).
Recte Constanter et Fortiter Rightly, constantly and bravely (Bavaria).
Recte Faciendo Neminem Timeas May you fear no one in doing right. (Solms-Laubach).
Rector Orbis Ruler of the world (Rome, Didius Julianus).
Rectus et Immotus Right and immovable (Hesse).
Redde Cuique Quod Suum Est Render to each that which is his own (England, Henry VIII).
Redeunt antiqui Gaudia Moris There return the joys of ancient custom (Regensburg).
Reg Pr Pol et Lith Saxon Dux Royal prince of Poland and Lithuania and duke of Saxony (Trier).
Regia Boruss Societas Asiat Embdae Royal Prussian Asiatic Society of Emden (Prussia).
Regier Mich Her Nach Deinen Wort Govern me here according to Thy word (Palatinate).
Regnans Capitulum Ecclesiae Cathedralis Ratisbonensis Sede Vacante Administering the chapter of the cathedral church at Regensburg, the see being vacant (Regensburg).
Regni Utr Sic et Hier Of the kingdom of the Two Sicilies and of Jerusalem (Naples and Sicily).
Religio Protestantium Leges Angliae Libertas Parliamenti The religion of the Protestants, the laws of England and the freedom of Parliament (England, Royalists, 1642).
Relinquo Vos Liberos ab Utroque Homine I leave you as children of each man (San Marino).
Restauracao da Independencia Restoration of inde-pendence (Portugal, 1990).
Restitutor Exercitus Restorer of the army (Rome, Aurelian).
Restitutor Galliarum Restorer of the Gauls (Rome, Gallienus).
Restitutor Generis Humani Restorer of mankind (Rome, Valerian).
Restitutor Libertatis Restorer of freedom (Rome, Constantine).
Restitutor Orbis Restorer of the world (Rome, Valerian).
Restitutor Orientis Restorer of the east (Rome, Valerian).
Restitutor Saeculi Restorer of the century (Rome, Valerian).
Restitutor Urbis Restorer of the city (Rome, Severus).
Rosa Americana Utile Dulci The American rose, useful and sweet (American colonies).
Rosa Sine Spina A rose without a thorn (England, Tudor coins).
Rutilans Rosa Sine Spina A dazzling rose without a thorn (England, Tudor gold coins).
S Annae Fundgruben Ausb Tha in N Oe Mining thaler of the St Anne mine in Lower Austria (Austria).
S Ap S Leg Nat Germ Primas Legate of the Holy Apostolic See, born Primate of Germany (Salzburg).
S Carolus Magnus Fundator Charlemagne founder (Munster).
S. Gertrudis Virgo Prudens Niviella St Gertrude the wise virgin of Nivelles (Nivelles).
SI Aul Reg Her & P Ge H Post Mag General hereditary postmaster, supreme of the imperial court of the hereditary kingdom and provinces (Paar).
S. Ian Bapt F. Zachari St John the Baptist, son of Zachary (Florence).
S. Kilianus Cum Sociis Francorum Apostoli St Kilian and his companions, apostles to the Franks (Wurzburg).
S. Lambertus Patronus Leodiensis St Lambert, patron of Liege (Liege).
Sac Nupt Celeb Berol For the holy matrimony celebrated at Berlin (Brandenburg-Ansbach).
Sac Rom Imp Holy Roman Empire (German states).
Sac Rom Imp Provisor Iterum Administrator of the Holy Roman Empire for the second time (Saxony).
Salus Generis Humani Safety of mankind (Rome, Vindex).
Salus Patriae Safety of the fatherland (Italy).
Salus Populi The safety of the people (Spain).
Salus Provinciarum Safety of the provinces (Rome, Postumus).
Salus Publica Salus Mea Public safety is my safety (Sweden).
Salus Reipublicae The safety of the republic (Rome, Theodosius II).
Salus Reipublicae Suprema Lex The safety of the republic is the supreme law (Poland).
Salvam Fac Rempublicam Tuam Make your state safe (San Marino).
Sanctus Iohannes Innoce St John the harmless (Gandersheim).
Sans Changer Without changing (Isle of Man).
Sans Eclat Without pomp (Bouchain siege, 1711).
Sapiente Diffidentia Wise distrust (Teschen).
Scutum Fidei Proteget Eum / Eam The shield of faith shall protect him / her (England, Edward VI and Elizabeth I).
Secundum Voluntatem Tuam Domine Your favourable will o Lord (Hesse).
Securitati Publicae For the public safety (Brandenburg-Ansbach).
Sede Vacante The see being vacant (Papal states, Vatican and ecclesiastical coinage).
Sena Vetus Alpha et W Principum et Finis Old Siena alpha and omega, the beginning and the end (Siena).
Senatus Populus QR Senate and people of Rome (Rome, 1188).
Si Deus Nobiscum Quis Contra Nos If God is with us who can oppose us (Hesse).

Si Deus Pro Nobis Quis Contra Nos If God is for us who can oppose us (Roemhild).
Sieh Deine Seeligkeit Steht Fest Ins Vaters Liebe Behold thy salvation stands surely in thy Father's love (Gotha).
Signis Receptis When the standards had been recovered (Rome, Augustus).
Signum Crucis The sign of the cross (Groningen).
Sincere et Constanter Truthfully and steadfastly (Hesse-Darmstadt).
Sit Nomen Domini Benedictum Blessed be the name of the Lord (Burgundy, Strasbourg).
St T X Adiuto Reg Iste Domba Let it be to you, o Christ, the assistant to the king of Dombes (Dombes).
Sit Tibi Xpe Dat q'tu Regis Iste Ducat May this duchy which Thou rulest be given to Thee, O Christ (Venice, ducat).
Sit Unio Haec Perennis May this union last for ever (Hohenlohe-Langenberg).
Sola Bona Quae Honesta The only good things are those which are honest (Brunswick).
Sola Facta Deum Sequor Through deeds alone I strive to follow God (Milan).
Soli Deo Honor et Gloria To God alone be honour and glory (Nassau).
Soli Reduci To him, the only one restored (Naples and Sicily).
Solius Virtutis Flos Perpetuus The flower of Virtue alone is perpetual (Strasbourg).
Spes Confisa Deo Nunquam Confusa Recedit Hope entrusted in God never retreats in a disorderly fashion (Lippe).
Spes Nr Deus God is our hope (Oudenarde siege, 1582).
Spes Rei Publicae The hope of the republic (Rome, Valens).
Strena ex Argyrocopeo Vallis S Christoph A New Year's gift from the silver-bearing valley of St Christopher (Wurttemberg, 1625).
Sub His Secura Spes Clupeus Omnibus in Te Sperantibus Under these hope is safe, a shield for all who reside hope in Thee (Bavaria).
Sub Pondere Under weight (Fulda).
Sub Protectione Caesarea Under imperial protection (Soragna).
Sub Tuum Praesidium Confug We flee to Thy protection (Salzburg).
Sub Umbra Alarum Tuarum Under the shadow of Thy wings (lever, Scotland, James V).
Subditorum Salus Felicitas Summa The safety of the subjects is the highest happiness (Lubeck).
Sufficit Mihi Gratia Tua Domine Sufficient to me is Thy grace, o Lord (Ploen).
Supra Firmam Petram Upon a firm rock (Papacy).
Susceptor Noster Deus God is our defence (Tuscany).
Sydera Favent Industriae The stars favour industry (Furstenberg).
Sylvarum Culturae Praemium Prize for the culture of the forest (Brandenburg-Ansbach).
Tali Dicata Signo Mens Fluctuari Nequit Consecrated by such a sign the mind cannot waver (England, Henry VIII George noble).
Tandem Bona Caus Triumphat A good cause eventually triumphs (Dillenburg).
Tandem Fortuna Obstetrice With good luck ultimately as the midwife (Wittgenstein).
Te Stante Virebo With you at my side I shall be strong (Moravia).
Tene Mensuram et Respice Finem Hold the measure and look to the end (Burgundy).
Tert Ducat Secular Tercentenary of the duchy (Wurttemberg).
Thu Recht Schev Niemand Go with right and fear no one (Saxe-Lauenburg).
Tibi Laus et Gloria To Thee be praise and glory (Venice).
Timor Domini Fons Vitae The fear of the Lord is a fountain of life (England, Edward VI shillings).
Tout Avec Dieu Everything with God (Brunswick, 1626).
Traiectum ad Mosam The crossing of the Maas (Maastricht).
Transvolat Nubila Virtus Marriageable virtue soon flies past (Grueyeres).
Travail, Famille, Patrie Work, family, country (Vichy France).
Triumphator Gent Barb Victor over the barbarian people (Byzantine Empire, Arcadius).
Tueatur Unita Deus May God guard these united (Kingdoms) (England, James I; Britain, 1847).
Turck Blegert Wien Vienna besieged by the Turks (Vienna, 1531).
Tut Mar Gab Pr Vid de Lobk Nat Pr Sab Car et Aug Pr de Lobk Regency of Maria Gabriela, widow of the prince of Lobkowitz, born princess of Savoy-Carignan, and August prince of Lobkowitz (Lobkowitz).
Tutela Italiae The guardianship of Italy (Rome, Nerva).
Ubi Vult Spirat He breathes where he will (Papacy).
Ubique Pax Peace everywhere (Rome, Gallienus).
Union et Force Union and strength (France).
Urbe Obsessa The city under siege (Maastricht).
Urbem Virgo Tuam Serva Protects thy city o virgin (Mary) (Strasbourg).
USC & RAM Cons Int Gen C Mar & Nob Praet H Turmae Capit Privy councillor of both their holy imperial and royal apostolic majesties, general field marshal and captain of the noble praetorian Hungarian squadrons (Eszterhazy).
Veni Luumen Cordium Come light of hearts (Vatican).
Veni Sancte Spiritus Come Holy Ghost (Vatican).
Verbum Domini Manet in Aeternum The word of the Lord abides forever (Hesse-Darmstadt, Veldenz).

Veritas Lex Tua The truth is your law (Salzburg).
Veritas Temporis Filia Truth is the daughter of time (England and Ireland, Mary Tudor).
Veritate et Labore By truth and work (Wittgenstein).
Veritate et Iustitia By truth and justice (German states).
Victoria Principum The victory of princes (Ostrogoths).
Videant Pauperes et Laetentur Let the poor see and rejoice (Tuscany).
Virgo Maria Protege Civitatem Savonae Virgin Mary Protect the city of Savona (Savona).
Viribus Unitis With united strength (Austria).
Virtute et Fidelitate By virtue and faithfulness (Hesse-Cassel).
Virtute et Prudentia With virtue and prudence (Auersperg).
Virtute Viam Dimetiar I shall mark the way with valour (Waldeck).
Virtutis Gloria Merces Glory is the reward of valour (Holstein-Gottorp).
Vis Unita Concordia Fratrum Fortior United power is the stronger harmony of brothers (Mansfeld).
Visitavit Nos Oriens ex Alto He has visited us arising on high (Luneburg).
Vivit Post Funera He lives after death (Bremen).
Vota Optata Romae Fel Vows taken for the luck of Rome (Rome, Maxentius).
Vox de Throno A voice from the throne (Papacy).
Was Got Beschert Bleibet Unerwert What God hath endowed leave undisturbed
Wider macht und List Mein Fels Gott Ist Against might and trickery God is my rock (Hesse-Cassel).
Xpc Vincit Xpc Regnat Christ conquers, Christ reigns (Scotland, Spain).
Xpc Vivet Xpc Regnat Xpc Impat Christ lives, Christ reigns, Christ commands (Cambrai).
Xpe Resurescit Christ lives again (Venice).
Xpistiana Religio Christian religion (Carolingian Empire).
Xps Ihs Elegit me Regem Populo Jesus Christ chose me as king to the people (Norway).
Zelator Fidei Usque ad Montem An upholder of the faith through and through (Portugal).
Zum Besten des Vaterlands To the best of the fatherland (Bamberg).

Care of coins

There is no point in going to a great deal of trouble and expense in selecting the best coins you can afford, only to let them deteriorate in value by neglect and mishandling. Unless you give some thought to the proper care of your coins, your collection is unlikely to make a profit for you if and when you come to sell it. Housing your coins is the biggest problem of all, so it is important to give a lot of attention to this.

Storage

The ideal, but admittedly the most expensive, method is the coin cabinet, constructed of air-dried mahogany, walnut or rosewood (*never* oak, cedar or any highly resinous timber likely to cause chemical tarnish). These cabinets have banks of shallow drawers containing trays made of the same wood, with half-drilled holes of various sizes to accommodate the different denominations of coins. Such cabinets are handsome pieces of furniture but, being largely handmade, tend to be rather expensive. Occasionally good specimens can be picked up in secondhand furniture shops, or at the dispersal of house contents by auction, but the best bet is still to purchase a new cabinet, tailored to your own requirements. Only plantation-grown Honduras mahogany is used to resolve any environmental concerns.

Peter Nichols of 3 Norman Road, St Leonards-on-Sea, East Sussex TN37 6NH (telephone 01424 436682) is a specialist manufacturer of display and storage systems who has also been producing coin and medal cabinets to suit every need for more than a quarter of a century. He can produce a cabinet to fit into a wall safe or some other form of security box. He can match existing work, and thus replicate cabinets which you may already be using, or even produce designs to suit your specific requirements. A nice touch is that all the products in the Nichols repertoire take their names from Elizabethan mint-marks.

Nichols produces a wide range of cabinets from the seven-tray Pheon all the way up to the massive 40-tray specials designed for the British Museum. All cabinets are fitted with double doors. Prices start at around £80 and go up to about £350 for the thirty-tray Coronet. They are not cheap, but you have the satisfaction of acquiring exquisite examples of the cabinet maker's craft.

Spink & Son are distributors for the Abafil series manufactured in Milan. These cases are of stout wooden construction covered with simulated leather and lined with red plush. The trays to fit the cases are also manufactured in wood lined with plush although a less expensive lined plastic alternative is also available. The Diplomat range is designed primarily for secure transportation, but the Mini-diplomat makes a good static cabinet,

Below: The Mascle Classic—the ideal "entry-level" coin cabinet for collectors. Right: The Crozier—a cabinet for the connoisseur.

The Diplomat, Abafil's plush flagship of the portable Diplomat range.

and can take up to three trays holding a maximum of 241 coins, while the Custom case holds 14 de luxe or 20 standard trays and will house up to 1,500 coins. Even cheaper is the Mignon case holding up to 105 coins, ideally suited for carrying in a briefcase or travel bag.

An excellent compromise is provided by a number of firms who manufacture coin trays in durable, felt-lined materials with shallow compartments to suit the various sizes of coins. Most of these trays interlock so that they build up into a cabinet of the desired size, and there are also versions designed as carrying cases, which are ideal for transporting coins.

The popular and extensive Lighthouse range is available from The Duncannon Partnership, 4 Beaufort Road, Reigate, RH2 9DJ (telephone 01737 244222, www.duncannon.co.uk) or Token Publishing Ltd (telephone 01404 44167, www.tokenpublishing.com). This range includes a wide variety of cases and albums for the general collector in basic or de luxe styles as required, as well as printed albums for the specialist. Their cases, including the popular aluminium range, are manufactured to the highest standards, lined with blue plush which displays any coin to its best advantage. The red-lined single trays come in deep or standard size and make an ideal cabinet when stacked together or housed in their attractive aluminium case, which is available separately. The trays themselves come with a variety of compartments for every size of coin. As with most distributors nowadays their complete range can be viewed on-line.

***Adding on to the stacking** Lindner range is easy.*

The extensive Lindner range is supplied in the UK by Prinze Publications of 3A Hayle Industrial Park, Hayle, Cornwall TR27 5JR (telephone 01736 751914, www.prinz.co.uk or from Token Publishing Ltd telephone 01404 44167, www.tokenpublishing.com). Well-known for their wide range of philatelic and numismatic accessories, but these include a full array of coin boxes, capsules, carrying cases and trays . The basic Lindner coin box is, in fact, a shallow tray available in a standard version or a smoked glass version. These trays have a crystal clear frame, red felt inserts and holes for various diameters of coins and medals. A novel feature of these trays is the rounded insert which facilitates the removal of coins from their spaces with the minimum of handling. These boxes are designed in such a manner that they interlock and can be built up into banks of trays, each fitted with a draw-handle and sliding in and out easily. Various types of chemically inert plastic capsules and envelopes have been designed for use in combination with plain shallow trays, without holes drilled. Lindner also manufacture a range of luxury cases lined in velvet and Atlas silk with padded covers and gold embossing on the spines, producing a most tasteful and elegant appearance.

Safe Albums of 16 Falcon Business Park, 38 Ivanhoe Road, Finchampstead, Berkshire RG40 4QQ (telephone 0118 932 8976, www.safealbums.co.uk) are the UK agents for the German Stapel-Element, a drawer-stacking system with clear plasticiser-free trays that fit into standard bookshelves. The sliding coin compartments, lined with blue velvet, can be angled for display to best advantage. Stackable drawers can be built up to any height desired. A wide range of drawer sizes is available, with compartments suitable for the smallest coins right up to four-compartment trays designed for very large artefacts such as card-cases or cigarette cases. The Mobel-Element cabinet is a superb specialised cabinet constructed of the finest timber with a steel frame and steel grip bars which can be securely locked. It thus combines elegance with security and is the ideal medium for the most valuable coins and medals.

There are also various storage systems, such as Coindex, which operate on the principle of

Safe's cabinet combines elegance with security.

narrow drawers in which the coins are stored in envelopes of chemically-inert plastic. A strip across the top holds a little slip giving a brief description, catalogue number and the price of each coin. Safe Albums' products are also available from Token Publishing Ltd (telephone 01404 44167, www.tokenpublishing.com)

The Sydney Museum in Australia, for example, keeps its coins in manila envelopes stored in plastic lunch-boxes which seemed to do the job pretty well!

Coin Albums

When coin collecting became a popular hobby in the 1960s, several firms marketed ranges of coin albums. They had clear plastic sleeves divided into tiny compartments of various sizes and had the merit of being cheap and taking up little room on a bookshelf.

They had several drawbacks, however, not the least being the tendency of the pages to sag with the weight of the coins, or even, in extreme cases, to pull away from the pegs or rings holding them on to the spine. They required very careful handling as the coins could easily fall out of the top row as the pages were turned. The more expensive albums had little flaps that folded over the top of the coin to overcome this problem.

Arguably the worst aspect of these albums was the use of polyvinyl chloride (PVC) in the construction of the sleeves. Collectors soon discovered to their horror that this reacted chemically with their coins, especially those made of silver, causing a rather disgusting yellow slime to adhere to the coins' surface. I shudder to think how many fine collections were ruined as a result, or of the countless coins that required highly expert treatment in a bid to restore them to as near the original condition as possible.

Fortunately the lesson has been learned and the coin albums now on the market are quite safe. Lighthouse and Lindner offer a wide range of albums designed to house coins, medals or banknotes. The old problem about sagging pages is overcome by the use of a multi-ring binding welded to a very stout spine, while the sleeves contain neither Styrol nor PVC and will not affect any metals at all. In addition to pages with pockets of uniform size, the Karat range of albums operates on a slide principle which enables the user to insert vertical strips of different sizes on the same page, so that the coins of one country or series, or perhaps a thematic display of coins from different countries, can be displayed side by side.

Safe Albums offer a wide range of albums in the Coinholder System and Coin-Combi ranges.

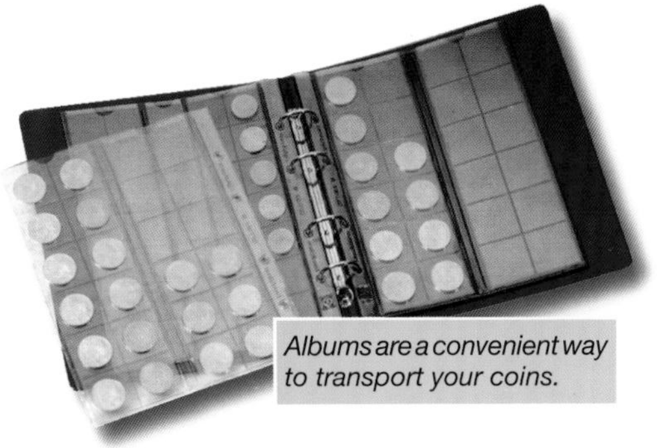

Albums are a convenient way to transport your coins.

These, too, offer the choice of fixed pages with uniform-sized pockets, or interchangeable sliding inserts for different sizes side by side.

Token Publishing Ltd now stock a complete and varied range of coin accessories following their take over of the well-known and much respected Lodge Hill Accessories originally founded by Mike Veissid of Collectors Gallery. They now stock everything from magnifying glasses to coin albums. To find out more, simply log onto www.tokenpublishing.com or call 01404 44167 for an up-to-date illustrated, colour catalogue.

The Lighthouse range includes a wide selection of de luxe and printed albums.

Cleaning

coins

This is like matrimony—it should not be embarked on lightly. Indeed, the advice given by the magazine *Punch* in regard to marriage is equally sound in this case—don't do it! It is far better to have a dirty coin than an irretrievably damaged one. Every dealer has horror stories of handling coins that previous owners have cleaned, to their detriment. The worst example I ever saw was a display of coins found by a metal detectorist who "improved" his finds by abrading them in the kind of rotary drum used by lapidarists to polish gemstones. If you really must remove the dirt and grease from coins, it is advisable to practise on coins of little value.

Warm water containing a mild household detergent or washing-up liquid will work wonders in removing surface dirt and grease from most coins, but silver is best washed in a weak solution of ammonia and warm water—one part ammonia to ten parts water. Gold coins can be cleaned with diluted citric acid, such as lemon juice. Copper or bronze coins present more of a problem, but patches of verdigris can usually be removed by careful washing in a 20 per cent solution of sodium sesquicarbonate. Wartime coins made of tin, zinc, iron or steel can be cleaned in a 5 per cent solution of caustic soda containing some aluminium or zinc foil or filings, but they must be rinsed afterwards in clean water and carefully dried. Cotton buds are ideal for gently prising dirt out of coin legends and crevices in the designs. Soft brushes (with animal bristles—*never* nylon or other artificial bristles) designed for cleaning silver are most suitable for gently cleaning coins.

Coins recovered from the soil or the sea bed present special problems, due to chemical reaction between the metals and the salts in the earth or sea water. In such cases, the best advice is to take them to the nearest museum and let the professional experts decide on what can or should be done.

Both Lindner and Safe Albums offer a range of coin-cleaning kits and materials suitable for gold, silver, copper and other base alloys respectively. Safe (living up to their name) also provide a stern warning that rubber gloves should be worn and care taken to avoid breathing fumes or getting splashes of liquid in your eyes or on your skin. Obviously, the whole business of cleaning is a matter that should not be entered into without the utmost care and forethought.

POLISHING: A WARNING

If cleaning should only be approached with the greatest trepidation, polishing is definitely *out!* Beginners sometimes fall into the appalling error of thinking that a smart rub with metal polish might improve the appearance of their coins. Short of actually punching a hole through it, there can hardly be a more destructive act. Polishing a coin may improve its superficial appearance for a few days, but such abrasive action will destroy the patina and reduce the fineness of the high points of the surface.

Even if a coin is only polished once, it will never be quite the same again, and an expert can tell this a mile off.

Celtic coinage of Britain

Celtic coins were the first coins made in Britain. They were issued for a century and a half before the Roman invasion, and possibly a little later in some areas. They were issued by 11 tribal groups or administrative authorities situated southeast of a line from the Humber to the Severn. In this short article Celtic specialist CHRIS RUDD introduces this increasingly popular area.

The earliest coins were uninscribed and often abstract in design. Later ones carried the names of local leaders and tribal centres, and in the southeast became increasingly Roman in style, sometimes copying classical images quite closely.

Most Celtic coins were struck between two dies on flans of gold, silver, billion and bronze. Some were cast in strip moulds in tin-rich bronze alloy called "potin".

Because the Celts wrote no books and left no written records of their activities, little is known about the people and places behind their coins. Who made them? When? Where? And why? These are questions that are still largely unanswered, except in the very vaguest terms. Celtic cataloguers talk about gold quarters, silver units and silver minims. But the truth is we don't even know what the Celts themselves called their coins.

British Celtic coins are among the most fascinating ever fashioned and perhaps the least familiar to the average collector because of their rarity. Like the Celts themselves, Celtic coin designs are wild, free flowing, flamboyant and full of fun. Yes, Celtic moneyers had a great sense of humour!

Celtic coins bear a vast variety of gods and goddesses, armed warriors, chariot wheels, hidden faces, decapitated heads, suns, moons, stars, thunderbolts, floral motifs, magic signs and phallic symbols. Plus a menagerie of antelopes, bears, boars, bulls, cocks, crabs, cranes, dogs, dolphins, ducks, eagles, hares, all kinds of horses (some with wings, some with human heads, many with three tails, a few breathing fire), goats, lions, lizards, owls, rams, rats, ravens, snakes, stags, starfish, worms and wolves. Not to mention dragons, griffins, hippocamps, sphinxes and ram-horned serpents.

Ask any metal detectorist how many Celtic coins he or she has found and you will immediately realise they are rarer than Roman coins in this country—at least a thousand times rarer on average. This is because far fewer Celtic coins were minted, in smaller runs, over a much shorter time span. Though some may have been made as early as 80 BC, the majority of British Celtic coins were struck from 54 BC to AD 43; barely 100 years of production, and most of that seems to have been sporadic.

However, the greater rarity of Celtic coins doesn't mean they are necessarily more costly than other ancient coins: in fact, they are often cheaper. You see, in the coin market, demand determines price. The more collectors that want a coin, the higher its price.

A recent survey revealed "worldwide there may be no more than 150 regular private collectors of

Method that may have been used for striking Celtic coins (drawing by Simon Pressey).

Celtic coins, buying on average one or more coins per month". Whereas there are literally thousands of people collecting the other major series of ancient and medieval coins. That is why Celtic coins are still comparatively less costly than Greek, Anglo-Saxon and English hammered coins. The Celtic market is smaller, though expanding. For example a very fine Celtic gold stater typically costs half the price of a Greek gold stater or an English gold noble of comparable quality and rarity. The price differential can be even more dramatic at major international auctions. But the disparity is diminishing as more and more collectors are beginning to appreciate the hitherto unrecognised beauty, scarcity and good value of British Celtic coins. So now could be a good time to start collecting Celtic coins, before their prices begin climbing more steeply.

Thirty years ago collecting British Celtic coins was a rich man's hobby and understanding

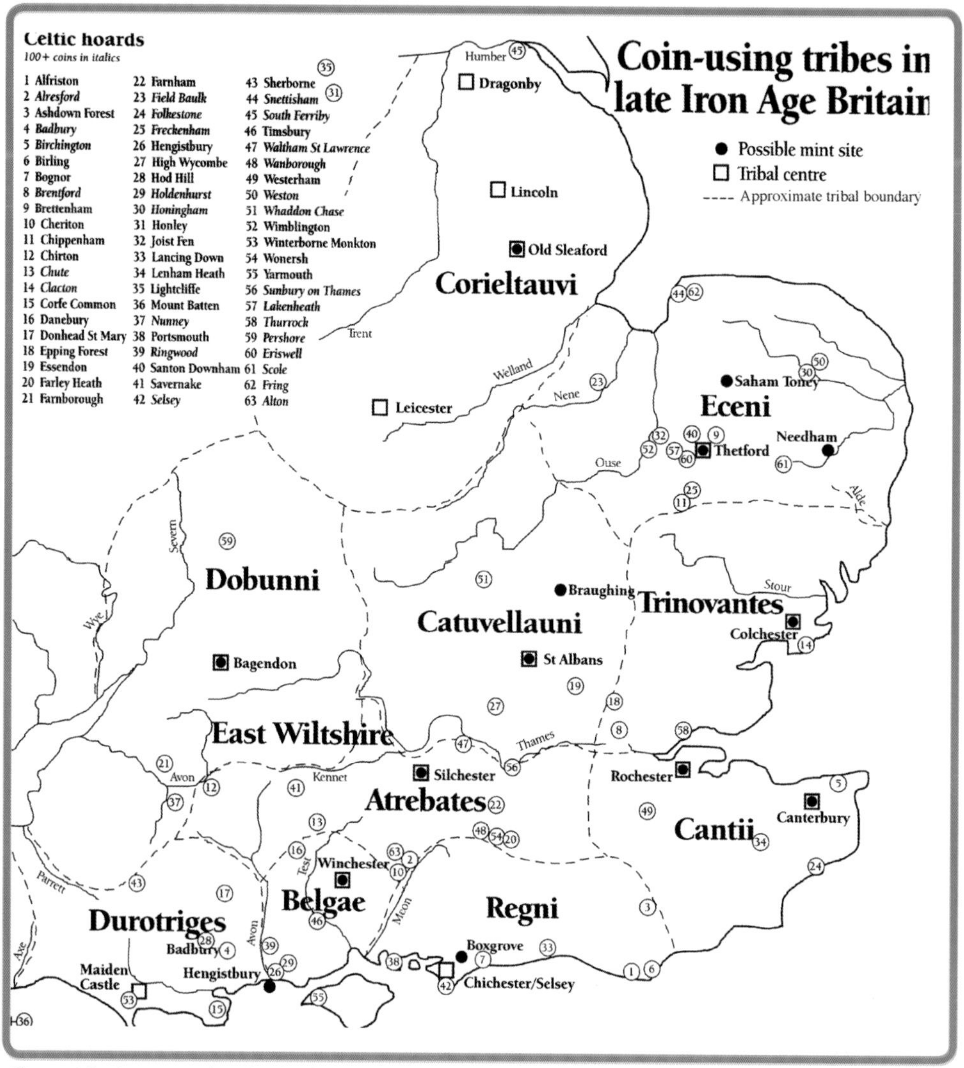

Eleven tribal groups minted coins in late Iron Age Britain, c. 80 BC–AD 45. The boundaries shown here are guesstimates, not actual, and often follow rivers, many of which are still known by their Celtic names.

Silver unit attributed to King Esuprastus of the Eceni, whose death resulted in the revolt of Queen Boudica, AD 60 (drawn four times actual size by Susan White).

them was the lonely pursuit of a few scholarly numismatists. Today, thanks to the popularity of metal detecting, Celtic coins are more plentiful and almost everyone can afford to collect them. Most ancient coin dealers sell Celtic coins, some for as little as £20 each, and you will always find a few trays of them at every coin fair.

British Celtic coins are also easier to study today, thanks to the publication of some excellent books on the subject. The Celtic collector's bible is *Celtic Coinage of Britain* by Robert D. Van Arsdell (Spink, 1989)—well researched, well written, well illustrated, always quoted in dealers' catalogues, often controversial when dates are discussed and hopefully to be republished soon in a revised edition. For the dedicated Celtic devotee *British Iron Age Coins in the British Museum* by Richard Hobbs (British Museum Press, 1996) is an invaluable companion volume to Van Arsdell—more cautious, less speculative.

By far the best introductory book is *Celtic Coinage in Britain* by Dr Philip de Jersey (Shire Archaeology, 1996) who manages the Celtic Coin Index, a photographic record of over 31,000 British coins at the Institute of Archaeology, Oxford. In plain language Dr Philip de Jersey explains how Celtic coins and the images they carry can reveal information on the political, economic and social life of the Celts. *Celtic Coinage in Britain* contains clear twice-size photos of over a hundred Celtic coins, some of them rarely seen before. It gives the names, addresses and phone numbers of the museums in England, Scotland and Wales with the best and most accessible collections of Celtic coins.

In short, if you want to know more about British Celtic coins, *Celtic Coinage in Britain* is where you start reading and keep reading. This is the best little book ever written about British Celtic coins and outstanding value for money at £4.99.

How should you start collecting British Celtic coins? First, get a few of the commoner uninscribed types from each of the 11 tribal areas, aiming for the highest grade you can comfortably afford. Then you may wish to get an inscribed coin of each of the main rulers. You would also be well advised to acquire some Gaulish coins at the same time, because many British coins were influenced by Gallic prototypes.

How much do British Celtic coins cost? Very little, considering how scarce they are. Types with legends usually cost more than those without and top quality bronze is frequently more pricey than top quality silver (which may surprise you) because silver is commoner and generally survives better after 2,000 years underground.

Chris Rudd is a well-known dealer who specialises in Celtic coins.

Collecting Ancient coins

Ancient coins differ from most other series which are collected in Britain in that every piece has spent the major part of the last two thousand years in the ground. As JOHN CUMMINGS, dealer in ancient coins and antiquities explains here, the effect that burial has had on the surface of the coin determines more than anything else the value of a particular piece. With more modern coins, the only things which affect price are rarity and grade. There may be a premium for coins exhibiting particularly fine tone, or with outstanding pedigrees, but an 1887 crown in "extremely fine" condition has virtually the same value as every other piece with the same grade and of the same date. With ancient coins the story is very different.

A large number of different criteria affect the price of an ancient coin. Factors affecting prices can be broken down into several categories:

Condition

The most important factor by far in determining price. Ancient coins were struck by hand and can exhibit striking faults. Value suffers if the coin is struck with the designs off-centre, is weakly struck, or if the flan is irregular in shape. Many of the Celtic tribes issued coins of varying fineness and those made from low quality gold or silver are worth less than similar specimens where the metal quality is better. Conversely, coins on exceptional flans, particularly well struck, or with fine patinas command a premium.

Many ancient coins have suffered during their stay in the ground. It must be borne in mind that the prices given in the price guide are for uncorroded, undamaged examples. A Roman denarius should be graded using the same criteria as those used for grading modern coins. The surfaces must be good, and the coin intact. The fact that the coin is 2,000 years old is irrelevant as far as grading is concerned. Coins which are not perfectly preserved are not without value but the value for a given grade decreases with the degree of fault.

Rarity

As with all other series, rare coins usually command higher prices than common ones although this is not written in stone. A unique variety of a small fourth century Roman bronze coin, even in perfect condition, can be worth much less than a more worn and common piece from an earlier part of the empire. In the Celtic series, there is an almost infinite variety of minor types and a unique variety of an uninscribed type will rarely outbid an inscribed issue of a known king.

Historical and local significance

Types which have historical or local interest can command a price far above their scarcity value. Denarii of the emperor Tiberius are believed to have been referred to in the New Testament and command a far higher price than a less interesting piece of similar rarity. Similarly, pieces which have British reverse types such as the "VICT BRIT" reverse of the third century AD are more expensive than their scarcity would indicate. The 12 Caesars are ever popular especially in the American market and this affects prices throughout the world. In the Celtic series, coins of Cunobelin or Boudicca are far more popular than pieces which have no historical interest but which are far scarcer.

Reverse types

All Roman emperors who survived for a reasonable time issued coins with many different reverse types. The most common of these usually show various Roman gods. When a coin has an unusual reverse it always enhances the value.

Particularly popular are architectural scenes, animals, references to Judaism, and legionary types.

Artistic merit

The Roman coinage is blessed with a large number of bust varieties and these can have a startling effect on price. For example, a common coin with the bust facing left instead of right can be worth several times the price of a normal specimen. Like many of the emperors, the coinage of Hadrian has a large number of bust varieties, some of which are extremely artistic and these, too, can command a premium.

The coinage used in Britain from the time of the invasion in AD 43 was the same as that introduced throughout the Empire by the emperor Augustus around 20 BC. The simple divisions of 2 asses equal to one dupondius, 2 dupondii equal to 1 sestertius, 4 sestertii equal to one denarius and 25 denarii equal to one aureus continued in use until the reformation of the coinage by Caracalla in AD 214.

Aureus (gold)

Denarius (silver)

Sestertius (bronze)

Dupondius (copper)

As (copper)

Introducing Hammered coinage

The hammered currency of medieval Britain is among some of the most interesting coinage in the world. The turbulent history of these islands is reflected in the fascinating changes in size, design, fineness and workmanship, culminating in the many strange examples that emanated from the strife of the Civil War.

The Norman Conquest of England in 1066 and succeeding years had far-reaching effects on all aspects of life. Surprisingly, however, it had little impact on the coinage. William the Conqueror was anxious to emphasise the continuity of his reign, so far as the ordinary people were concerned, and therefore he retained the fabric, size and general design pattern of the silver penny. Almost 70 mints were in operation during this reign, but by the middle of the 12th century the number was reduced to 55 and under Henry II (1154–89) it fell to 30 and latterly to only eleven. By the early 14th century the production of coins had been centralised on London and Canterbury, together with the ecclesiastical mints at York and Canterbury. The silver penny was the principal denomination throughout the Norman period, pieces cut along the lines of the cross on the reverse continuing to serve as halfpence and farthings.

Eight types of penny were struck under William I and five under his son William Rufus, both profiles (left and right) and facing portraits being used in both reigns allied to crosses of various types. Fifteen types were minted under Henry I (1100–35), portraiture having now degenerated to crude caricature, the lines engraved on the coinage dies being built up by means of various punches. Halfpence modelled on the same pattern were also struck, but very sparingly and are very rare.

On Henry's death the succession was contested by his daughter Matilda and his nephew Stephen of Blois. Civil war broke out in 1138 and continued till 1153. Stephen controlled London and its mint, but Matilda and her supporters occupied the West Country and struck their own coins at Bristol. Several of the powerful barons struck their own coins, and there were distinct regional variants of the regal coinage. Of particular interest are the coins

Silver pennies of, from left to right, William I, William Rufus, Henry I and Stephen.

struck from obverse dies with Stephen's portrait erased or defaced, believed to date from 1148 when the usurper was under papal interdict.

Peace was restored in 1153 when it was agreed that Matilda's son Henry should succeed Stephen. On the latter's death the following year, Henry II ascended the throne. Coins of Stephen's last type continued to be minted till 1158, but Henry then took the opportunity to overhaul the coinage which had become irregular and sub-standard during the civil war. The new "Cross Crosslet" coins, usually known as the Tealby coinage (from the hoard of over 5,000 pennies found at Tealby, Lincolnshire in 1807), were produced at 30 mints, but when the recoinage was completed this number was reduced to a dozen. The design of Henry's coins remained virtually the same throughout more than two decades, apart from minor variants. Then, in 1180, a new type, known as the Short Cross coinage, was introduced. This was a vast improvement over the poorly struck Cross Crosslet coins and continued without alteration, not only to the end of the reign of Henry II in 1189, but throughout the reigns of his sons Richard (1189–99) and John (1199–1216) and the first half of the reign of his grandson Henry III (1216–46). Throughout that 66 year period, however, there were minor variations in portraits and lettering which enable numismatists to attribute the HENRICUS coins to specific reigns and periods.

"Tealby" type penny (top), and "Short Cross" penny of Henry II.

The style and workmanship of the Short Cross coinage deteriorated in the reign of Henry III. By the 1220s coin production was confined to the regal mints at London and Canterbury, the sole exception being the ecclesiastical mint maintained by the Abbot of Bury St Edmunds. Halfpence and farthings were briefly struck in 1221–30, though halfpence are now extremely rare and so far only a solitary farthing has been discovered.

By the middle of this reign the coinage was in a deplorable state, being poorly struck, badly worn and often ruthlessly clipped. In 1247 Henry ordered a new coinage and in this the arms of the cross on the reverse were extended to the rim as a safeguard against clipping. This established a pattern of facing portrait and long cross on obverse and reverse respectively that was to continue till the beginning of the 16th century. Several provincial mints were re-activated to assist with the recoinage but they were all closed down again by 1250, only the regal mints at London and Canterbury and the ecclesiastical mints at Durham and Bury St Edmunds remaining active.

"Long Cross" pennies of Henry III (top), and Edward I.

In 1257 Henry tentatively introduced a gold penny (worth 20 silver pence and twice the weight of a silver penny). The coin was undervalued and soon disappeared from circulation.

The Long Cross coinage of Henry III continued under Edward I till 1279 when the king introduced a new coinage in his own name. The penny continued the style of its predecessors, though much better designed and executed; but new denominations were now added. Henceforward halfpence and farthings became a regular issue and, at the same time, a fourpenny coin known as the groat (from French *gros*) was briefly introduced (minting ceased in 1282 and was not revived till 1351). Due to the centralisation of coin production the name of the moneyer was now generally dropped, although it lingered on a few years at Bury St Edmunds. The provincial mints were again revived in 1299–1302 to recoin the lightweight foreign imitations of pennies which had flooded in from the Continent.

The coinage of Edward II (1307–27) differed only in minor respects from that of his father, and a similar pattern prevailed in the first years of Edward III. In 1335 halfpence and farthings below the sterling fineness were struck. More importantly, further attempts were made to introduce gold coins. In 1344 the florin or double

Pre-Treaty Noble of Edward III which contained reference to France in the legend.

leopard of six shillings was introduced, along with its half and quarter. This coinage was not successful and was soon replaced by a heavier series based on the noble of 80 pence (6*s.* 8*d.*), half a mark or one third of a pound. The noble originally weighed 138.5 grains but it was successively reduced to120 grains, at which weight it continued from 1351. During this reign the protracted conflict with France known as the Hundred Years' War erupted. Edward III, through his mother, claimed the French throne and inscribed this title on his coins. By the Treaty of Bretigny (1361) Edward temporarily gave up his claim and the reference to France

Noble of Edward IV, issued before he was forced to abandon the throne of England.

was dropped from the coins, but when war was renewed in 1369 the title was resumed, and remained on many English coins until the end of the 18th century. The silver coinage followed the pattern of the previous reign, but in 1351 the groat was re-introduced and with it came the twopence or half-groat. Another innovation was the use of mintmarks at the beginning of the inscriptions. Seven types of cross and one crown were employed from 1334 onwards and their sequence enables numismatists to date coins fairly accurately.

The full range of gold (noble, half-noble and quarter-noble) and silver (groat, half-groat, penny, halfpenny and farthing) continued under Richard II (1377–99). Little attempt was made to alter the facing portrait on the silver coins, by now little more than a stylised caricature anyway.

Noble of Henry IV which was reduced in weight due to the shortage of gold.

Under Henry IV (1399–1413) the pattern of previous reigns prevailed, but in 1412 the weights of the coinage were reduced due to a shortage of bullion. The noble was reduced to 108 grains and its sub-divisions lightened proportionately. The penny was reduced by 3 grains, and its multiples and sub-divisions correspondingly reduced. One interesting change was the reduction of the fleur de lis of France from four to three in the heraldic shield on the reverse of the noble; this change corresponded with the alteration in the arms used in France itself. The Calais mint, opened by Edward III in 1363, was closed in 1411. There was no change in the designs used for the coins of Henry V (1413–22) but greater use was now made of mintmarks to distinguish the various periods of production. Coins were by now produced mainly at London, although the episcopal mints at Durham and York were permitted to strike pennies.

The supply of gold dwindled early in the reign of Henry VI and few nobles were struck after 1426. The Calais mint was re-opened in 1424 and struck a large amount of gold before closing finally in 1440. A regal mint briefly operated at York in 1423–24. Mintmarks were now much more widely used and tended to correspond more closely to the annual trials of the Pyx. The series of civil upheavals known as the Wars of the Roses erupted in this period.

In 1461 Henry VI was deposed by the Yorkist Earl of March after he defeated the Lancastrians at Mortimer's Cross. The Yorkists advanced on London where the victor was crowned Edward IV. At first he continued the gold series of his predecessor, issuing nobles and quarter-nobles, but in 1464 the weight of the penny was reduced to 12 grains and the value of the noble was raised to 100 pence (8*s*. 4*d*.).The ryal or rose-

Groat of Richard III (1483–85).

noble of 120 grains, together with its half and quarter, was introduced in 1465 and tariffed at ten shillings or half a pound. The need for a coin worth a third of a pound, however, led to the issue of the angel of 80 grains, worth 6*s*. 8*d*., but this was initially unsucessful and very few examples are now extant. The angel derived its name from the figure of the Archangel Michael on the obverse; a cross surmounting a shield appeared on the reverse.

In 1470 Edward was forced to flee to Holland and Henry VI was briefly restored. During this brief period (to April 1471) the ryal was discontinued but a substantial issue of angels and half-angels was made both at London and Bristol. Silver coins were struck at York as well as London and Bristol, the issues of the provincial mints being identified by the initials B or E (Eboracum, Latin for York). Edward defeated the Lancastrians at Tewkesbury and deposed the luckless Henry once more. In his second reign Edward struck only angels and half-angels as well as silver from the groat to halfpenny. In addition to the three existing mints, silver coins were struck at Canterbury, Durham and the archiepiscopal mint at York. Mintmarks were now much more frequent and varied. Coins with a mark of a halved sun and rose are usually assigned to the reign of Edward IV, but they were probably also struck in the nominal reign of Edward V, the twelve-year-old prince held in the Tower of London under the protection of his uncle Richard, Duke of Gloucester. Coins with this mark on the reverse had an obverse mark of a boar's head, Richard's personal emblem. The brief reign of Richard III (1483–5) came to an end with his defeat at Bosworth and the relatively scarce coins of this period followed the pattern of the previous reigns, distinguished by the sequence of mint marks and the inscription RICAD or RICARD.

In the early years of Henry VII's reign the coinage likewise followed the previous patterns, but in 1489 the first of several radical changes was effected, with the introduction of the gold sovereign of 20 shillings showing a full-length portrait of the monarch seated on an elaborate throne. For reverse, this coin depicted a Tudor rose surmounted by a heraldic shield. A similar reverse appeared on the ryal of 10 shillings, but the angel and angelet retained previous motifs. The silver coins at first adhered to the medieval pattern, with the stylised facing portrait and long cross, but at the beginning of the 16th century a large silver coin, the testoon or shilling of 12 pence, was introduced and adopted a realistic profile of the king, allied to a reverse showing a cross surmounted by the royal arms. The same design was also used for the later issue of groat and half groat.

First coinage Angel of Henry VIII which retained the traditional 23.5 carat fineness.

This established a pattern which was to continue till the reign of Charles I. In the reign of Henry VIII, however, the coinage was subject to considerable debasement. This led to the eventual introduction of 22 carat (.916 fine) gold for the crown while the traditional 23 1/2 carat gold was retained for the angel and ryal. This dual system continued until the angel was discontinued at the outset of the Civil War in 1642; latterly it had been associated with the ceremony of touching for "King's Evil" or scrofula, a ritual used by the early Stuart monarchs to bolster their belief in the divine right of kings.

Under the Tudors and Stuarts the range and complexity of the gold coinage increased, but it was not until the reign of Edward VI that the silver series was expanded. In 1551 he introduced the silver crown of five shillings, the first English coin to bear a clear date on the obverse. Under Mary dates were extended to the shilling and sixpence.

The mixture of dated and undated coins continued under Elizabeth I, a reign remarkable for the range of denominations—nine gold and eight silver. The latter included the sixpence, threepence, threehalfpence and threefarthings, distinguished by the rose which appeared behind the Queen's head.

The coinage of James I was even more complex, reflecting the king's attempts to unite his dominions. The first issue bore the legend ANG: SCO (England and Scotland), but from 1604 this was altered to MAG: BRIT (Great Britain). This period witnessed new denominations, such as the rose-ryal and spur-ryal, the unite, the Britain crown and the thistle crown, and finally the laurel of 20 shillings and its sub-divisions.

In the reign of Elizabeth experiments began with milled coinage under Eloi Mestrell. These continued sporadically in the 17th century, culminating in the beautiful coins struck by Nicholas Briot (1631–39). A branch mint was established at Aberystwyth in 1637 to refine and coin silver from the Welsh mines. Relations between King and Parliament deteriorated in the reign of Charles I and led to the Civil War (1642). Parliament controlled London but continued to strike coins in the King's name. The Royalists struck coins, both in pre-war and new types, at Shrewsbury, Oxford, Bristol, Worcester, Exeter, Chester, Hereford and other Royalist strongholds, while curious siege pieces were pressed into service at Newark, Pontefract and Scarborough.

After the execution of Charles I in 1649 the Commonwealth was proclaimed and gold and silver coins were now inscribed in English instead of Latin. Patterns portraying Cromwell and a crowned shield restored Latin in 1656. Plans for milled coinage were already being considered before the Restoration of the monarchy in 1660. Hammered coinage appeared initially, resuming the style of coins under Charles I, but in 1662 the hand-hammering of coins was abandoned in favour of coins struck on the mill and screw press. The hammered coins of 1660–62 were undated and bore a crown mintmark, the last vestiges of medievalism in British coinage.

The magnificent second coinage Rose-Ryal of James I (1603–25).

Images courtesy of Spink.

coin Grading

Condition is the secret to the value of virtually anything, whether it be antiques, jewellery, horses or second-hand cars—and coins are certainly no exception. When collecting coins it is vital to understand the recognised standard British system of grading, i.e. accurately assessing a coin's condition or state of wear. Grading is an art which can only be learned by experience and so often it remains one person's opinion against another's, therefore it is important for the beginner or inexperienced collector to seek assistance from a reputable dealer or knowledgeable numismatist when making major purchases.

The standard grades as used in the Price Guide are as follows:	
UNC	**Uncirculated** A coin that has never been in circulation, although it may show signs of contact with other coins during the minting process.
EF	**Extremely Fine** A coin in this grade may appear uncirculated to the naked eye but on closer examination will show signs of minor friction on the highest surface.
VF	**Very Fine** A coin that has had very little use, but shows signs of wear on the high surfaces.
F	**Fine** A coin that has been in circulation and shows general signs of wear, but with all legends and date clearly visible.
Other grades used in the normal grading system are:	
BU	**Brilliant Uncirculated** As the name implies, a coin retaining its mint lustre.
Fair	A coin extensively worn but still quite recognisable and legends readable.
Poor	A coin very worn and only just recognisable.
Other abbreviations used in the Price Guide are:	
Obv	**Obverse**
Rev	**Reverse**
Other abbreviations, mintmarks, etc. can be identified under the appropriate section of this Yearbook.	

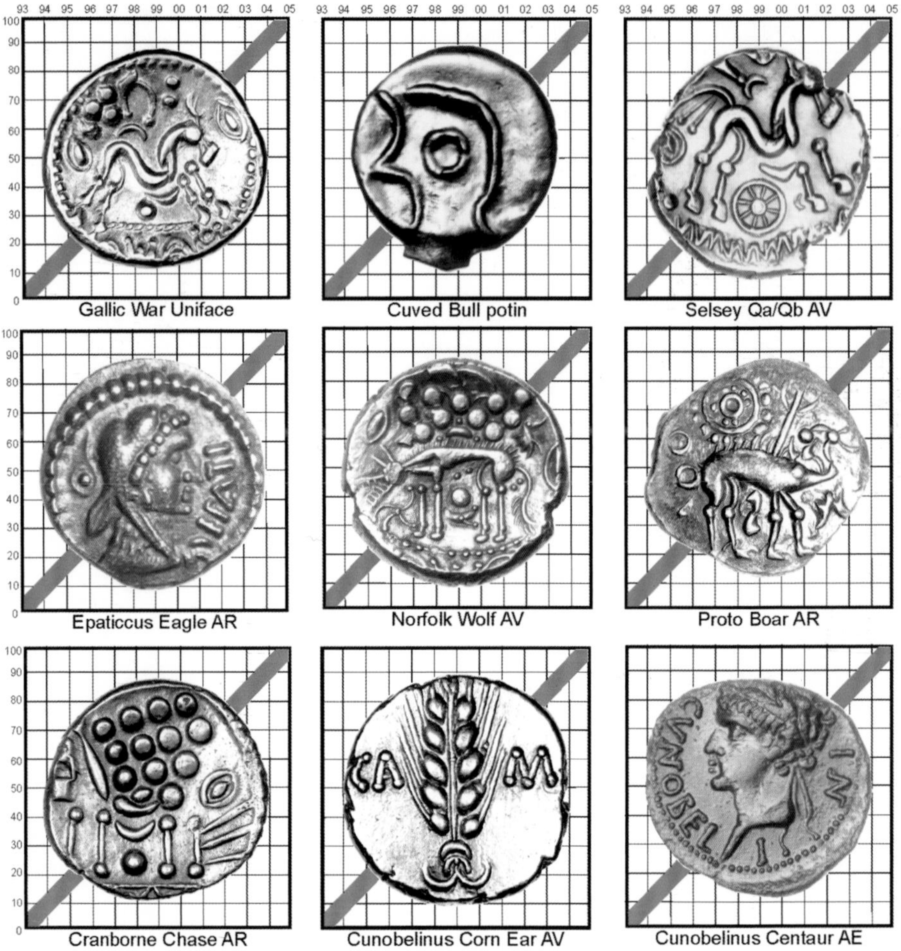

Schema of average percentage increments of retail values of selected commoner types of Late Iron Age coins monitored 1993-2005 with annual fluctuations flattened out. Source: EC Retail Review 8/05.

A SIMPLIFIED PRICE GUIDE
TO

ANCIENT COINS USED IN BRITAIN

PART I
CELTIC

The prices given in this section are those that you would expect to pay from a reputable dealer and not the prices at which you could expect to sell coins.

The list below, which has been generously provided by Celtic coin dealer Chris Rudd, contains most of the commonly available types: a full comprehensive guide is beyond the scope of this book. Prices are for coins with good surfaces which are not weakly struck or struck from worn dies. Examples which are struck from worn or damaged dies can be worth considerably less. Particularly attractive examples of bronze Celtic coins command a very high premium. Where a price is given for an issue of which there are many varieties, the price is for the most common type.

UNINSCRIBED COINAGE

	F	VF	EF
GOLD STATERS			
Gallo-Belgic A	£650	£1500	£5500
Gallo-Belgic E (Ambiani)	£150	£250	£500
Chute type	£150	£275	£450
Cheriton type			
normally rather "brassy" metal	£200	£400	£850
Corieltavi (various types)	£150	£350	£750
Norfolk "wolf" type			
fine gold	£200	£400	£1000
brassy gold	£125	£250	£600
very debased	£85	£175	£375
Whaddon Chase types	£200	£400	£1000
Wonersh type	£200	£400	£1500
Eceni (various types)	£250	£450	£1000
Remic type	£200	£350	£650
Dobunni	£250	£450	£850
GOLD QUARTER STATERS			
North Thames types	£155	£250	£450
North Kent types	£155	£250	£450
Eceni	£145	£200	£375
Sussex types	£100	£175	£325
Dobunni	£150	£250	£500
SILVER COINAGE			
North Thames types	£85	£155	£300
South Thames types	£85	£155	£300
Durotriges full stater			
fine silver	£65	£155	£275
base silver	£20	£50	£125
Durotriges small silver	£10	£30	£60
Dobunni	£50	£100	£250

(Note—Most examples are for base coins as better quality items are appreciably higher)

Cheriton Smiler gold stater

Cranborne Chase silver stater

	F	VF	EF
Corieltavi	£45	£100	£200
Eceni ("crescent" types)	£30	£75	£150
Eceni ("Norfolk god" types)	£50	£100	£250
Armorican Billon staters	£75	£150	£400

POTIN COINAGE

	F	VF	EF
Kent	£20	£50	£100

BRONZE COINAGE

	F	VF	EF
Durotriges debased stater	£25	£55	£100
Durotriges cast bronzes	£60	£120	£200
North Thames types. Various issues from:	£40	£100	£400

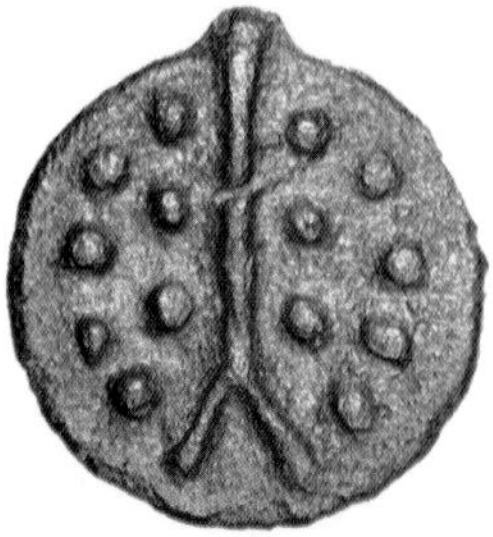

Hengistbury cast bronze

INSCRIBED CELTIC COINAGE

ATTREBATES & REGNI

	F	VF	EF
Commios			
stater	£550	£1500	£2850
silver unit	£75	£150	£300
silver minim	£60	£120	£250
Tincomarus			
stater	£420	£850	£2000
quarter stater	£145	£250	£450
silver unit	£75	£140	£275
silver minim	£60	£120	£175
Eppillus			
quarter stater	£145	£235	£425
silver unit	£75	£145	£300
bronze			Rare
Verica			
stater	£255	£550	£1000
quarter stater	£155	£275	£425
silver unit	£55	£150	£250
silver minim	£50	£120	£225
Epaticcus			
stater	£1000	£2000	£4000
silver unit	£50	£100	£265
silver minim	£55	£110	£275
Caratacos			
silver unit	£165	£320	£465
silver minim	£110	£220	£325

Tincomarus gold stater

Verica gold stater

CANTIACI

	F	VF	EF
Dubnovellaunos			
stater	£280	£565	£900
silver unit	£130	£210	£500
bronze unit	£55	£150	£350
Vosenos			
stater	£1000	£2500	£5000
quarter stater	£275	£585	£1200
silver unit	£135	£285	£650
Sam			
silver unit	£175	£350	£750
bronze unit	£100	£250	£500
Eppillus			
stater	£1000	£2000	£4250
quarter stater	£145	£255	£500
silver unit	£65	£145	£350
bronze unit	£55	£125	£450
bronze minim	£85	£150	£275
Amminus			
silver unit	£155	£320	£650
silver minim	£110	£215	£450
bronze unit	£80	£155	£500
Solidu			
silver unit	£500	£1000	£2250
silver minim	£500	£1000	£1500

Vosenos gold quarter stater

	F	VF	EF
DUROTRIGES			
Crab			
silver	£155	£320	£650
silver minim	£100	£250	£400
TRINOVANTES			
Addedomaros			
stater	£265	£500	£800
quarter stater	£155	£320	£550
bronze	£30	£65	£150
Dubnovellaunos			
stater	£255	£455	£775
quarter stater	£155	£310	£550
bronze unit	£55	£130	£450
CATUVELLAUNI			
Tasciovanos			
stater	£225	£425	£1200
quarter stater	£130	£235	£450
silver unit	£80	£165	£375
bronze unit	£55	£135	£350
bronze half unit	£55	£135	£275
Sego			
stater	£1000	£3000	£4000
quarter stater	£600	£1750	£3000
silver unit	£250	£500	£1000
bronze unit	£80	£200	£400
Dias			
silver unit	£100	£200	£400
bronze unit	£50	£150	£400
Rues			
bronze unit	£50	£150	£400
Andoco			
stater	£510	£1250	£2750
quarter stater	£210	£420	£755
silver unit	£155	£400	£750
bronze	£85	£215	£355
Cunobelin			
stater	£200	£455	£1200
quarter stater	£145	£265	£420
silver unit	£85	£165	£360
bronze unit	£65	£145	£320
AGR			
quarter stater	£600	£1500	£3000
silver unit	£500	£1000	£2000
DOBUNNI			
Anted			
stater	£325	£650	£1350
silver unit	£55	£120	£300
Eisu			
stater	£450	£750	£1500
silver unit	£55	£125	£325
Catti			
stater	£255	£525	£1250
Comux			
stater	£800	£1650	£3500
Corio			
stater	£265	£525	£1000
quarter stater	£200	£355	£625
Boduoc			
stater	£1000	£2250	£3000
silver unit	£200	£500	£850

Addedomaros gold stater

Tasciovanos gold stater

Cunobelinus gold stater

Catti gold stater

	F	VF	EF
ECENI			
Cani Duro			
silver unit	£110	£265	£550
Anted			
stater	£425	£1000	£2500
silver unit	£35	£65	£185
silver half unit	£45	£95	£200
Ecen			
silver unit	£40	£75	£185
silver half unit	£45	£95	£200
Saenu			
silver unit	£65	£125	£285
Aesu			
silver unit	£65	£125	£285
Esuprastus			
silver unit	£420	£1,000	£1850
Ale Scavo			
silver unit	£355	£765	£1550
CORIELTAVI			
Cat			
silver unit	£400	£1000	£2000
Vep			
stater	£400	£1000	£2500
silver unit	£75	£150	£300
Aunt Cost			
stater	£255	£565	£1000
silver unit	£85	£185	£315
silver half unit	£85	£160	£300
Esuprasu			
stater	£330	£675	£1250
silver unit	£155	£310	£550
Vep Corf			
stater	£410	£1000	£2150
silver unit	£80	£185	£300
silver half unit	£100	£215	£450
Dumno Tigir Seno			
stater	£755	£1850	£3150
silver unit	£100	£185	£500
Volisios Dumnocoveros			
stater	£300	£675	£1250
silver unit	£100	£185	£475
silver half unit	£100	£185	£450
Volisios Dumnovellaunos			
stater	£310	£725	£1550
silver half unit	£150	£335	£655
Volisios Cartivellaunos			
stater	£1000	£2000	£4000
silver half unit	£300	£620	£1150
Latios Ison			
stater	£1000	£2000	£4000
silver unit	£155	£420	£1150

Ale Scavo silver unit

Vep CorF gold stater

Dumno Tigir Seno gold stater

Illustrations by courtesy of Chris Rudd

A SIMPLIFIED PRICE GUIDE
TO

ANCIENT COINS USED IN BRITAIN

PART II
ROMAN BRITAIN

The list below has been generously provided by coin dealer Mike Vosper. These prices are for the most common types unless otherwise noted. In most cases, especially with large bronze coins, the price for coins in extremely fine condition will be _much_ higher than the price for the same coin in very fine condition as early bronze coins are seldom found in hoards and perfect, undamaged examples are rarely available.

The illustrations provided are a representative guide to assist with identification only.

REPUBLICAN COINAGE 280–41 BC

	FROM F	VF	EF
Republican			
Quadrigatus (Janus/Quadriga)	£75	£220	£685
Victoriatus (Jupiter/Victory)	£25	£60	£195
Denarius (Roma/Biga)	£25	£60	£1200
Denarius (other types)	£28	£65	£210
Denarius (Gallic warrior, L. Hostilius Saserna)	£280	£825	£2500
Quinarius	£25	£55	£185
Cast Aes Grave, As	£185	£510	–
Struck As/Semis/Litra	£55	£160	–
Struck Triens/Quadrands	£42	£115	–

Gnaeus Pompey Junior

IMPERATORIAL COINAGE 49–27 BC

	FROM F	VF	EF
Pompey the Great			
Denarius (Hd. of Pompilius/Prow)	£110	£290	£875
Scipio			
Denarius (Jupiter/Elephant)	£48	£135	£410
Cato Uticensis			
Quinarius (Bacchus/Victory)	£35	£100	£310
Gnaeus Pompey Junior			
Denarius (Roma/Hispania)	£75	£215	£585
Sextus Pompey			
Denarius (his bust)	£220	£675	£2200
Denarius (other types)	£130	£480	£1550
As	£160	£415	–
Julius Caesar			
Aureus	£525	£1550	£3225
Denarius ("elephant" type)	£75	£220	£575
Denarius (Caesar portrait)	£260	£785	£2600
Denarius (heads of godesses)	£75	£185	£650

Julius Caesar

	FROM F	VF	EF
Brutus			
Denarius (his portrait/EID MAR)	£13000	£39000	£105,000
Denarius (others)	£140	£385	£1200
Cassius			
Denarius...	£110	£295	£900
Ahenobarbus			
Denarius	£260	£800	£2750
Mark Antony			
Denarius ("Galley" type)	£50	£130	£405
Denarius (with portrait)	£100	£295	£750
Denarius (other types)	£75	£220	£600
AR quinarius	£45	£110	£315
Mark Antony & Lepidus			
AR quinarius	£40	£110	£320
Mark Antony & Octavian			
AR denarius	£140	£390	£1200
Quninarius	£35	£95	£270
Mark Antony & Lucius Antony			
AR denarius	£235	£700	£2100
Mark Antony & Octavia			
AR Cistophorus	£150	£495	£1600
Cleopatra VII & Mark Antony			
AR denarius	£700	£2750	£9000
Fulvia			
AR quinarius	£75	£200	£600
Octavian (later known as Augustus)			
Gold Aureus	£1000	£2500	£7,000
Denarius	£90	£240	£725
Quinarius (ASIA RECEPTA)..............	£40	£100	£300
Octavian & Divos Julius Caesar			
AE sestertius	£260	£800	–
Octavian & Mark Antony			
AR denarius	£135	£395	£1,250
Quinarius	£35	£90	£285

Brutus

Mark Antony & Octavian

IMPERIAL COINAGE—Julio-Claudian Dynasty 27BC–69 AD

	FROM F	VF	EF
Augustus			
Gold Aureus (Caius & Lucius Caesar)	£565	£1500	£4800
AR Cistophorus................................	£115	£325	£1200
Denarius (Caius & Lucius Caesar)	£50	£145	£420
Denarius (other types)	£65	£195	£535
AR quinarius	£50	£135	£385
Sestertius (large SC)	£90	£325	£1,300
Dupondius or as (large SC)..............	£45	£145	£475
Quadrans	£15	£45	£120
Divus Augustus (struck under Tiberius)			
As	£55	£170	£525
Augustus & Agrippa			
Dupondius (Crocodile rev)	£58	£185	£800
Livia			
Sestertius	£135	£470	£2250
Dupondius	£135	£465	£2250
Gaius Caesar			
AR denarius	£295	£895	£2750
Tiberius			
Aureus (Tribute penny)	£520	£1500	£4500
Denarius (Tribute penny)	£70	£195	£500
Sestertius	£140	£495	£2100
Dupondius	£160	£495	£1750
As	£60	£160	£600
Drusus			
Sestertius..	£220	£675	£2950

Augustus

Tiberius

	FROM F	VF	EF
As (Large S C	£70	£190	£600
Caligula			
Denarius (rev. portrait)	£430	£1290	£3850
Sestertius (PIETAS & Temple)	£300	£1000	£4200
As	£80	£275	£925
Agrippa (struck under Caligula)			
As (VESTA)	£60	£170	£625
Germanicus (struck under Caligula or Claudius)			
As (Large S C)	£70	£190	£625
Agrippina Senior (struck under Caligula)			
Sestertius (Carpentum)	£435	£1400	£5600
Nero & Drusus (struck under Caligula)			
Dupondius (On horseback, galloping)	£180	£550	£2200
Claudius			
Aureus ("DE BRITANN" type)	£950	£260	£7000
Denarius as above	£315	£900	£2850
Didrachm as above	£270	£795	£2000
Denarius other types	£255	£685	£2200
Sestertius	£150	£420	£2200
Dupondius	£60	£190	£675
As	£55	£145	£500
Quadrans	£20	£45	£165
Irregular British Sestertius	£30	£85	£300
Irregular British As	£22	£60	£190
Claudius & Agrippina Junior or Nero			
Denarius	£345	£1200	£3000
Nero Cludius Drusus (struck under Claudius)			
Sestertius	£180	£500	£2500
Antonia (struck under Claudius)			
Dupondius	£100	£325	£1200
Britannicus			
Sestertius	£10500	£35000	—
Nero			
Aureus	£485	£1200	£3200
Denarius	£95	£260	£800
Sestertius	£155	£500	£2500
Sestertius (Port of Ostia)	£1100	£3500	£22,000
Dupondius	£85	£230	£850
As	£50	£140	£575
Semis	£42	£110	£395
Quadrans	£22	£54	£165
Civil War			
Denarius	£170	£485	£1725
Galba			
Denarius	£100	£340	£1250
Sestertius	£220	£655	£3300
Dupondius	£110	£295	£1200
As	£795	£235	£1000
Otho			
Denarius	£200	£555	£1950
Vitellius			
Denarius	£95	£275	£995
Sestertius	£710	£2200	£9000
Dupondius	£230	£650	£2750
As	£125	£360	£1300

IMPERIAL COINAGE—Flavian Dynasty 69–96 AD

	FROM F	VF	EF
Vespasian			
Aureus	£500	£1200	£3600
Denarius	£35	£70	£220
Denarious (IVDAEA)	£70	£190	£635
Sestertius	£100	£295	£1200
Dupondius	£50	£130	£500
As	£40	£115	£475

Caligula

Agrippina Senior

Claudius

Nero

Galba

	FROM F	VF	EF
Titus			
Aureus	£460	£1300	£4250
Denarius as Caesar	£40	£110	£350
Denarius as Augustus	£45	£125	£400
Sestertius	£135	£395	£1600
Dupondius	£55	£160	£595
As	£50	£145	£560
As (IVDAEA CAPTA)	£160	£465	£1950
Julia Titi			
Denarious	£190	£565	£1900
Domitian			
Aureus	£485	£1265	£4250
Cistophorus	£115	£320	£965
Denarius as Caesar	£30	£80	£250
Denarius as Augustus	£25	£60	£195
Sestertius	£95	£300	£1000
Dupondius	£40	£120	£375
As	£40	£115	£340
Ae Semis	£35	£90	£285
Ae Quadrands	£20	£60	£185
Domitia			
Cistophorus	£235	£695	£1900

Titus

Domitian

IMPERIAL COINAGE—Adoptive Emperors 96–138 AD

	FROM F	VF	EF
Nerva			
Aureus	£1000	£2900	£8950
Denarius	£50	£125	£425
Sestertius	£155	£465	£1900
Sestertius (Palm-tree)	£500	£1500	£6250
Dupondius	£70	£225	£700
As	£55	£170	£600
Trajan			
Aureus	£430	£1100	£3500
Denarius	£25	£55	£195
Denarius (Trajan's Column)	£40	£115	£350
Sestertius	£65	£215	£745
Sestertius (Dacian rev.)	£70	£245	£855
Dupondius or as	£35	£95	£350
Ae Quadrands	£25	£60	£200
Plotina, Marciana or Matidia			
Denarius	£425	£1300	£4250
Hadrian			
Aureus	£495	£1250	£4000
Cistophourus	£100	£325	£1000
Denarius (provinces)	£45	£120	£350
Denarius other types	£25	£65	£225
Sestertius	£80	£235	£750
Sertertius (RETITVTORI province types)	£135	£425	£1650
Sestertius (Britannia std)	£2400	£7950	—
Dupondius or As	£35	£120	£395
As (Britannia std)	£170	£500	—
Ae Semiis or Quadrands	£30	£85	£225
Eygpt. Alexandrian Billon Tetradrachm	£30	£85	£345
Sabina			
Denarius	£30	£85	£275
Sestertius	£115	£350	£1450
As or Dupondius	£65	£185	£700
Aelius Ceasar			
Denarius	£70	£225	£650
Sestertius	£145	£445	£1650
As or Dupondius	£60	£175	£700

Nerva

Trajan

Hadrian

IMPERIAL COINAGE—The Antonines 138–193 AD

	FROM F	VF	EF
Antoninus Pius			
Aureus	£365	£950	£3100
Denarius	£18	£45	£165
Sestertius Britannia seated	£465	£1350	£5900
Sestertius other types	£45	£145	£600
As – Britannia rev.	£65	£195	£875
Dupondius or As other types	£30	£70	£300
Antoninus Pius & Marcus Aurelius			
Denarius (bust each side)	£32	£82	£275
Diva Faustina Senior			
Denarius	£18	£42	£165
Sestertius	£38	£145	£595
As or Dupondius	£25	£75	£300
Marcus Aurelius			
Aureus	£395	£995	£3250
Denarius as Caesar	£18	£50	£165
*Denarius as Augustus	£17	£45	£165
Sestertius	£45	£145	£600
As or Dupondius	£25	£75	£300
Faustina Junior			
Denarius	£18	£45	£210
Sestertius	£40	£175	£710
As or Dupondius	£22	£70	£350
Lucius Verus			
Denarius	£20	£60	£210
Sestertius	£55	£185	£710
As or Dupondius	£28	£85	£350
Lucilla			
Denarius	£20	£55	£200
Sestertius	£55	£170	£600
As or Dupondius	£30	£85	£310
Commodus			
Aureus	£465	£1300	£4250
Denarius as Caesar	£28	£60	£200
Denarius as Augustus	£18	£45	£200
Sestertius	£45	£135	£575
Sestertius (VICT BRIT)	£95	£295	£1300
As or Dupondius	£22	£70	£275
Crispina			
Denarius	£22	£60	£250
Sestertius	£68	£200	£800
As or Dupondius	£32	£95	£395

Antoninus Pius

Marcus Aurelius

Faustina Junior

Lucius Verus

IMPERIAL COINAGE—The Severan Dynasty 193–235 AD

	FROM F	VF	EF
Pertinax			
Denarius	£200	£595	£1600
Sestertius	£375	£1000	£3900
Didius Julianus			
Denarius	£350	£900	£2350
Sestertius or Dupondius	£250	£700	£2850
Manlia Scantilla or Didia Clara			
Denarius	£350	£1000	£2700
Pescennius Niger			
Denarius	£225	£650	£2000
Clodius Albinus			
Denarius as Caesar	£42	£120	£350
Denarius as Augustus	£75	£235	£750
Sestertius	£165	£525	£2200
As	£80	£235	£1000
Septimius Severus			
Aureus	£500	£1350	£4250

Commodus

	FROM F	VF	EF
Aureus (VICT BRIT)	£965	£3100	£10,000
Denarius (Mint of Rome)	£15	£35	£150
Denarius (Mints of Emesa & Laodicea)	£13	£35	£125
Denarius (LEG XIII)	£22	£70	£250
Denarius (VICT BRIT)	£22	£80	£275
Sestertius other types	£70	£200	£800
Sestertius (VICT BRIT)	£285	£850	£3600
Dupondius or as	£50	£135	£520
Dupondius or As (VICT BRIT)	£110	£300	£1300
Julia Domna			
Denarius	£14	£35	£125
Sestertius	£68	£200	£895
As or Dupondius	£48	£135	£525
Caracalla			
Aureus (VICT BRIT)	£1050	£3200	£12,000
Denarius as Caesar	£14	£40	£135
Denarius as Augustus	£14	£34	£125
Denarius (VICT BRIT)	£30	£85	£275
Antoninianus	£30	£75	£245
Sestertius	£80	£235	£1000
Sestertius (VICT BRIT)	£245	£750	£3000
Dupondius or As	£45	£135	£510
Dupondius or As (VICT BRIT)	£100	£260	£900
Plautilla			
Denarius	£25	£55	£195
Geta			
Denarius as Caesar	£18	£40	£125
Denarius as Augustus	£20	£60	£200
Denarius (VICT BRIT)	£30	£85	£275
Sestertius	£115	£320	£1300
Sestertius (VICT BRIT)	£245	£695	£2750
Dupondius or as	£70	£200	£800
As (VICT BRIT)	£100	£300	£1000
Macrinus			
Antoninianus	£90	£265	£775
Denarius	£30	£95	£300
Sestertius	£200	£300	£2600
Diadumenian			
Denarius	£55	£170	£575
Dupondius or As	£125	£350	£1500
Elagabalus			
Aureus	£660	£2000	£6000
Antoninianus	£20	£55	£185
Denarius	£15	£35	£125
Sestertius	£90	£275	£1200
Dupondius or As	£60	£150	£595
Julia Paula			
Denarius	£30	£90	£300
Aquilla Severa			
Denarius	£55	£155	£595
Julia Soaemias			
Denarius	£28	£65	£210
Dupondius or As	£65	£200	£710
Julia Maesa			
Denarius	£15	£45	£145
Sestertius	£85	£240	£910
Severus Alexander			
Aureus	£360	£1000	£3250
Denarius as Caesar	£65	£175	£525
Denarius as Augustus	£12	£32	£110
Sestertius	£35	£90	£365
Dupondius or As	£25	£75	£295
Orbiana			
Denarius	£58	£165	£500
As	£90	£250	£900

Septimus Severus

Julia Domna

Geta

Macrinus

Elagabalus

Julia Maesa

	FROM F	VF	EF
Julia Mamaea			
Denarius	£14	£35	£115
Sestertius	£35	£95	£375

IMPERIAL COINAGE—Military Anarchy 235–270 AD

	FROM F	VF	EF
Maximinus I			
Denarius	£14	£38	£125
Sestertius, Dupondius or As	£38	£110	£410
Diva Paula			
Denarius	£115	£315	£1000
Maximus Caesar			
Denarius	£55	£158	£575
Sestertius	£55	£155	£600
Gordian I & II, Africanus			
Denarius	£310	£910	£3500
Sestertius	£380	£1050	£450
Balbinus & Pupienus			
Antoninanus	£68	£190	£595
Denarius	£58	£185	£500
Gordian III			
Antoninianus	£7	£18	£65
Denarius	£10	£28	£100
Sestertius or As	£25	£78	£300
Tranquillina			
Common Colonial	£32	£110	£395
Philip I			
Antoninianus "Animal"			
Lion, stag, antelope, wolf & twins ...	£16	£48	£165
Other Antoninianus	£8	£18	£65
Sestertius, Dupondius or As	£28	£82	£295
Otacilla Severa			
Antoniniaus	£9	£20	£70
Antoninianus "Hipo"	£18	£58	£195
Sestertius	£28	£85	£300
Philip II			
Antoninianus	£8	£20	£70
Antoninianus "Goat"	£18	£58	£195
Sestertius, Dupondius or As	£30	£90	£325
Pacatian			
Antoninianus	£1300	£3775	–
Trajan Decius			
Antoninianus	£7	£19	£70
Antoninianus (DIVI series Augustus, Trajan etc)	£35	£82	£275
Double Sestertius	£175	£555	£2500
Sestertius, Dupondius or As	£30	£88	£350
Herennius Etruscilla			
Antoniniaus	£8	£19	£70
Sestertius, Dupondius or As	£35	£98	£325
Herennius Etruscus			
Antoninianus	£18	£48	£165
Sesterius, Dupondius or As	£58	£180	£650
Hostilian			
Antoninianus as Caesar	£30	£85	£295
Antoninianus as Augustus	£68	£220	£625
Trebonianus Gallus			
Antoninianus	£10	£21	£75
Sestertius or As	£28	£90	£325
Volusian			
Antoninianus	£12	£28	£90
Sestertius	£30	£90	£360
Aemilian			
Antoninianus	£50	£140	£425

Orbiana

Julia Mamaea

Diva Paula

Gordian III

Trajan Decius

Hostilian

	FROM F	VF	EF
Valerian I			
Antoninianus	£8	£20	£65
Sestertius & As	£48	£148	£550
Diva Mariniana			
Antoninianus	£38	£112	£395
Gallienus			
Silver Antoninianus	£10	£25	£65
AE Antoninianus	£6	£14	£55
Ae Antoninianus (Military bust)	£10	£26	£90
AE Antoninianus (Legionary)	£55	£180	—
Ae Sestertius	£45	£135	£525
Ae Denarius	£48	£130	£425
Saloninus			
Ae Antoninianus	£8	£18	£60
Valerian II			
Billon Antoninianus	£12	£32	£125
Saloninus			
Antoninianus	£14	£38	£120
Macrianus & Quietus			
Billon Antoninianus	£42	£110	£345
Regalianus or Dryantilla			
Billon Antoninianus	£1525	£5100	—
Postumus			
Silver Antoninianus	£10	£28	£80
Ae Antoninianus	£10	£18	£55
Radiated sestertius	£48	£158	£650
Laelianus			
Ae Antoninianus	£100	£280	£875
Marius			
Ae Antoninianus	£38	£105	£350
Victorinus			
Ae Antoninianus	£8	£18	£60
Tetricus I & II			
Ae Antoninianus	£8	£18	£60
Claudius II Gothicus			
Ae Antoninianus	£5	£16	£58
Egypt, Alexandrian Billon tetradrachm	£6	£16	£58
DIVO Ae Antoninianus	£6	£22	£70
Quintillus			
Ae Antoninianus	£14	£40	£120

Postumus

Aurelian

Severina

IMPERIAL COINAGE—The Illyrian Emperors—270–285 AD

	FROM F	VF	EF
Aurelian			
Ae Antoninianus	£9	£25	£80
Ae Denarius	£20	£58	£200
Vabalathus & Aurelian			
Ae Antoninianus (bust both sides)	£28	£62	£225
Vabalathus			
Ae Antoninianus	£210	£510	—
Severina			
Ae Antoninianus	£18	£45	£150
Ae As	£38	£110	£375
Zenobia			
Eygpt, Alexandrian Billon Tetradrachm	£510	£1800	—
Tacitus			
Ae Antoninianus	£14	£35	£125
Florian			
Ae Antoninianus	£28	£80	£300
Probus			
Gold Aureus	£1050	£2600	£6750

Tacitus

Florian

	FROM F	VF	EF
Ae Antoninianus	£8	£20	£80
Antoninianus (military or imp. Busts RIC G or H)	£12	£32	£125
Antoninianus (Other military or imp NOT BUSTS G or H)	£16	£46	£185
Antoninianus (VICTOR GERM rev.) ..	£14	£34	£125
Egypt, Alexandrian Billon tetradrachm	£3	£12	£45
Carus			
Ae Antoninianus	£14	£40	£155
Numerian			
Ae Antoninianus	£13	£40	£145
Carinus			
Ae Antoninianus	£13	£32	£125
Magna Urbica			
Ae Antoninianus	£56	£172	£550
Julian of Pannonia			
Ae Antoninianus	£212	£655	£2300

Diocletian

Maximianus

IMPERIAL COINAGE—The Tetrarchy 285–307 AD

	FROM F	VF	EF
Diocletian			
Gold Aureus	£598	£1765	£5600
AR Argenteus	£88	£260	£700
Ae Antoninianus & Radiates	£8	£25	£80
Ae Follis (London Mint)	£13	£42	£145
As above with LON mint mark	£112	£290	£825
Ae Follis (other mints)	£10	£28	£90
Ae Follis (Imperial bust)....................	£25	£78	£250
Maximianus			
AR Argenteus	£86	£255	£695
Ae Follis (London mint)	£13	£42	£145
Ae Follis (other mints)	£11	£28	£90
Ae Follis (MONETA rev.)	£11	£36	£125
Carausius			
Aureus	£5550	£17500	—
Denarius	£265	£765	£260
Ae Antoninianus (PAX).......................	£28	£70	£310
As above but full silvering	£32	£100	£440
Legionary Antoninianus	£72	£200	£810
Expectate Veni Antoninianus	£92	£285	—
In the name of Diocletian or Maximian	£32	£100	£445
Allectus			
Aureus	£6550	£22500	—
Ae Antoninianus	£26	£82	£365
As above but full silvering	£42	£120	£535
Quinarius	£26	£85	£375
Constantius I			
AR Argenteus	£92	£278	£750
Ae Follis (London Mint)	£15	£42	£150
Ae Follis (other mints)	£10	£28	£95
Ae Follis (SALVS rev.)	£12	£36	£135
Ae 4 (Lion or Eagle)	£10	£30	£105
Galerius			
Ae Follis (London mint)	£13	£32	£120
Ae Follis (other mints)	£10	£26	£85
Galeria Valeria			
Ae Follis	£30	£78	£265
Severus II			
Ae Follis (London mint)	£36	£98	£325
Ae Follis (other mints)	£28	£76	£275
Ae Radiate	£16	£46	£150
Ae Denarius	£30	£88	£295
Maximinus II			
Ae Follis (London mint)	£13	£38	£135
Ae Follis (other mints)	£7	£19	£65
Ae Radiate	£9	£28	£95

Carausius

Severus II

Maximinus II

	FROM F	VF	EF
Maxentius			
Ae Follis	£9	£28	£95
Romulus			
Ae Follis	£42	£135	£500
Licinius I			
Billon Argenteus	£62	£195	£650
Ae Follis (London mint)	£8	£22	£85
Ae Follis (other mints)	£7	£18	£75
AE3	£7	£16	£70
Licinius II			
AE3	£8	£22	£85
Alexander or Martinian			
AE	£1265	£4100	–

Licinius II

IMPERIAL COINAGE—Family of Constantine 307–350 AD

	FROM F	VF	EF
Constantine I			
Billon Argenteus	£52	£155	£525
Ae Follis (London mint)	£9	£25	£95
As above—helmeted bust	£14	£45	£175
Ae Follis (other mints) as Caesar	£14	£48	£165
Ae Follis (other mints) as Augustus	£5	£14	£65
AE3	£5	£14	£55
AE3 (London mint)	£8	£22	£85
AE3 (SARMATIA rev)	£12	£32	£125
Urbs Roma / Wolf & twins AE3/4	£5	£15	£65
Constantinopolis AE3/4	£4	£14	£55
Fausta & Helena			
AE3 (London mint)	£52	£150	£475
AE3 (other mints)	£15	£42	£165
Theodora			
AE4	£8	£26	£95
Crispus			
AE3 (London mint)	£9	£26	£95
AE3	£8	£20	£75
Delmatius			
AE3/4	£14	£42	£135
Hanniballianus Rex			
AE4	£84	£235	£785
Constantine II			
AE3 (London mint)	£9	£25	£95
AE3	£6	£18	£75
AE3/4	£4	£9	£45
Constans			
AE2 (centenionalis)	£10	£28	£95
AE3 (half centenionalis)	£6	£22	£75
AE4	£5	£9	£45
Constantius II			
Gold Solidus	£190	£460	£1350
Siliqua	£25	£68	£225
AE2 (or centenionalis)	£8	£25	£85
AE3 (or half centenionalis)	£7	£18	£65
AE3 (London mint)	£22	£65	£225
AE3	£3	£8	£35

Constantine I

Constantine II

Magnentius

IMPERIAL COINAGE—Late period to the collapse of the Empire 350 AD to end

	FROM F	VF	EF
Magnentius			
Gold Solidus	£530	£1650	£5200
Silver Siliqua	£215	£765	£2800
Double centenionalis	£48	£165	£700
Centenionalis	£16	£48	£200
Decentius			
Double centenionalis	£68	£230	£850
Centenionalis	£18	£58	£250
Vetranio			
AE2 (centenionalis)	£36	£118	£375
AE3 (half centenionalis)	£30	£100	£295

Vetranio

	FROM F	VF	EF
Nepotian			
AE2 (centenionalis)	£1765	£5600	–
Constantius Gallus			
AE2 (centenionalis)	£12	£38	£115
AE3 (half centenionalis)	£6	£18	£60
Julian II			
Siliqua	£25	£70	£210
AE1	£42	£135	£395
AE3 (helmeted bust)	£10	£28	£85
Anonymous, Serapis + Jupiter AE3	£178	£525	–
Jovian			
AE1	£66	£215	£630
AE3	£13	£40	£115
Valentinian I			
Sold Solidus	£122	£295	£685
Silver Milliarense	£168	£525	£1500
Siliqua	£28	£80	£225
AE3	£6	£20	£65
Valens			
Gold Solidus	£122	£295	£695
Silver Milliarense	£195	£580	£1700
Siliqua	£25	£75	£225
AE3	£6	£20	£65
Procopius			
AE3	£48	£128	£450
Gratian			
Silver Milliarense	£170	£525	£1500
Siliqua	£26	£75	£225
AE3	£5	£18	£75
AE4	£5	£14	£60
Valentinian II			
Solidus	£162	£400	£900
Siliqua	£26	£78	£235
AE2	£13	£30	£90
AE4	£5	£14	£50
Theodosius I			
Solidus	£162	£415	£1000
Siliqua	£29	£90	£255
AE2	£12	£35	£100
AE3	£9	£28	£90
Aelia Flaccilla			
AE2	£30	£90	£295
AE4	£19	£45	£145
Magnus Maximus			
Solidus (AVGOB)	£4550	£11500	–
Solidus	£725	£1850	£4600
Siliqua	£32	£95	£275
Siliqua (AVGPS)	£725	£1,850	–
AE2	£19	£60	£185
Flavius Victor			
Silver Sliqua	£100	£315	£795
AE4	£36	£90	£295
Eugenius			
Silver Siliqua	£112	£340	£1000
Arcadius			
Gold Solidus	£112	£275	£675
Silver Siliqua	£28	£80	£250
Silver Half-siliqua	£92	£270	£750
AE2	£14	£30	£95
AE4	£5	£12	£35
Eudoxia			
AE3	£26	£68	£195

Julian II

Jovian

Valentinian I

Valens

Theodosius I

Arcadius

	FROM F	VF	EF
Honorius			
Gold Solidus	£110	£270	£600
Silver Siliqua	£30	£85	£240
AE4	£6	£18	£50
Constantine III			
Silver Siliqua	£100	£310	£800
Theodosius II			
Gold Solidus	£110	£270	£600
Johannes			
AE4	£110	£425	—
Valentinian III			
Gold Soldius	£110	£265	£575
AE4	£28	£75	£265

Honorius

Theodosius II

Ae = bronze; AE 1, 2, 3, 4 = bronze coins in descending order of size.

Illustrations by courtesy of Classical Numismatic Group/Seaby Coins.

Mike R. Vosper

Celtic, Roman, Greek & Hammered Coins Bought & Sold

Fine styled 3/4 Facing Gold Solidus. **Mint state colonial of Philip I.** Magnificent Cunobelin stater.

quisite Byzantine gold depicting Christ. Classic example of Caligula. One of the finest known 'Crispus' thrymsa.

A splendid example of the rare SOLIDV. A pleasing example of a Gold Noble. A handsome example of a Burgred.

Stunning pictorial Greek, one of many we've sold. Superb Anglo-Gallic Gold. One of the unpublished 1/4 staters we've had.

To view our extensive stock please log onto

www.vosper4coins.co.uk

P.O. Box 32, Hockwold, BRANDON, IP26 4HX, U.K.

Tel/Fax: +44 (0) 1-842-828292

Email: mike.vosper@vosper4coins.co.uk Website: www.vosper4coins.co.uk

Are you wishing to sell a comprehensive collection of coins?

We will obtain retail prices through our

COIN CONVEYANCE PROGRAMME (contact us for more details)

BNTA BNTA

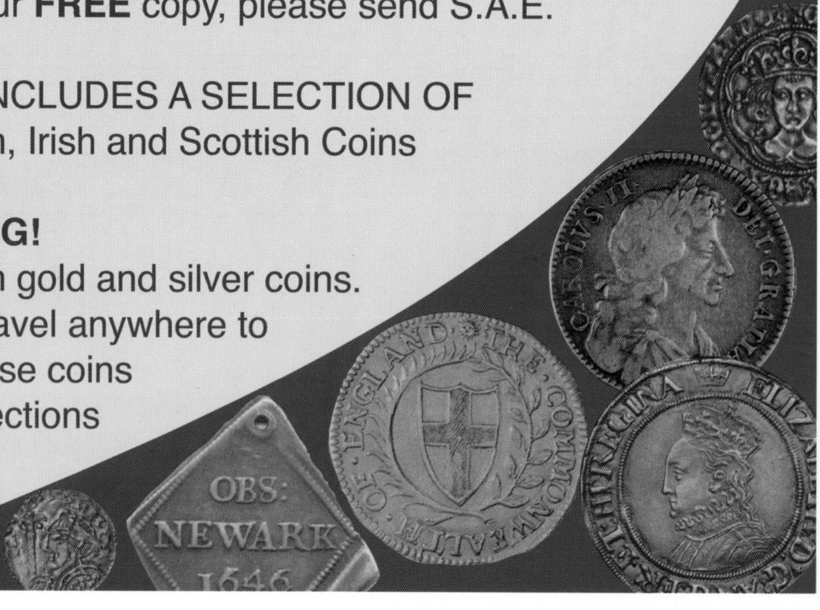
OBS:
NEWARK

A SIMPLIFIED PRICE GUIDE
TO

ENGLISH HAMMERED COINS

PART I
959–1485

INTRODUCTION

We have taken our starting point for hammered coin prices back to the Anglo-Saxon reign of Edgar; who could reasonably claim to be the first king of All England. Also it is from this time onwards that we start to get regular "portraits" as well as moneyers and mints on most issues. This gives a total of eight rulers to the list of kings prior to the Norman Conquest and most of these have coin issues that can be purchased quite reasonably. It is also worth pointing out here that of course coins had previously been struck in England for approximately 1000 years prior to our listings by Celtic, Roman and earlier Saxon rulers, details of which can be found in more specific publications.

PRICING

The prices given in the following pages are intended to be used as a "Pocket book guide" to the values of the *most common* coins within any denomination of any one reign. The price quoted is what a collector may expect to pay for such a piece in the condition indicated. For more detailed information we recommend the reader to one of the many specialist publications.

GRADING

The prices quoted are for three different grades of condition: Fine (F), Very Fine (VF) and Extremely Fine (EF). A "Fine" coin is assumed to be a fairly worn, circulated, piece but with all or most of the main features and lettering still clear. "Very Fine" is a middle grade with a small amount of wear and most details fairly clear. For this edition we have included the prices for coins in Extremely Fine condition where appropriate, although very few hammered coins actually turn up in this grade (i.e. nearly mint state with hardly any wear). In some instances the prices quoted are theoretically based and are only included to provide a guide. It is important to note that on all hammered coins the very nature of striking, i.e. individually, by hand, means hammered coinage is rarely a straight grade and when listed by a dealer the overall condition will often be qualified by terms such as: *weak in parts, struck off-centre, cracked or chipped flan, double struck,* etc. When applicable the price should be adjusted accordingly.

HISTORY

Below the heading for each monarch we have given a few historical notes as and when they apply to significant changes in the coinage.

EDGAR
(959–975)

	F	VF	EF
Edgar Penny, non portrait (2 line inscription)...............................	£200	£450	–

EDWARD THE MARTYR
(975–978)

	F	VF	EF
Edward, Penny, Portrait.......................	£1100	£3000	–

AETHELRED II
(978–1016)

	F	VF	EF
Aethelred II, Penny, last small cross type (First hand type illustrated)	£120	£260	£500

CNUT
(1016–1035)

	F	VF	EF
Cnut, Penny (short cross type).............. (*Quatrefoil type illustrated*)	£100	£175	£375

HAROLD I (1035–40)

	F	VF	EF
Harold I, Penny	£275	£680	–

HARTHACANUTE (1035–42)

	F	VF	EF
Harthacanute, Penny, English Mint (in his own name)	£900	£2400	–
Harthacanute, Penny, Danish type	£275	£575	–

Danish type

EDWARD THE CONFESSOR (1042–66)

	F	VF	EF
Edward the Confessor, Penny	£130	£240	–

HAROLD II (1066)

	F	VF	EF
Harold II, Penny	£700	£1550	–

WILLIAM I
(1066–87)

The Norman Conquest had very little immediate effect on the coinage of England. The Anglo-Saxon standard of minting silver pennies was very high and the practice of the moneyer putting his name and mint town on the reverse continued as before, except with William's portrait of course. It is worth noting here that non-realistic, stylised portraits were used until the reign of Henry VII.
There are eight major types of pennies of which the last, the PAXS type, is by far the commonest.

	F	VF	EF
William I, Penny	£250	£450	£900

WILLIAM II
(1087–1100)

Very little change from his father's reign except that five new types were issued, most of which were much more crudely designed than previous, all are scarce.

	F	VF	EF
William II, Penny	£625	£1400	–

HENRY I
(1100–35)

There are fifteen different types of penny for this reign of which the last two are the most common. Most issues are of a very poor standard both in workmanship and metal, the prices reflect a poor quality of issue.

	F	VF	EF
Henry I, Penny	£175	£425	–

STEPHEN (1135–54)

This is historically a very complicated time for the coinage, mainly due to civil war and a consequential lack of central control in the country which resulted in very poor quality and deliberately damaged pieces. Coins were struck not only in the name of Stephen and his main rival claimant Matilda but also by their supporters. The commonest issue is the "Watford" type; so named, as are many issues, after the area in which a hoard was found.

	F	VF	EF
Stephen, Penny	£250	£600	–

HENRY II (1154–89)

There were two distinct issues struck during this reign. The first, Cross and Crosslets or "Tealby" coinage (named after Tealby in Lincolnshire), continued to be very poorly made and lasted 20 years. However, in 1180 the new and superior "Short Cross" issue commenced, being issued from only twelve major

	F	VF	EF
Henry II, Penny, Tealby	£90	£250	–
Henry II, Penny, Short Cross	£45	£130	–

RICHARD I (1189–1199)

There were no major changes during this reign, in fact pennies continued to be struck with his father Henry's name throughout the reign. The coins struck under Richard tend to be rather crude in style.

	F	VF	EF
Richard I, Penny	£75	£200	–

JOHN (1199–1216)

As with his brother before him, there were no major changes during the reign of King John, and pennies with his father's name were struck throughout the reign, although they tended to be somewhat neater in style than those struck during the reign of Richard I.

	F	VF	EF
John, Penny	£50	£125	£240

HENRY III (1216–72)

The coinage during Henry III's reign continued as before with the short cross issue. However, in 1247 a new long cross design was introduced to prevent clipping. This design was to last in one form or another for many centuries.

	F	VF	EF
Henry III, Penny, Short Cross	£30	£85	£175
Henry III, Penny, Long Cross	£25	£50	£125

EDWARD I (1272–1307)

After a few years of issuing similar pieces to his father, in 1279 Edward I ordered a major re-coinage. This consisted of well-made pennies, halfpennies and farthings in relatively large quantities, and for a brief period a groat (four pence) was produced. The pennies are amongst the most common of all hammered coins.

	F	VF	EF
Edward I (and Edward II)			
Groat (often damaged)	£2000	£6250	—
Penny	£20	£50	£135
Halfpenny	£20	£65	£175
Farthing	£20	£60	£170

Edward I penny

EDWARD II
(1307–1327)

The coinage of Edward II differs in only a very few minor details from that of Edward I and are of similar value for the common types.

EDWARD III
(1327–77)

This was a long reign which saw major changes in the coinage, the most significant being the introduction of a gold coinage (based on the Noble, valued at 6s 8d, and its fractions) and a regular issue of a large silver groat (and half groat). The mints were limited to a few episcopal cities but coins of English type were also struck in the newly-acquired Calais.

	F	VF	EF
Gold			
Noble	£550	£1350	£3000
Half Noble	£365	£900	£1800
Quarter Noble	£225	£500	£900
Silver			
Groat	£50	£170	£650
Half Groat	£30	£100	£300
Penny	£25	£80	£225
Half Penny	£18	£55	£170
Farthing	£30	£80	£200

Gold Noble

RICHARD II
(1377–1399)

The denominations continued during this reign much as before. However, coins are quite rare mainly due to the lack of bullion gold and silver going into the mints, mainly because of an inbalance with European weights and fineness.

	F	VF	EF
Gold			
Noble	£750	£1850	£4500
Half Noble	£800	£2250	—
Quarter Noble	£375	£850	£1500
Silver			
Groat	£450	£1500	—
Half Groat	£225	£700	—
Penny	£65	£200	—
Half Penny	£40	£125	—
Farthing	£125	£285	—

Gold Noble

HENRY IV
(1399–1413)

Because of the continuing problems with the scarcity of gold and silver the coinage was reduced in weight in 1412, towards the end of the reign. All coins of this reign are quite scarce.

	F	VF
Gold		
Noble	£1500	£3800
Half Noble	£2000	£5250
Quarter Noble	£550	£1350
Silver		
Groat	£1900	£5700
Half Groat	£650	£1750
Penny	£325	£900
Half Penny	£275	£650
Farthing	£625	£1600

Noble

HENRY V
(1413–22)

Monetary reform introduced towards the end of his father's reign in 1412 improved the supply of bullion and hence coins of Henry V are far more common. All of the main denominations continued as before.

	F	VF	EF
Gold			
Noble	£750	£1775	£3750
Half Noble	£635	£1500	—
Quarter Noble	£285	£675	£1150
Silver			
Groat	£165	£450	—
Half Groat	£120	£350	—
Penny	£40	£150	—
Half Penny	£30	£95	—
Farthing	£200	£600	—

Groat

HENRY VI
(1422–61 and again 1470–71)

Although there were no new denominations during these reigns (see Edward IV below), Henry's first reign saw eleven different issues, each for a few years and distinguished by privy marks, i.e. crosses, pellets, annulets, etc.

HENRY VI *continued*

	F	VF	EF
Gold			
First reign—			
Noble	£700	£1750	£3250
Half Noble	£475	£1150	£2100
Quarter Noble	£240	£575	£1000
2nd reign—			
Angel	£1375	£3400	—
Half Angel	£1750	£5250	—
Silver			
Groat	£50	£125	£250
Half Groat	£35	£90	£200
Penny	£30	£100	£225
Half Penny	£20	£65	£140
Farthing	£100	£250	—

Noble

EDWARD IV
(1461–70 and again 1471–83)

The significant changes during these reigns were the replacement of the noble by the rose ryal (and revalued at 10 shillings) and the introduction of the angel at the old noble value. We also start to see mint-marks or initial marks appearing, usually at the top of the coin, they were used to denote the period of issue for dating purposes and often lasted for two to three years.

	F	VF	EF
Gold			
Ryal	£650	£1500	£2650
Half Ryal	£550	£1325	£2250
Quarter Ryal	£350	£800	£1450
Angel	£575	£1250	£2350
Half Angel	£550	£1200	£2250
Silver			
Groat	£50	£140	£375
Half Groat	£45	£140	£325
Penny	£30	£85	£225
Half Penny	£25	£85	—
Farthing	£250	£675	—

Angel

RICHARD III
(1483–85)

The close of the Yorkist Plantagenet and the beginning of the Medieval period come together at this time. There are no new significant numismatic changes but most coins of Richard whilst not really rare, continue to be very popular and priced quite high.

	F	VF	EF
Gold			
Angel	£2000	£5250	—
Half Angel	£3500	£10,750	—
Silver			
Groat	£600	£1500	—
Half Groat	£800	£2000	—
Penny	£300	£800	—
Half Penny	£235	£600	—
Farthing	£1000	£2500	—

Groat

PART II: 1485–1663

Among the more significant features of the post-Renaissance period as it affected coinage is the introduction of realistic portraiture during the reign of Henry VII. We also have a much wider and varied number of new and revised denominations, for example eleven different gold denominations of Henry VIII and the same number of silver for Elizabeth I. Here we only mention the introduction or changes in the main denominations, giving a value for all of them, once again listing the commonest type.

HENRY VII (1485–1509)

The gold sovereign of 20 shillings makes its first appearance in 1489 as does the testoon (later shilling) in about 1500. The silver penny was re-designed to a rather crude likeness of the sovereign.

	F	VF	EF
Gold			
Sovereign	£15,000	£45,000	—
Ryal	£16,000	£50,000	—
Angel	£550	£1300	—
Half Angel	£525	£1250	—
Silver			
Testoon 1/-	£11,500	£22,000	—
Groat	£70	£175	£500
Half Groat	£40	£100	£275
Penny	£35	£95	£225
Half Penny	£25	£85	—
Farthing	£275	£800	—

Profile Groat

HENRY VIII (1509–47)

After a long initial period of very little change in the coinage, in 1526 there were many, with an attempt to bring the gold/silver ratio in line with the continental currencies. Some gold coins only lasted a short time and are very rare. The crown (in gold) makes its first appearance. Towards the end of the reign we see large issues of debased silver coins (with a high copper content) bearing the well-known facing portrait of the ageing King. These tend to turn up in poor condition.

	F	VF	EF
Gold			
Sovereign	£4000	£11,500	—
Half Sovereign	£650	£1750	—
Angel	£575	£1250	£2400
Half Angel	£525	£1200	£2000
Quarter Angel	£500	£1250	—
George Noble	£6000	£17,500	—
Half George Noble	Rare	Rare	—
Crown of the rose	Rare	Rare	—
Crown of the double rose	£500	£1200	£2000
Half Crown of the double rose	£450	£1000	—
Silver			
Testoon 1/-	£775	£3250	—
Groat	£100	£285	£650
Half Groat	£50	£140	£375
Penny	£35	£135	£250
Half Penny	£225	£650	—
Farthing	£225	£650	—

Gold Sovereign

EDWARD VI (1547–53)

Some of the coins struck in the first few years of this short reign could really be called Henry VIII posthumous issues as there is continuity in both name and style from his father's last issue. However, overlapping this period are portrait issues of the boy King, particularly shillings (usually poor quality coins). This period also sees the first dated English coin (shown in Roman numerals). In 1551 however, a new coinage was introduced with a restored silver quality from the Crown (dated 1551) down to the new sixpence and threepence.

	F	VF	EF
Gold			
Sovereign (30s)	£4000	£12,000	–
Half Sovereign	£1300	£3400	–
Crown	£1300	£4000	–
Half Crown	£1150	£3250	–
Angel	£6000	£15000	–
Half Angel	–	–	–
Sovereign (20s)	£3000	£7750	–
Silver			
Crown	£900	£2350	–
Half Crown	£700	£1600	–
Shilling	£100	£400	£1200
Sixpence	£115	£475	–
Groat	£750	£2250	–
Threepence	£185	£700	–
Half Groat	£355	£1000	–
Penny	£60	£200	–
Half Penny	£150	£500	–
Farthing	£800	£2500	–

Crowned bust half sovereign

MARY (1553–54)

The early coins of Mary's sole reign are limited and continue to use the same denominations as Edward, except that the gold ryal was reintroduced.

	F	VF
Gold		
Sovereign (30s)	£4000	£11,000
Ryal	£15,000	–
Angel	£1500	£3600
Half Angel	£2500	£7250
Silver		
Groat	£145	£450
Half Groat	£700	£2000
Penny	£565	£1800

Groat

PHILIP & MARY
(1554–58)

After a very short reign alone, Mary married Philip of Spain and they technically ruled jointly (although not for very long in practise) until her death. After her marriage we see both her and Philip on the shillings and sixpences.

	F	VF
Gold		
Angel	£3000	£7750
Half Angel	£5250	–
Silver		
Shilling	£385	£1500
Sixpence	£400	£1500
Groat	£150	£475
Half Groat	£400	£1150
Penny	£90	£235

Shilling

ELIZABETH I
(1558–1603)

As might be expected with a long reign there are a number of significant changes in the coinage which include several new denominations—so many in silver that every value from the shilling downwards was marked and dated to distinguish them. Early on we have old base Edward VI shillings countermarked to a new reduced value (not priced here). Also due to a lack of small change and the expense of making a miniscule farthing we have a new threehalfpence and threefarthings. Finally we see the beginnings of a milled (machine produced) coinage for a brief period from 1561–71.

	F	VF	EF
Gold			
Sovereign (30s)	£3650	£9000	–
Ryal (15s)	£8250	£22,500	–
Angel	£800	£2000	–
Half Angel	£725	£1750	–
Quarter Angel	£650	£1650	–
Pound (20s)	£1850	£5250	–
Half Pound	£1100	£2750	–
Crown	£775	£2150	–
Half Crown	£725	£1900	–
Silver			
Crown	£1300	£3150	–
Half Crown	£950	£2400	–
Shilling	£120	£360	£1000
Sixpence	£60	£180	£600
Groat	£70	£200	£450
Threepence	£40	£140	£350
Half Groat	£35	£85	–
Threehalfpence	£45	£145	–
Penny	£30	£85	£180
Threefarthings	£80	£220	–
Half Penny	£40	£90	£140

Shilling

JAMES I
(1603–25)

Although the size of the gold coinage remains much the same as Elizabeth's reign, the name and weight or value of the denominations have several changes, i.e. Pound = Sovereign = Unite = Laurel. A new four shilling gold coin (thistle crown) was introduced. A number of the silver coins now have their value in Roman numerals on the coin. Relatively few angels were made from this period onwards and they are usually found pierced.

	F	VF	EF
Gold			
Sovereign (20s)	£1500	£4750	–
Unite	£475	£1250	£2350
Double crown/half unite	£325	£850	£1750
Crown	£200	£500	£1200
Thistle Crown	£225	£625	£1250
Half Crown	£175	£400	–
Rose Ryal (30s)	£2000	£5250	–
Spur Ryal (15s)	£3500	£9500	–
Angel (pierced)	£575	£1150	–
Half Angel (Unpierced)	£1400	£4750	–
Laurel	£550	£1200	2150
Half Laurel	£400	£850	1750
Quarter Laurel	£225	£500	£1150
Silver			
Crown	£725	£1800	–
Half Crown	£275	£750	–
Shilling	£75	£240	–
Sixpence	£75	£200	–
Half Groat	£25	£55	£105
Penny	£20	£40	£90
Half Penny	£15	£35	£60

Halfcrown

CHARLES I
(1625–49)

This reign is probably the most difficult to simplify as there are so many different issues and whole books have been produced on this period alone. From the beginning of the King's reign and throughout the Civil War, a number of mints operated for varying lengths of time, producing both regular and irregular issues. The Tower mint was taken over by Parliament in 1642 but before this a small quantity of milled coinage was produced alongside the regular hammered issues. The Court then moved to Oxford from where, for the next three years, large quantities of gold and silver were struck (including rare triple unites and large silver pounds). The most prolific of the provincial mints were those situated at Aberystwyth, York, Oxford, Shrewsbury, Bristol, Exeter, Truro, Chester and Worcester as well as some smaller mints mainly situated in the West Country. Among the more interesting coins of the period are the pieces struck on unusually-shaped flans at Newark and Pontefract whilst those towns were under siege. As many of the coins struck during the Civil War were crudely struck on hastily gathered bullion and plate, they provide a fascinating area of study. The prices indicated below are the minimum for the commonest examples of each denomination irrespective of town of origin.

	F	VF	EF
Gold			
Triple Unite (£3)	£8000	£20,000	—
Unite	£500	£1250	—
Double crown/Half unite	£350	£850	—
Crown	£225	£475	—
Angel (pierced)	£700	£1750	—
Angel (unpierced)	£1750	£6000	—
Silver			
Pound (20 shillings)	£2200	£5250	—
Half Pound	£1200	£2500	—
Crown	£400	£1000	—
Half Crown	£70	£185	—
Shilling	£40	£170	£600
Sixpence	£55	£185	£550
Groat	£65	£170	£375
Threepence	£50	£150	£345
Half Groat	£20	£60	£130
Penny	£20	£50	£125
Half Penny	£15	£30	£50

Triple unite

Oxford Halfcrown

Above: Newark siege shilling.

THE COMMONWEALTH (1649–60)

After the execution of Charles I, Parliament changed the design of the coinage. They are simple non- portrait pieces with an English legend.

	F	VF	EF
Gold			
Unite	£1500	£3250	–
Double crown/Half unite	£750	£1800	–
Crown	£750	£1800	–
Silver			
Crown	£750	£1650	£3500
Half Crown	£260	£600	£1850
Shilling	£170	£385	£1400
Sixpence	£150	£375	£1200
Half Groat	£35	£100	£250
Penny	£35	£100	£250
Halfpenny	£30	£75	£150

Crown

CHARLES II (1660–85)

Although milled coins had been produced for Oliver Cromwell in 1656–58, after the Restoration of the monarchy hammered coins continued to be produced until 1663, when the machinery was ready to manufacture large quantities of good milled pieces.

	F	VF	EF
Gold			
Unite	£1150	£2850	–
Double crown/Half unite	£800	£2300	–
Crown	£900	£2600	–
Silver			
Half Crown	£240	£725	–
Shilling	£165	£500	–
Sixpence	£140	£425	–
Fourpence	£35	£100	£180
Threepence	£30	£100	£170
Twopence	£20	£50	£110
Penny	£25	£70	£130

Milled halfcrown

A COMPREHENSIVE PRICE GUIDE TO THE COINS OF

THE UNITED KINGDOM 1656–2009

including

ENGLAND
SCOTLAND
ISLE OF MAN
GUERNSEY, JERSEY, ALDERNEY

also

IRELAND

When referring to this price guide one must bear a number of important points in mind. The points listed here have been taken into consideration during the preparation of this guide and we hope that the prices given will provide a true reflection of the market at the time of going to press. Nevertheless, the publishers can accept no liability for the accuracy of the prices quoted.

1. "As struck" examples with flaws will be worth less than the indicated price.
2. Any coin which is particularly outstanding, with an attractive natural toning or in superb state will command a much *higher* price than that shown.
3. These prices refer strictly to the British market, and do not reflect outside opinions.
4. Some prices given for coins not seen in recent years are estimates based on a knowledge of the market.
5. In the case of coins of high rarity, prices are not generally given.
6. In the listing, "—" indicates, where applicable, one of the following:
    a. Metal or bullion value only
    b. Not usually found in this grade
    c. Not collected in this condition
7. Proof coins are listed in FDC under the UNC column.
8. All prices are quoted in £ sterling, exclusive of VAT (where applicable).

FIVE GUINEAS

CHARLES II (1660–85)

	F	VF	EF
1668 First bust	£1750	£4000	£9000
1668 — Elephant	£1750	£4000	£9500
1669 —	£1900	£4000	—
1669 — Elephant	£2000	£4500	—
1670 —	£1800	£4000	£10000
1671 —	£1800	£4000	£10000
1672 —	£1800	£4000	£10000
1673 —	£1800	£4000	£10500
1674 —	£2000	£4500	£10000
1675 —	£1700	£4200	£9750
1675 — Elephant	£1700	£4250	—
1675 — Elephant & Castle		Extremely rare	
1676 —	£1900	£4500	£10000
1676 — Elephant & Castle	£1750	£4200	£9000
1677 —	£1800	£4000	£9000
1677/5 — Elephant		Extremely rare	
1677 — Elephant & Castle	£1800	£4200	£10000
1678 —	£1800	£4200	£10000
1678 — Elephant & Castle	£2000	£4800	£1000
1678/7 —	£1800	£4000	£9000
1678/7 — Elephant & Castle	£1800	£4200	£9000
1678/7 Second Bust	£1800	£4000	£9000
1679 —	£1800	£4000	£9000
1680 —	£1800	£4000	£8500
1680 — Elephant & Castle		Extremely rare	
1681 —	£2000	£4200	£9000
1681 — Elephant & Castle	£2000	£5000	£10000
1682 —	£1800	£4000	£9000
1682 — Elephant & Castle	£1800	£4000	£9500
1683 —	£1900	£4000	£9000
1683 — Elephant & Castle	£2200	£5000	£11000
1684 —	£1800	£4000	£9000
1684 — Elephant & Castle	£1800	£4200	£9000

Charles II

JAMES II (1685–88)

	F	VF	EF
1686	£1850	£6000	£13000
1687	£1700	£5000	£11000
1687 Elephant & Castle	£1850	£5000	£11000
1688	£1850	£5000	£11000
1688 Elephant & Castle	£1900	£5000	£12500

WILLIAM AND MARY (1688–94)

	F	VF	EF
1691	£1500	£4000	£9500
1691 Elephant & Castle	£1800	£4000	£10000
1692	£1500	£4000	£9500
1692 Elephant & Castle	£1750	£4500	£11000
1693	£1550	£4000	£9500
1693 Elephant & Castle	£2000	£4500	£12000
1694	£1750	£5250	£11000
1694 Elephant & Castle	£1850	£4800	£12000

WILLIAM III (1694–1702)

	F	VF	EF
1699 First bust	£1750	£5000	£11000
1699 — Elephant & Castle	£1900	£5000	£12000
1700 —	£1800	£5000	£11000
1701 Second bust "fine work"	£1800	£5000	£12500

William & Mary

ANNE (1702–14)

	F	VF	EF
Pre-Union with Scotland			
1703 VIGO below bust	£20000	£50000	£140000
1705	£1800	£4500	£12000
1706	£1650	£4000	£11000
Post-Union (different shields)			
1706	£2000	£4000	£10000
1709 Narrow shields	£1850	£4000	£10000
1711 Broader shields	£1850	£4000	£10000
1713 —	£1850	£4500	£11000
1714 —	£1850	£4500	£12000
1714/3	£2000	£5000	£12500

GEORGE I (1714–27)

	F	VF	EF
1716	£2000	£4500	£12000
1717	£2200	£6000	£15000
1720	£2700	£7000	£18000
1726	£2000	£5000	£12000

GEORGE II (1727–60)

	F	VF	EF
1729 Young head	£1900	£4700	£10500
1729 — E.I.C. below head	£1800	£4500	£9500
1731 —	£1750	£5000	£10000
1735 —	£1750	£4600	£12500
1738 —	£2200	£5000	£12000
1741 —	£1750	£4000	£10000
1746 Old head, LIMA	£1750	£4000	£10000
1748 —	£1750	£4000	£10000
1753 —	£1800	£4500	£10000

GEORGE III (1760–1820)

	F	VF	EF
1770 Patterns	–	–	£90000
1773	–	–	£80000
1777	–	–	£70000

Anne

IMPORTANT NOTE:

The prices quoted in this guide are set at August 2009 with the price of gold at £595 per ounce and silver £8.75 per ounce—market fluctuations can have a marked effect on the values of modern precious metal coins.

TWO GUINEAS

Charles II

CHARLES II (1660–85)

	F	VF	EF
1664 First bust	£900	£2500	£5500
1664 — Elephant	£800	£2200	£4750
1665 —		Extremely rare	
1669 —		Extremely rare	
1671 —	£900	£4000	£11000
1675 Second bust	£1000	£4000	—
1676 —	£900	£3500	—
1676 — Elephant & Castle	£900	£3500	£7000
1677 —	£900	£3500	£6750
1677 — Elephant & Castle		Extremely rare	
1678/7 —	£900	£3000	£6000
1678 — Elephant		Extremely rare	
1678 — Elephant & Castle	£900	£3000	£6000
1679 —	£1000	£3500	£6000
1680 —	£1000	£3500	£6500
1681 —	£800	£2750	£6000
1682 — Elephant & Castle	£900	£3500	£7000
1683 —	£1000	£3000	£6000
1683 — Elephant & Castle	£1000	£3250	£6250
1684 —	£900	£3750	£6750
1684 — Elephant & Castle	£1000	£3750	£7250

James II

JAMES II (1685–88)

	F	VF	EF
1687	£1000	£3000	£6000
1688/7	£1100	£3500	£7000

WILLIAM AND MARY (1688–94)

	F	VF	EF
1691 Elephant & Castle		Extremely rare	
1693	£1000	£2700	£6000
1693 Elephant & Castle	£1000	£2700	£6000
1694 — 4 over 3	£900	£2400	£5500
1694 Elephant & Castle	£1000	£2700	£6000

WILLIAM III (1694–1702)

	F	VF	EF
1701 "fine work"	£1400	£4000	£6500

Anne

ANNE (1702–14)

	F	VF	EF
1709	£850	£2200	£5200
1711	£850	£2000	£5000
1713	£850	£2000	£5000
1714	£900	£2200	£5500

GEORGE I (1714–27)

	F	VF	EF
1717	£850	£2000	£5000
1720	£850	£2000	£5000
1720/17	£850	£2000	£5200
1726	£750	£1850	£4600

GEORGE II (1727–60)

	F	VF	EF
1733 Proof only FDC		£20000 plus	
§1734 Young head 4 over 3	£1600	£4000	—
1735 —	£700	£1500	£3500
1738 —	£600	£1000	£2200
1739 —	£600	£1000	£2100
1739 Intermediate head	£700	£1100	£2200
1740 —	£700	£1100	£2200
1748 Old head	£700	£1100	£3000
1753 —	£750	£1600	£4000

George II

GEORGE III (1760–1820)

	F	VF	EF
1768 Patterns only	—	Extremely Rare	
1773 Patterns only	—	Extremely Rare	
1777 Patterns only	—	Extremely Rare	

GUINEAS

CHARLES II (1660–85)

	F	VF	EF
1663 First bust	£750	£2700	£6500
1663 — Elephant below	£750	£2500	—
1664 Second bust	£600	£2500	—
1664 — Elephant		Extremely rare	
1664 Third bust	£600	£2000	£5000
1664 — Elephant	£600	£2200	£5000
1665 —	£650	£2200	£5000
1665 — Elephant	£700	£2500	£6000
1666 —	£600	£2300	£5000
1667 —	£550	£2000	£5000
1668 —	£550	£2200	£5000
1668 — Elephant		Extremely rare	
1669 —	£550	£2750	—
1670 —	£500	£2500	£5500
1671 —	£500	£2200	£5200
1672 —	£550	£2500	£5500
1672 Fourth bust	£450	£2000	£4500
1673 Third bust	£600	£2850	—
1673 Fourth bust	£450	£2000	£5000
1674 —	£450	£2000	—
1674 — Elephant & Castle		Extremely rare	
1675 —	£500	£2000	£5000
1675 — CRAOLVS Error		Extremely rare	
1675 — Elephant & Castle	£550	£2000	£5000
1676 —	£400	£1200	£4000
1676 — Elephant & Castle	£450	£1600	£4000
1677 —	£450	£1500	£3700
1677/5 — Elephant 7 over 5		Extremely rare	
1677 — Elephant & Castle	£300	£1800	£4500
1678 —	£325	£1500	£3500
1678 — Elephant		Extremely rare	
1678 — Elephant & Castle	£500	£2000	—

Charles II, third bust

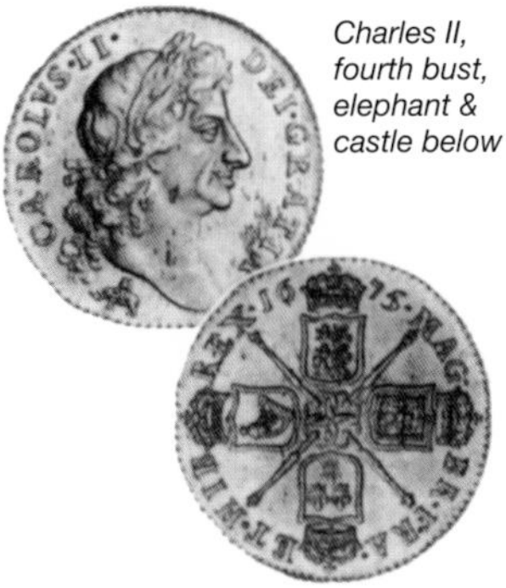

Charles II, fourth bust, elephant & castle below

	F	VF	EF
1679 —	£400	£1250	£3500
1679 — Elephant & Castle	£500	£1800	£5000
1680 —	£500	£1800	£5000
1680 — Elephant & Castle	£600	£2250	—
1681 —	£425	£2000	£4500
1681 — Elephant & Castle	£500	£2000	—
1682 —	£400	£1600	£4000
1682 — Elephant & Castle	£450	£1800	£4500
1683 —	£350	£1300	£3500
1683 — Elephant & Castle	£600	£2500	£5500
1684 —	£450	£1800	£4500
1684 — Elephant & Castle	£475	£1800	£4750

James II, first bust, elephant & castle below

JAMES II (1685–1688)

	F	VF	EF
1685 First bust	£400	£1800	£5000
1685 — Elephant & Castle	£500	£2200	£4500
1686 —	£450	£2000	£4000
1686 — Elephant & Castle		Extremely rare	
1686 Second bust	£350	£1500	£3500
1686 — Elephant & Castle	£500	£2500	£5500
1687 —	£350	£1700	£3500
1687 —Elephant & Castle	£400	£1700	£4500
1688 —	£400	£1700	£5000
1688 — Elephant & Castle	£400	£2000	£5000

James II, second bust

WILLIAM AND MARY (1688–94)

	F	VF	EF
1689	£400	£1800	£4500
1689 Elephant & Castle	£400	£1800	£4500
1690	£400	£1800	£4500
1690 Elephant & Castle	£550	£2000	£5500
1691	£400	£1800	£4500
1691 Elephant & Castle	£400	£1800	£4500
1692	£400	£1800	£4500
1692 Elephant	£600	£2400	£6000
1692 Elephant & Castle	£450	£2400	£4500
1693	£400	£2000	£4500
1693 Elephant		Extremely rare	
1693 Elephant & Castle		Extremely rare	
1694	£400	£2000	£4750
1694 Elephant & Castle	£400	£2200	£4600

WILLIAM III (1694–1702)

	F	VF	EF
1695 First bust	£300	£1700	£3750
1695 — Elephant & Castle	£400	£1900	£4500
1696 —	£325	£1800	£4000
1696 — Elephant & Castle		Extremely rare	
1697 —	£350	£1800	£4500
1697 Second bust	£300	£1700	£4300
1697 — Elephant & Castle	£800	£4000	—
1698 —	£350	£1600	£3250
1698 — Elephant & Castle	£400	£1800	£4500
1699 —	£400	£1600	£4500
1699 — Elephant & Castle		Extremely rare	
1700 —	£300	£1500	£3600
1700 — Elephant & Castle	£900	£3750	—
1701 —	£300	£1500	£3250
1701 — Elephant & Castle		Extremely rare	
1701 Third bust "fine work"	£500	£2750	£5500

William III, second bust

ANNE (1702–1714)

	F	VF	EF
1702 (Pre-Union) First bust	£400	£1700	£4250
1703 — VIGO below	£7000	£22000	£45000
1705 —	£600	£1800	£5000
1706 —	£600	£1800	£5000
1707 —	£600	£2000	£4800
1707 — (Post-Union)	£500	£2000	£3000
1707 — Elephant & Castle	£750	£1750	–
1707 Second bust		Extremely rare	
1708 First bust		Extremely rare	
1708 Second bust	£400	£1100	£3750
1708 — Elephant & Castle	£800	£1900	£4000
1709 —	£400	£1100	£3200
1709 — Elephant & Castle	£800	£1700	£4250
1710 Third bust	£400	£1100	£2650
1711 —	£400	£1000	£2500
1712 —	£400	£1000	£2500
1713 —	£400	£1000	£2200
1714 —	£400	£1000	£2200
1714 GR•TI•	£700	£1500	£3500

Anne, second bust

GEORGE I (1714–27)

	F	VF	EF
1714 First bust (Prince Elector)	£1000	£2750	£5500
1715 Second bust	£450	£1500	£3300
1715 Third bust	£450	£1500	£3300
1716 —	£450	£1500	£3300
1716 Fourth bust	£400	£1200	£3000
1717 —	£400	£1200	£3000
1718 —		Extremely rare	
1719 —	£400	£1400	£2600
1720 —	£400	£1400	£3000
1721 —	£400	£1400	£3000
1721 — Elephant & Castle		Extremely rare	
1722 —	£400	£1300	£3000
1722 — Elephant & Castle		Extremely rare	
1723 —	£400	£1300	£3000
1723 Fifth bust	£400	£1200	£3000
1724 —	£450	£1300	£3250
1725 —	£400	£1200	£3000
1726 —	£375	£1200	£2800
1726 — Elephant & Castle	£1200	£3750	£10000
1727 —	£400	£1800	£4500

George I, third bust

GEORGE II (1727–60)

	F	VF	EF
1727 First young head, early large shield	£750	£2000	£4000
1727 — Larger lettering, early small shield	£400	£1200	£3000
1728 — —	£400	£1200	£3000
1729 2nd young head E.I.C. below	£500	£1500	£4000
1729 — Proof			Very Rare
1730 —	£400	£1500	£3500
1731 —	£375	£1300	£3200
1731 — E.I.C. below	£500	£1500	£3500
1732 —	£400	£1350	£2800
1732 — E.I.C. below	£450	£1350	£3500
1732 — Larger lettering obverse	£375	£1350	£3000
1732 — — E.I.C. below	£450	£1700	£3500
1733 — —	£300	£1250	£2500
1734 — —	£300	£1250	£2500
1735 — —	£300	£1250	£2500
1736 — —	£300	£1300	£2700
1737 — —	£350	£1350	£3000

George II, 1759, old head, larger lettering

	F	VF	EF
1738 — —	£325	£1250	£3000
1739 Intermediate head	£325	£1000	£2500
1739 — E.I.C. below	£450	£1400	£3500
1740 —	£325	£1100	£3000
1741/39 —		Extremely rare	
1743 —		Extremely rare	
1745 — Larger lettering obv. Older bust	£325	£1100	£3500
1745 — LIMA below	£900	£2250	£5000
1746 — (GEORGIVS) Larger lettering obv.	£325	£900	£2800
1747 Old head, large lettering	£300	£700	£1800
1748 —	£300	£700	£1800
1749 —	£300	£700	£1800
1750 —	£300	£700	£1800
1751 — small lettering	£300	£700	£1800
1753 —	£300	£700	£1800
1755 —	£300	£700	£1800
1756 —	£300	£700	£1800
1758 —	£300	£700	£1800
1759 —	£300	£700	£1800
1760 —	£300	£700	£1800

George III first head

GEORGE III (1760–1820)

1761 First head	£950	£2700	£5500
1763 Second head	£900	£2000	£5000
1764 —	£700	£2000	£4500
1765 Third head	£225	£450	£950
1766 —	£225	£450	£950
1767 —	£225	£450	£950
1768 —	£225	£450	£950
1769 —	£225	£450	£950
1770 —	£225	£450	£950
1771 —	£225	£450	£950
1772 —	£225	£450	£950
1773 —	£225	£450	£950
1774 Fourth head	£160	£325	£650
1775 —	£160	£325	£650
1776 —	£170	£350	£650
1777 —	£170	£350	£650
1778 —	£185	£450	£750
1779 —	£165	£400	£600
1781 —	£165	£400	£600
1782 —	£165	£400	£600
1783 —	£165	£400	£600
1784 —	£165	£400	£600
1785 —	£160	£350	£600
1786 —	£160	£375	£600
1787 Fifth head, "Spade" reverse	£160	£325	£550
1788 —	£160	£325	£550
1789 —	£160	£325	£550
1790 —	£160	£325	£550
1791 —	£160	£325	£550
1792 —	£160	£325	£550
1793 —	£160	£325	£550
1794 —	£160	£325	£550
1795 —	£160	£325	£550
1796 —	£150	£325	£550
1797 —	£130	£325	£550
1798 —	£120	£325	£450
1799 —	£170	£325	£675
1813 Sixth head, "Military" reverse	£600	£1300	£2500

(Beware of counterfeits of this series—many dangerous copies exist)

Fourth head

Fifth head, Spade reverse

Sixth "Military" head

HALF GUINEAS

CHARLES II (1660–85)

	F	VF	EF
1669 First bust	£325	£1000	£3750
1670 —	£300	£1000	£3000
1671 —	£350	£1000	£3750
1672 —	£350	£1000	£3750
1672 Second bust	£325	£900	£3000
1673 —	£450	£1300	£3750
1674 —	£500	£1600	£4000
1675 —		Extremely rare	
1676 —	£325	£1000	£3000
1676 — Elephant & Castle	£600	£2300	—
1677 —	£325	£1000	£3000
1677 — Elephant & Castle	£500	£1500	—
1678 —	£375	£1100	£3500
1678 — Elephant & Castle	£350	£1100	£3750
1679 —	£325	£1000	£3000
1680 —	£400	£1500	—
1680 — Elephant & Castle		Extremely rare	
1681 —	£400	£1500	—
1682 —	£400	£1300	£3500
1682 — Elephant & Castle	£500	£1700	—
1683 —	£350	£900	£3000
1683 — Elephant & Castle		Extremely rare	
1684 —	£350	£850	£3000
1684 — Elephant & Castle	£350	£1100	£3400

Charles II, first bust

JAMES II (1685–88)

	F	VF	EF
1686	£300	£1100	£3400
1686 Elephant & Castle	£700	£3750	£7000
1687	£400	£1300	£3800
1688	£325	£1300	£3800

WILLIAM AND MARY (1688–94)

	F	VF	EF
1689 First busts	£400	£1800	£4000
1690 Second busts	£400	£1850	£4200
1691 —	£425	£1800	£4000
1691 — Elephant & Castle	£350	£1700	£3800
1692 —	£350	£1500	£3200
1692 — Elephant		Extremely rare	
1692 — Elephant & Castle	£350	£1600	£3800
1693 —		Extremely rare	
1694 —	£350	£1600	£3500

Williuam & Mary, first busts

WILLIAM III (1694–1702)

	F	VF	EF
1695	£300	£750	£2800
1695 Elephant & Castle	£425	£1100	£3200
1696 —	£300	£950	£2800
1697 Larger Harp rev.	£300	£1000	£3000
1698	£300	£750	£2800
1698 Elephant & Castle	£350	£800	£3000
1699		Extremely rare	
1700	£225	£700	£2500
1701	£225	£700	£2500

William III, elephant & castle below bust

ANNE (1702–14)

Anne

	F	VF	EF
1702 (Pre-Union)	£450	£1800	£4500
1703 VIGO below bust	£4000	£10000	£22500
1705	£500	£1700	£4500
1707 (Post-Union)	£300	£900	£2500
1708	£325	£900	£2500
1709	£300	£900	£2500
1710	£275	£750	£2000
1711	£275	£750	£2000
1712	£275	£750	£2000
1713	£275	£750	£2000
1714	£275	£750	£2000

GEORGE I (1714–27)

George I, second bust

	F	VF	EF
1715 First bust	£350	£800	£2200
1717 —	£300	£650	£1600
1718 —	£300	£650	£1600
1719 —	£300	£650	£1600
1720 —	£325	£675	£1600
1721 —		Extremely rare	
1721 — Elephant & Castle		Extremely rare	
1722 —	£300	£600	£2000
1723 —		Extremely rare	
1724 —	£325	£700	£2000
1725 Second bust	£275	£500	£1400
1726 —	£275	£500	£1500
1727 —	£275	£500	£1550

GEORGE II (1727–60)

George II, young head

George II, old head

	F	VF	EF
1728 Young head	£275	£700	£2500
1729 —	£300	£700	£2350
1729 — E.I.C.	£325	£1000	£3000
1730 —	£550	£2000	—
1730 — E.I.C.	£600	£2000	—
1731 —	£300	£950	£3000
1731 — E.I.C.		Extremely rare	
1732 —	£300	£900	£3000
1732 — E.I.C.		Extremely rare	
1733 —			Unknown
1734 —	£300	£800	£2500
1735 —		Extremely rare	
1736 —	£300	£700	£3000
1737 —		Extremely rare	
1738 —	£300	£750	£2500
1739 —	£300	£750	£2500
1739 — E.I.C.		Extremely rare	
1740 Intermediate head	£375	£1000	£3000
1743 —		Extremely rare	
1745 —	£300	£900	£2850
1745 — LIMA	£800	£3500	—
1746 —	£275	£700	£2200
1747 Old head	£300	£700	£2200
1748 —	£240	£600	£1500
1749 —	£220	£600	£1750
1750 —	£240	£600	£1500
1751 —	£240	£600	£1500
1752 —	£240	£600	£1500
1753 —	£240	£600	£1500
1755 —	£240	£600	£1500

	F	VF	EF
1756 —	£240	£600	£1500
1758 —	£260	£650	£1650
1759 —	£240	£500	£1500
1760 —	£240	£500	£1500

GEORGE III (1760–1820)

	F	VF	EF
1762 First head	£420	£1250	£3000
1763 —	£500	£1500	£3500
1764 Second head	£140	£375	£900
1765 —	£400	£900	£2500
1766 —	£175	£400	£1000
1768 —	£200	£450	£1000
1769 —	£200	£455	£1000
1772 —		Extremely rare	
1773 —	£200	£400	£900
1774 —	£250	£550	£1600
1774 Third head		Extremely rare	
1775 —	£750	£1800	£4000
1775 Fourth head	£120	£275	£550
1775 — Proof		Extremely rare	
1776 —	£110	£250	£550
1777 —	£110	£250	£550
1778 —	£110	£225	£600
1779 —	£130	£325	£750
1781 —	£110	£300	£700
1783 —	£425	£1250	—
1784 —	£120	£300	£600
1785 —	£120	£300	£600
1786 —	£120	£300	£600
1787 Fifth head, "Spade" rev.	£115	£225	£500
1788 —	£115	£225	£500
1789 —	£115	£240	£600
1790 —	£115	£240	£500
1791 —	£115	£240	£500
1792 —	£500	£1600	—
1793 —	£115	£220	£500
1794 —	£115	£220	£500
1795 —	£150	£300	£600
1796 —	£115	£300	£550
1797 —	£115	£300	£550
1798 —	£115	£300	£550
1800 —	£250	£700	£1500
1801 Sixth head, Shield in Garter rev.	£70	£150	£350
1802 —	£75	£150	£350
1803 —	£75	£150	£350
1804 Seventh head	£75	£150	£350
1805		Extremely rare	
1806 —	£100	£170	£400
1808 —	£100	£150	£400
1899 —	£100	£150	£400
1810 —	£90	£150	£400
1811 —	£150	£300	£725
1813 —	£150	£300	£725

George III, second head

George III, fifth head, "spade" reverse

THIRD GUINEAS

GEORGE III (1760–1820)

DATE	F	VF	EF
1797 First head,date in legend	£60	£100	£225
1798 — —	£60	£100	£225
1799 — —	£70	£110	£250
1800 — —	£55	£100	£225
1801 Date under crown	£55	£100	£225
1802 —	£55	£100	£225
1803 —	£55	£100	£225
1804 Second head	£60	£100	£225
1806 —	£60	£100	£225
1808 —	£60	£100	£225
1809 —	£60	£100	£225
1810 —	£60	£100	£225
1811 —	£175	£400	£1000
1813 —	£125	£200	£550

George III, date in legend

George III, date under crown

QUARTER GUINEAS

GEORGE I (1714–27)

DATE	F	VF	EF
1718	£90	£190	£340

GEORGE III (1760–1820)

DATE	F	VF	EF
1762	£70	£160	£325

George I

FIVE POUNDS

GEORGE III (1760–1820)

DATE	Mintage	F	VF	EF	UNC
1820 (pattern only)	—			Extremely rare	

GEORGE IV (1820–30)

DATE	Mintage	F	VF	EF	UNC
1826 proof only	—	—	—	£6,000	£10,000

VICTORIA (1837–1901)

DATE	Mintage	F	VF	EF	UNC
1839 Proof Only (Una & The Lion) Many Varieties FDC £25,000 upwards					
1887	53,844	£750	£925	£1100	£1500
1887 Proof	797	—	—	—	£3,000
1887 S on ground on rev. (Sydney Mint)				Excessively rare	
1893	20,405	£750	£1200	£1800	£2400
1893 Proof	773	—	—	—	£3500

EDWARD VII (1902–10)

DATE	Mintage	F	VF	EF	UNC
1902	34,910	—	£750	£925	£1200
1902 Matt proof	8,066	—	—	—	£1100

DATE	MINTAGE	F	VF	EF	UNC

GEORGE V (1911–36)

DATE	MINTAGE	F	VF	EF	UNC
1911 Proof only	2,812	–	–	–	£2,000

GEORGE VI (1937–52)

DATE	MINTAGE	F	VF	EF	UNC
1937 Proof only	5,501	–	–	–	£1000

Later issues are listed in the Decimal section.

TWO POUNDS

GEORGE III (1760–1820)

DATE	MINTAGE	F	VF	EF	UNC
1820 (pattern only)	–	–	–		Extremely rare

GEORGE IV (1820–30)

DATE	MINTAGE	F	VF	EF	UNC
1823 St George reverse	–	£750	£1000	£1500	£2500
1826 Proof only, shield reverse	–	–	–	£2750	£5000

WILLIAM IV (1830–37)

DATE	MINTAGE	F	VF	EF	UNC
1831 Proof only	225	–	–	£3000	£5500

VICTORIA (1837–1901)

DATE	MINTAGE	F	VF	EF	UNC
1887...................................	91,345	£400	£600	£900	£1100
1887 Proof.........................	797	–	–	–	£1200
1887 S on ground of rev. (Sydney Mint)					Excessively rare
1893...................................	52,212	£550	£850	£1000	£1200
1893 Proof.........................	773	–	–	–	£1600

EDWARD VII (1902–10)

DATE	MINTAGE	F	VF	EF	UNC
1902...................................	45,807	£275	£380	£500	£650
1902 Matt proof.................	8,066	–	–	–	£475

GEORGE V (1911–36)

DATE	MINTAGE	F	VF	EF	UNC
1911 Proof only	2,812	–	–	–	£750

GEORGE VI (1937–52)

DATE	MINTAGE	F	VF	EF	UNC
1937 Proof only	5,501	–	–	–	£750

Later issues are listed in the Decimal section.

SOVEREIGNS

GEORGE III (1760–1820)

DATE	MINTAGE	F	VF	EF	UNC
1817	3,235,239	£200	£400	£800	£1500
1818	2,347,230	£200	£400	£800	£1500
1819	3,574			Exceedingly rare	
1820	931,994	£200	£400	£800	£1500

GEORGE IV (1820–30)

DATE	MINTAGE	F	VF	EF	UNC
1821 First bust, St George reverse	9,405,114	£200	£350	£800	£1800
1821 — Proof	incl. above	—	—	—	£3500
1822 —	5,356,787	£200	£350	£750	£1700
1823 —	616,770	£400	£1500	£4000	—
1824 —	3,767,904	£200	£400	£1000	£1800
1825 —	4,200,343	£325	£1000	£2800	£4000
1825 Second bust, shield reverse	incl. above	£220	£500	£800	£1800
1826 —	5,724,046	£200	£500	£800	£1650
1826 — Proof	—	—	—	—	£3000
1827 —	2,266,629	£200	£425	£900	£2000
1828 —	386,182	—	£400	£1250	—
1829 —	2,444,652	£300	£500	£900	£2000
1830 —	2,387,881	£300	£500	£900	£2000

George IV, shield reverse

WILLIAM IV (1830–37)

DATE	MINTAGE	F	VF	EF	UNC
1831	598,547	£220	£450	£1000	£2000
1831 Proof	—	—	—	—	£3000
1832	3,737,065	£240	£450	£1000	£1800
1833	1,225,269	£240	£450	£1000	£1800
1835	723,441	£240	£450	£1000	£1800
1836	1,714,349	£240	£450	£1000	£1800
1837	1,172,984	£250	£475	£1100	£2000

William IV

Note—from the Victoria reign onwards, the prices of coins in lower grade will be subject to the bullion price of gold.

VICTORIA (1837–1901)

Many of the gold coins struck at the colonial mints found their way into circulation in Britain, for the sake of completeness these coins are listed here. These can easily be identified by a tiny initial letter for the appropriate mint which can be found below the base of the reverse shield or, in the case of the St George reverse, below the bust on the obverse of the Young Head issues, or on the "ground" below the horse's hoof on the later issues.

YOUNG HEAD ISSUES

Shield reverse

(Note—Shield back sovereigns in Fine/VF condition, common dates, are normally traded as bullion + a percentage)

DATE	MINTAGE	F	VF	EF	UNC
1838	2,718,694	£160	£320	£1000	£3000
1839	503,695	£320	£2500	£4500	£5500
1839 Proof, plain edge	—	—	—	—	£5000
1841	124,054	£1200	£2500	£6500	—
1842	4,865,375	£160	£180	£250	£600
1843	5,981,968	£160	£180	£250	£600
1843 "Narrow shield" variety	incl. above				Rare
1844	3,000,445	£160	£180	£350	£600
1845	3,800,845	£160	£180	£350	£600
1846	3,802,947	£160	£180	£350	£600
1847	4,667,126	£160	£180	£350	£600

DATE	MINTAGE	F	VF	EF	UNC
1848	2,246,701	£160	£180	£300	£550
1849	1,755,399	£160	£180	£300	£550
1850	1,402,039	£160	£180	£300	£550
1851	4,013,624	£160	£180	£300	£550
1852	8,053,435	£160	£180	£300	£550
1853	10,597,993	£160	£180	£300	£550
1853 Proof	—	—	—	—	£7000
1854 Incuse WW	3,589,611	£160	£180	£300	£500
1854 Surface raised WW	3,589,611	£175	£300	£750	£1750
1855	4,806,160	£160	£180	£300	£500
1856	8,448,482	£160	£200	£350	£550
1857	4,495,748	£160	£180	£300	£500
1858	803,234	£160	£180	£300	£500
1859	1,547,603	£160	£180	£300	£500
1859 "Ansell" (additional line on lower part of hair ribbon)	—	£400	£800	£3500	—
1860	2,555,958	£160	£180	£275	£400
1861	7,624,736	£160	£180	£275	£400
1862	7,836,413	—	£180	£275	£400
1863	5,921,669	—	£180	£275	£375
1863 Die No 827 on Truncation...			Extremely rare		
1863 with Die number below shield	incl. above	£160	£180	£275	£450
1864 —	8,656,352	£160	£180	£275	£450
1865 —	1,450,238	£160	£180	£275	£450
1866 —	4,047,288	£160	£180	£275	£450
1868 —	1,653,384	£160	£180	£275	£450
1869 —	6,441,322	£160	£180	£275	£450
1870 —	2,189,960	£160	£180	£275	£450
1871 —	8,767,250	£160	£180	£275	£450
1872 —	8,767,250	£160	£180	£275	£450
1872 no Die number	incl. above	£160	£180	£275	£450
1873 with Die number	2,368,215	£160	£180	£275	£450
1874 —	520,713	£800	—	—	—

M below reverse shield (Melbourne Mint)

DATE	MINTAGE	F	VF	EF	UNC
1872	748,180	£160	£180	£275	£600
1873	—		Extremely rare		
1874	1,373,298	£160	£180	£275	£600
1879			Extremely rare		
1880	3,053,454	£300	£650	£2750	£1600
1881	2,325,303	£160	£180	£300	£1100
1882	2,465,781	£160	£180	£275	£600
1883	2,050,450	£160	£275	£600	—
1884	2,942,630	£160	£180	£275	£600
1885	2,967,143	£160	£180	£275	£600
1886	2,902,131	£550	£2000	£4000	£8000
1887	1,916,424	£350	£750	£2400	£5500

S below reverse shield (Sydney Mint)

DATE	MINTAGE	F	VF	EF	UNC
1871	2,814,000	£160	£180	£275	£550
1872	1,815,000	£160	£180	£275	£550
1873	1,478,000	£160	£180	£275	£550
1875	2,122,000	£160	£180	£275	£550
1877	1,590,000	£160	£180	£275	£550
1878	1,259,000	£160	£180	£275	£550
1879	1,366,000	£160	£180	£275	£550
1880	1,459,000	£160	£180	£275	£550
1881	1,360,000	£160	£180	£275	£550
1882	1,298,000	£160	£180	£275	£550
1883	1,108,000	£160	£180	£275	£550
1884	1,595,000	£160	£180	£275	£550
1885	1,486,000	£160	£180	£275	£550
1886	1,667,000	£160	£180	£275	£550
1887	1,000,000	£160	£180	£275	£550

The mint initial appears below the shield, i.e. "S" indicates that the coin was struck at the Sydney Mint

DATE	MINTAGE	F	VF	EF	UNC
St George & Dragon reverse					
1871	incl. above	£150	£170	£190	£220
1872	incl. above	£150	£170	£190	£220
1873	incl. above	£150	£170	£190	£220
1874	incl. above	£150	£170	£190	£220
1876	3,318,866	£150	£170	£190	£220
1878	1,091,275	£150	£170	£190	£220
1879	20,013	£200	£400	£1100	—
1880	3,650,080	£150	£170	£190	£220
1884	1,769,635	£150	£170	£190	£220
1885	717,723	£150	£170	£190	£220
M below bust on obverse (Melbourne Mint)					
1872	incl. above	£200	£400	£1000	£2500
1873	752,199	£150	£170	£190	£240
1874	incl. above	£150	£170	£190	£240
1875	incl. above	£150	£170	£190	£240
1876	2,124,445	£150	£170	£190	£240
1877	1,487,316	£150	£170	£190	£240
1878	2,171,457	£150	£170	£190	£240
1879	2,740,594	£150	£170	£190	£240
1880	incl. above	£150	£170	£190	£240
1881	incl. above	£150	£170	£190	£240
1882	incl. above	£150	£170	£190	£240
1883	incl. above	£150	£170	£190	£240
1884	incl. above	£150	£170	£190	£240
1885	incl. above	£150	£170	£190	£240
1886	incl. above	£150	£170	£190	£240
1887	incl. above	£150	£170	£190	£240
S below bust on obverse (Sydney Mint)					
1871	2,814,000	£150	£170	£190	£240
1872	incl. above	£150	£170	£190	£240
1873	incl. above	£150	£170	£190	£240
1874	1,899,000	£150	£170	£190	£240
1875	inc above	£150	£170	£190	£240
1876	1,613,000	£150	£170	£190	£240
1877	—			Extremely rare	
1879	incl. above	£150	£170	£190	£240
1880	incl. above	£150	£170	£190	£240
1881	incl. above	£150	£170	£190	£240
1882	incl. above	£150	£170	£190	£240
1883	incl. above	£150	£170	£190	£240
1884	incl. above	£150	£170	£190	£240
1885	incl. above	£150	£170	£190	£240
1886	incl. above	£150	£170	£190	£240
1887	incl. above	£150	£170	£190	£240
JUBILEE HEAD ISSUES					
1887	1,111,280	£150	£170	£190	£250
1887 Proof	797	—	—	—	£700
1888	2,717,424	£150	£170	£190	£250
1889	7,257,455	£150	£170	£190	£250
1890	6,529.887	£150	£170	£190	£250
1891	6,329,476	£150	£170	£190	£250
1892	7,104,720	£150	£170	£190	£250
M on ground on reverse (Melbourne Mint)					
1887	940,000	£150	£110	£190	£325
1888	2,830,612	£150	£110	£190	£250
1889	2,732,590	£150	£110	£190	£250
1890	2,473,537	£150	£110	£190	£250
1891	2,749,592	£150	£110	£190	£250
1892	3,488,750	£150	£110	£190	£250
1893	1,649,352	£175	£300	£600	£1200

"M" below the horse's hoof above the date indicates that the coin was struck at the Melbourne Mint

Jubilee head type

DATE	MINTAGE	F	VF	EF	UNC
S on ground on reverse (Sydney Mint)					
1887	1,002,000	£150	£200	£300	£550
1888	2,187,000	£150	£170	£190	£210
1889	3,262,000	£150	£170	£190	£210
1890	2,808,000	£150	£170	£190	£210
1891	2,596,000	£150	£170	£190	£210
1892	2,837,000	£150	£170	£190	£210
1893	1,498,000	£150	£170	£190	£210
OLD HEAD ISSUES					
1893	6,898,260	£150	£170	£190	£250
1893 Proof	773	—	—	—	£900
1894	3,782,611	£150	£170	£190	£210
1895	2,285,317	£150	£170	£190	£210
1896	3,334,065	£150	£170	£190	£210
1898	4,361,347	£150	£170	£190	£210
1899	7,515,978	£150	£170	£190	£210
1900	10,846,741	£150	£170	£190	£210
1901	1,578,948	£150	£170	£190	£210
M on ground on reverse (Melbourne Mint)					
1893	1,914,000	£150	£170	£190	£210
1894	4,166,874	£150	£170	£190	£210
1895	4,165,869	£150	£170	£190	£210
1896	4,456,932	£150	£170	£190	£210
1897	5,130,565	£150	£170	£190	£210
1898	5,509,138	£150	£170	£190	£210
1899	5,579,157	£150	£170	£190	£210
1900	4,305,904	£150	£170	£190	£210
1901	3,987,701	£150	£170	£190	£210
P on ground on reverse (Perth Mint)					
1899	690,992	£150	£170	£400	£1200
1900	1,886,089	£150	£170	£190	£210
1901	2,889,333	£150	£170	£190	£210
S on ground on reverse (Sydney Mint)					
1893	1,346,000	£150	£170	£190	£210
1894	3,067,000	£150	£170	£190	£210
1895	2,758,000	£150	£170	£190	£210
1896	2,544,000	£150	£170	£190	£250
1897	2,532,000	£150	£170	£190	£210
1898	2,548,000	£150	£170	£190	£210
1899	3,259,000	£150	£170	£190	£210
1900	3,586,000	£150	£170	£190	£210
1901	3,012,000	£150	£170	£190	£210

Old head type

EDWARD VII (1902–10)

DATE	MINTAGE	F	VF	EF	UNC
1902	4,737,796	£150	£170	£190	£250
1902 Matt proof	15,123	—	—	—	£275
1903	8,888,627	£150	£170	£190	£250
1904	10,041,369	£150	£170	£190	£250
1905	5,910,403	£150	£170	£190	£250
1906	10,466,981	£150	£170	£190	£250
1907	18,458,663	£150	£170	£190	£250
1908	11,729,006	£150	£170	£190	£250
1909	12,157,099	£150	£170	£190	£250
1910	22,379,624	£150	£170	£190	£250
C on ground on reverse (Ottawa Mint)					
1908 Satin finish Proof only	633			Extremely rare	
1909	16,300	£150	£170	£300	—
1910	28,020	£150	£170	£300	—

DATE	MINTAGE	F	VF	EF	UNC
M on ground on reverse (Melbourne Mint)					
1902	4,267,157	£150	£170	£195	£250
1903	3,521,780	£150	£170	£195	£250
1904	3,743,897	£150	£170	£195	£250
1905	3,633,838	£150	£170	£195	£250
1906	3,657,853	£150	£170	£195	£250
1907	3,332,691	£150	£170	£195	£250
1908	3,080,148	£150	£170	£195	£250
1909	3,029,538	£150	£170	£195	£250
1910	3,054,547	£150	£170	£195	£250
P on ground on reverse (Perth Mint)					
1902	3,289,122	£150	£170	£195	£250
1903	4,674,783	£150	£170	£195	£250
1904	4,506,756	£150	£170	£195	£250
1905	4,876,193	£150	£170	£195	£250
1906	4,829,817	£150	£170	£195	£250
1907	4,972,289	£150	£170	£195	£250
1908	4,875,617	£150	£170	£195	£250
1909	4,524,241	£150	£170	£195	£250
1910	4,690,625	£150	£170	£195	£250
S on ground on reverse (Sydney Mint)					
1902	2,813,000	£150	£170	£195	£250
1902 Proof	incl. above			Extremely rare	
1903	2,806,000	£150	£170	£195	£250
1904	2,986,000	£150	£170	£195	£250
1905	2,778,000	£150	£170	£195	£250
1906	2,792,000	£150	£170	£195	£250
1907	2,539,000	£150	£170	£195	£250
1908	2,017,000	£150	£170	£195	£250
1909	2,057,000	£150	£170	£195	£250
1910	2,135,000	£150	£170	£195	£250

GEORGE V (1911–36)

(Extra care should be exercised when purchasing as good quality forgeries exist of virtually all dates and mintmarks)

1911	30,044,105	£150	£170	£195	£250
1911 Proof	3,764	—	—	—	£500
1912	30,317,921	£150	£170	£195	£250
1913	24,539,672	£150	£170	£195	£250
1914	11,501,117	£150	£170	£195	£250
1915	20,295,280	£150	£170	£195	£250
1916	1,554,120	£150	£170	£195	£250
1917	1,014,714	£1500	£2000	£4500	—
1925	4,406,431	£150	£170	£195	£250
C on ground on reverse (Ottawa Mint)					
1911	256,946	£150	£170	£195	£250
1913	3,715	£200	£350	£900	—
1914	14,891	£150	£200	£500	—
1916	6,111			Extremely rare	
1917	58,845	£150	£170	£195	£250
1918	106,516	£150	£170	£195	£250
1919	135,889	£150	£170	£195	£250
I on ground on reverse (Bombay Mint)					
1918	1,295,372	£150	£170	£200	—
M on ground on reverse (Melbourne Mint)					
1911	2,851,451	£150	£170	£195	£250
1912	2,469,257	£150	£170	£195	£250
1913	2,323,180	£150	£170	£195	£250
1914	2,012,029	£150	£170	£195	£250
1915	1,637,839	£150	£170	£195	£250
1916	1,273,643	£150	£170	£195	£250
1917	934,469	£150	£170	£195	£250
1918	4,969,493	£150	£170	£195	£250

DATE	MINTAGE	F	VF	EF	UNC
1919	514,257	£150	£170	£195	£250
1920	530,266	£150	£1500	£2500	—
1921	240,121	£150	£170	£5500	£10000
1922	608,306	£150	£2500	£4500	—
1923	510,870	£150	£170	£195	£250
1924	278,140	£150	£170	£195	£250
1925	3,311,622	£150	£170	£195	£250
1926	211,107	£150	£170	£195	£250
1928	413,208	£200	£550	£1250	£2000
1929	436,719	£200	£500	£1500	£2000
1930	77,547	£150	£170	£190	£300
1931	57,779	£150	£190	£300	£425
P on ground on reverse (Perth Mint)					
1911	4,373,165	£150	£170	£195	£250
1912	4,278,144	£150	£170	£195	£250
1913	4,635,287	£150	£170	£195	£250
1914	4,815,996	£150	£170	£195	£250
1915	4,373,596	£150	£170	£195	£250
1916	4,096,771	£150	£170	£195	£250
1917	4,110,286	£150	£170	£195	£250
1918	3,812,884	£150	£170	£195	£250
1919	2,995,216	£150	£170	£195	£250
1920	2,421,196	£150	£170	£195	£250
1921	2,134,360	£150	£170	£195	£250
1922	2,298,884	£150	£170	£195	£250
1923	2,124,154	£150	£170	£195	£250
1924	1,464,416	£150	£170	£195	£250
1925	1,837,901	£150	£170	£195	£300
1926	1,313,578	£300	£600	£1500	£1800
1927	1,383,544	£150	£175	£300	£450
1928	1,333,417	£150	£170	£195	£250
1929	1,606,625	£150	£170	£195	£250
1930	1,915,352	£150	£170	£195	£250
1931	1,173,568	£150	£170	£195	£250
S on ground on reverse (Sydney Mint)					
1911	2,519,000	£150	£170	£195	£250
1912	2,227,000	£150	£170	£195	£250
1913	2,249,000	£150	£170	£195	£250
1914	1,774,000	£150	£170	£195	£250
1915	1,346,000	£150	£170	£195	£250
1916	1,242,000	£150	£170	£195	£250
1917	1,666,000	£150	£170	£195	£250
1918	3,716,000	£150	£170	£195	£250
1919	1,835,000	£150	£170	£195	£250
1920	—			Excessively rare	
1921	839,000	£300	£650	£1200	£1700
1922	578,000			Extremely rare	
1923	416,000			Extremely rare	
1924	394,000	£300	£550	£800	£1250
1925	5,632,000	£150	£170	£195	£250
1926	1,031,050			Extremely rare	
SA on ground on reverse (Pretoria Mint)					
1923	719	£400	£800	£1800	£3750
1923 Proof	655			Extremely rare	
1924	3,184	—	£1500	£3250	—
1925	6,086,264	£150	£170	£195	£250
1926	11,107,611	£150	£170	£195	£250
1927	16,379,704	£150	£170	£195	£250
1928	18,235,057	£150	£170	£195	£250
1929	12,024,107	£150	£170	£195	£250
1930	10,027,756	£150	£170	£195	£250
1931	8,511,792	£150	£170	£195	£250
1932	1,066,680	£150	£170	£195	£250

GEORGE VI (1937–52)

DATE	MINTAGE	F	VF	EF	UNC
1937 Proof only	5,501	—	—	£725	£1200

ELIZABETH II (1952–)

Pre Decimal Issues

DATE	MINTAGE	F	VF	EF	UNC
1957	2,072,000	£150	£170	£195	£250
1958	8,700,140	£150	£170	£195	£250
1959	1,358,228	£150	£170	£195	£250
1962	3,000,000	£150	£170	£195	£250
1963	7,400,000	£150	£170	£195	£250
1964	3,000,000	£150	£170	£195	£250
1965	3,800,000	£150	£170	£195	£250
1966	7,050,000	£150	£170	£195	£250
1967	5,000,000	£150	£170	£195	£250
1968	4,203,000	£150	£170	£195	£250

Later issues are included in the Decimal section.

HALF SOVEREIGNS

GEORGE III (1760–1820)

DATE	MINTAGE	F	VF	EF	UNC
1817	2,080,197	£80	£125	£300	£500
1818	1,030,286	£80	£125	£300	£500
1820	35,043	£80	£125	£300	£500

GEORGE IV (1820–30)

DATE	MINTAGE	F	VF	EF	UNC
1821 First bust, ornate shield reverse	231,288	£200	£600	£1500	£2750
1821 — Proof	unrecorded	—	—	£2000	£3000
1823 First bust, Plain shield rev.	224,280	£80	£150	£400	£700
1824 —	591,538	£80	£150	£425	£700
1825 —	761,150	£80	£150	£425	£700
1826 bare head, shield with full legend reverse	344,830	£80	£140	£400	£700
1826 — Proof	unrecorded	—	—	£750	£1100
1827 —	492,014	£85	£150	£400	£750
1828 —	1,224,754	£75	£140	£400	£800

WILLIAM IV (1830–37)

DATE	MINTAGE	F	VF	EF	UNC
1831 Proof only	unrecorded	—	—	£750	£1600
1834	133,899	£100	£200	£500	£1000
1835	772,554	£100	£300	£425	£950
1836	146,865	£90	£200	£500	£1000
1836 obverse from 6d die	incl. above	£600	£1200	£2500	—
1837	160,207	£100	£200	£475	£950

VICTORIA (1837–1901)

YOUNG HEAD ISSUES

Shield reverse

DATE	MINTAGE	F	VF	EF	UNC
1838	273,341	£75	£90	£225	£600
1839 Proof only	1,230	—	—	—	£2000
1841	508,835	£75	£90	£260	£700
1842	2,223,352	—	£85	£200	£500
1843	1,251,762	£75	£90	£260	£650

DATE	MINTAGE	F	VF	EF	UNC
1844	1,127,007	£70	£85	£240	£500
1845	887,526	£100	£300	£700	£1400
1846	1,063,928	£75	£85	£220	£500
1847	982,636	£75	£85	£220	£500
1848	410,595	£75	£85	£220	£500
1849	845,112	—	£85	£180	£450
1850	179,595	£100	£200	£500	£1100
1851	773,573	—	£85	£200	
£5001852	1,377,671	—	£90	£200	£500
1853	2,708,796	—	£85	£180	£450
1853 Proof	unrecorded	—	—	—	£4000
1854	1,125,144		Extremely rare		
1855	1,120,362	—	£95	£180	£425
1856	2,391,909	—	£95	£180	£425
1857	728,223	—	£85	£190	£450
1858	855,578	—	£85	£190	£450
1859	2,203,813	—	£85	£180	£425
1860	1,131,500	—	£85	£180	£425
1861	1,130,867	—	£85	£180	£425
1862	unrecorded	£400	£100	£4000	—
1863	1,571,574	—	£85	£180	£425
1863 with Die number	incl. above	—	£85	£180	£425
1864 —	1,758,490	—	£95	£180	£425
1865 —	1,834,750	—	£95	£180	£425
1866 —	2,058,776	—	£95	£180	£425
1867 —	992,795	—	£95	£180	£425
1869 —	1,861,764	—	£85	£180	£425
1870 —	1,159,544	—	£85	£175	£350
1871 —	2,062,970	—	£85	£150	£350
1872 —	3,248,627	—	£85	£150	£350
1873 —	1,927,050	—	£85	£150	£350
1874 —	1,884,432	—	£85	£150	£350
1875 —	516,240	—	£85	£150	£350
1876 —	2,785,187	—	£85	£150	£350
1877 —	2,197,482	—	£85	£130	£350
1878 —	2,081,941	—	£85	£130	£350
1879 —	35,201	—	£85	£140	£350
1880 —	1,009,049	—	£85	£140	£350
1880 no Die number	incl. above	—	£85	£140	£350
1883 —	2,870,457	—	£85	£135	£300
1884 —	1,113,756	—	£85	£125	£300
1885 —	4,468,871	—	£85	£125	£300

Date	Mintage	F	VF	EF	UNC
M below shield (Melbourne Mint)					
1873	165,034	£75	£120	£500	—
1877	80,016	£75	£120	£450	—
1881	42,009	£80	£175	£550	—
1882	107,522	£80	£100	£500	—
1884	48,009	£80	£100	£500	—
1885	11,003	£75	£200	£1200	—
1886	38,008	£75	£110	£1200	—
1887	64,013	£110	£300	£1200	£4000
S below shield (Sydney Mint)					
1871	180,000 (?)	£90	£125	£600	—
1872	356,000	£95	£125	£600	—
1875	unrecorded	£75	£125	£600	—
1879	94,000	£75	£100	£750	—
1880	80,000	£75	£900	£750	—
1881	62,000	£75	£100	£750	—
1882	52,000	£140	£500	£3000	—
1883	220,000	£75	£80	£500	—
1886	82,000	£75	£80	£450	—
1887	134,000	£75	£100	£650	£2000
JUBILEE HEAD ISSUES					
1887	871,770	£75	£85	£70	£95
1887 Proof	797	£75	£85	—	£475
1890	2.266,023	£75	£85	£70	£125
1891	1,079,286	£75	£85	£70	£125
1892	13,680,486	£75	£85	£60	£125
1893	4,426,625	£75	£85	£65	£125
M below shield (Melbourne Mint)					
1887	incl. above	£75	£100	£275	£450
1893	110,024	£85	£125	£375	—
S below shield (Sydney Mint)					
1887	incl. above	£75	£90	£250	£400
1889	64,000	£80	£100	£250	—
1891	154,000	£80	£120	£275	—
OLD HEAD ISSUES					
1893	incl. above	£75	£90	£125	£150
1893 Proof	773	—	—	—	£575
1894	3,794,591	£75	£90	£125	£150
1895	2,869,183	£75	£90	£125	£150
1896	2,946,605	£75	£90	£125	£150
1897	3,568,156	£75	£90	£125	£150
1898	2,868,527	£75	£90	£125	£150
1899	3,361,881	£75	£90	£125	£150
1900	4,307,372	£75	£90	£125	£150
1901	2,037,664	£75	£90	£125	£150
M on ground on reverse (Melbourne Mint)					
1893	*unrecorded*			Extremely rare	
1896	218,946	£75	£100	£400	—
1899	97,221	£75	£100	£400	—
1900	112,920	£75	£100	£400	—
P on ground on reverse (Perth Mint)					
1899			Proof Unique		
1900	119,376	£125	£300	£500	—
S on ground on reverse (Sydney Mint)					
1893	250,000	£75	£100	£300	—
1897	*unrecorded*	£75	£90	£275	—
1900	260,00	£75	£80	£275	—

EDWARD VII (1902–10)

Date	Mintage	F	VF	EF	UNC
1902	4,244,457	£75	£80	£85	£90
1902 Matt proof	15,123	—	—	—	£125
1903	2,522,057	£75	£80	£85	£90

DATE		F	VF	EF	UNC
1904	1,717,440	£75	£80	£85	£90
1905	3,023,993	£75	£80	£85	£90
1906	4,245,437	£75	£80	£85	£90
1907	4,233,421	£75	£80	£85	£90
1908	3,996,992	£75	£80	£85	£85
1909	4,010,715	£75	£80	£85	£85
1910	5,023,881	£75	£80	£85	£85
M on ground on reverse (Melbourne Mint)					
1906	82,042	£75	£80	£100	£300
1907	405,034	£75	£80	£85	£250
1908	incl. above	£75	£80	£85	£300
1909	186,094	£75	£80	£85	£250
P on ground on reverse (Perth Mint)					
1904	60,030	£100	£150	£550	—
1908	24,668	£100	£150	£550	—
1909	44,022	£75	£130	£450	—
S on ground on reverse (Sydney Mint)					
1902	84,000	£75	£80	£100	£300
1902 Proof				Extremely rare	
1903	231,000				£250
1906	308,00	£75	£80	£100	£275
1908	538,000	£75	£80	£100	£275
1910	474,000	£75	£80	£100	£275

GEORGE V (1911–36)

1911	6,104,106	£75	£80	£85	£100
1911 Proof	3,764	—	—	—	£275
1912	6,224,316	£75	£80	£85	£100
1913	6,094,290	£75	£80	£85	£100
1914	7,251,124	£75	£80	£85	£100
1915	2,042,747	£75	£80	£85	£100
M on ground on reverse (Melbourne Mint)					
1915	125,664	—	—	£75	£125
P on ground on reverse (Perth Mint)					
1911	130,373	—	—	£100	£200
1915	136,219	—	—	£100	£200
1918	unrecorded	£120	£275	£600	£900
S on ground on reverse (Sydney Mint)					
1911	252,000	£75	£80	£85	£110
1912	278,000	£75	£80	£85	£110
1914	322,000	£75	£80	£85	£110
1915	892,000	£75	£80	£85	£110
1916	448,000	£75	£80	£85	£110
SA on ground on reverse (Pretoria Mint)					
1923 Proof only	655	—	—	—	£350
1925	946,615	£75	£80	£85	£100
1926	806,540	£75	£80	£85	£100

GEORGE VI (1937–52)

1937 Proof only	5,501	—	—	—	£375

Later issues are included in the Decimal section.

Leading the way

in Numismatics

CROWNS

DATE	F	VF	EF	UNC

OLIVER CROMWELL

DATE	F	VF	EF	UNC
1658 8 over 7 (always)	£1800	£3250	£5000	–
1658 Dutch Copy			Extremely rare	
1658 Patterns. In Various Metals			Extremely rare	

CHARLES II (1660–85)

DATE	F	VF	EF	UNC
1662 First bust, rose (2 varieties)	£150	£700	£3500	–
1662 — no rose (2 varieties)	£150	£700	£3500	–
1663 —	£160	£700	£3750	–
1664 Second bust	£130	£600	£3500	–
1665 —	£900	–	–	–
1666 —	£175	£900	£4000	–
1666 — error RE.X for REX			Extremely rare	
1666 — Elephant below bust	£350	£1500	£5000	–
1667 —	£130	£500	£3000	–
1668/7 — 8 over 7	£120	£500	–	–
1668 —	£120	£500	£3000	–
1669/8 — 9 over 8	£350	£800	–	–
1669 —	£300	£900	£4000	–
1670/69 — 70 over 69	£150	£800	–	–
1670 —	£130	£600	£3500	–
1671	£120	£600	£3000	–
1671 Third bust	£120	£500	£3000	–
1672 —	£120	£500	£3000	–
1673 —	£120	£500	£3000	–
1674 —			Extremely rare	
1675 —	£1500	–	–	–
1675/3 —	£700	£2200	–	–
1676 —	£115	£550	£3000	–
1677 —	£120	£550	£3000	–
1677/6 — 7 over 6	£150	£900	–	–
1678/7 —	£150	£900	–	–
1678/7 — 8 over 7	£200	–	–	–
1679 —	£120	£600	£3000	–
1679 Fourth bust	£120	£600	£3000	–
1680 Third bust	£120	£800	£3500	–
1680/79 — 80 over 79	£140	£800	–	–
1680 Fourth bust	£120	£650	£3500	–
1680/79 — 80 over 79	£160	£1000	–	–
1681 —	£120	£600	£3000	–
1681 — Elephant & Castle below bust	£3000	£6000	–	–
1682/1 —	£120	£600	£3000	–
1682 — edge error QVRRTO for QVARTO	£400	–	–	–
1683 —	£400	£1000	£4000	–
1684 —	£400	£1300	–	–

JAMES II (1685–88)

DATE	F	VF	EF	UNC
1686 First bust	£225	£800	£3700	–
1686 — No stops on obv	£325	£1200	–	–
1687 Second bust	£220	£600	£3000	–
1688/7 — 8 over 7	£230	£800	–	–
1688 —	£220	£800	£3000	–

WILLIAM AND MARY (1688–94)

DATE	F	VF	EF	UNC
1691	£350	£1000	£4000	–
1692	£350	£1000	£4000	–
1692 2 over upside down 2	£350	£1000	£4000	–

WILLIAM III (1694–1702)

DATE	F	VF	EF	UNC
1695 First bust	£80	£250	£1500	–
1696 —	£75	£240	£1200	–
1696 — no stops on obv.	£225	£250	–	–
1996 — no stops obv./rev.	£250	£250	–	–
1696 — GEI for DEI	£400	£1300	–	–
1696 Second bust				Unique
1696 Third bust	£80	£250	£1200	–
1697 —	£800	£2000	£3500	–
1700 Third bust variety edge year DUODECIMO	£90	£400	£1400	–
1700 — edge year DUODECIMO TERTIO..	£90	£400	£1400	–

ANNE (1702–14)

DATE	F	VF	EF	UNC
1703 First bust, VIGO	£260	£900	£3500	–
1705 — Plumes in angles on rev.	£500	£1500	£5000	–
1706 — Roses & Plumes in angles on rev...	£140	£600	£2000	–
1707 — —	£140	£600	£2000	–
1707 Second bust, E below	£130	£500	£1600	–
1707 — Plain	£130	£500	£1600	–
1708 — E below	£130	£500	£1600	–
1708/7 — 8 over 7	£160	£800	–	–
1708 — Plain	£130	£600	£1600	–
1708 — — error BR for BRI			Extremely rare	
1708 — Plumes in angles on rev.	£175	£650	£2200	–
1713 Third bust, Roses & Plumes in angles on rev.	£175	£650	£1850	–

GEORGE I (1714–27)

DATE	F	VF	EF	UNC
1716	£425	£1200	£4500	–
1718 8 over 6	£425	£1200	£4500	–
1720 20 over 18	£425	£1200	£4500	–
1723 SSC in angles on rev. (South Sea Co.)	£425	£1200	£4200	–
1726	£425	£1200	£4500	–

GEORGE II (1727–60)

DATE	F	VF	EF	UNC
1732 Young head, Plain, Proof	–	–	£6000	
1732 — Roses & Plumes in angles on rev ..	£175	£700	£2200	–
1734 — —	£175	£700	£2200	–
1735 — —	£175	£700	£2200	–
1736 — —	£185	£700	£2200	–
1739 — Roses in angles on rev	£175	£600	£2000	–
1741 — —	£175	£600	£2000	–
1743 Old head, Roses in angles on rev	£160	£600	£1800	–
1746 — — LIMA below bust	£160	£600	£1800	–
1746 — Plain, Proof	–	£800	£4000	–
1750 — —	£300	£900	£2800	–
1751 — —	£400	£1050	£3000	–

GEORGE III (1760–1820)

DATE	F	VF	EF	UNC
Dollar with oval counterstamp	£125	£400	£750	–
Dollar with octagonal counterstamp	£175	£500	£800	–
1804 Bank of England Dollar, Britannia rev.	£100	£225	£500	–
1818 LVIII	£25	£70	£250	£700
1818 LIX	£25	£70	£250	£700
1819 LIX	£25	£70	£250	£700
1819 LIX 9 over 8	£30	£125	£400	–
1819 LIX no stops on edge	£50	£120	£300	£900
1819 LX	£30	£70	£325	£800
1820 LX	£25	£70	£300	£700
1820 LX 20 over 19	£55	£200	£500	–

GEORGE IV (1820–30)

DATE	MINTAGE	F	VF	EF	UNC
1821 First bust, St George rev. SECUNDO on edge	437,976	£35	£160	£500	£11000
1821 — — Proof	Incl. above	£35	£160	—	£4000
1821 — — Proof TERTIO (error edge)	Incl above	£35	£160	—	£4000
1822 — — SECUNDO	124,929	£35	£160	£500	£1000
1822 — — TERTIO	Incl above	£35	£160	£500	£1000
1823 — — Proof only				Extremely rare	
1826 Second bust, shield rev, SEPTIMO Proof only		—	—	£2000	£4500

WILLIAM IV (1830–37)

DATE			UNC
1831 Proof only W.W. on truncation	—	—	£11000
1831 Proof only W. WYON on truncation	—	—	£12500
1834 Proof only	—	—	—£18000

VICTORIA (1837–1901)

YOUNG HEAD ISSUES

DATE	MINTAGE	F	VF	EF	UNC
1839 Proof only	—	—	—	—	£4500
1844 Star stops on edge	94,248	£40	£200	£1000	£2750
1844 Cinquefoil stops on edge	incl. above	£40	£200	£1000	£2750
1845 Star stops on edge	159,192	£40	£200	£1000	£2750
1845 Cinquefoil stops on edge	incl. above	£40	£200	£1000	£2750
1847	140,976	£50	£200	£1100	£3000

GOTHIC HEAD ISSUES (Proof only)

DATE	MINTAGE	F	VF	EF	UNC
1847 mdcccxlvii UNDECIMO on edge	8,000	£400	£800	£1600	£2800
1847 — Plain edge	—	—	—	—	£3400
1853 mdcccliii SEPTIMO on edge	460	—	—	—	£6000
1853 — Plain edge	—	—	—	—	£8000

JUBILEE HEAD ISSUES

DATE	MINTAGE	F	VF	EF	UNC
1887	173,581	£12	£24	£55	£120
1887 Proof	1,084	—	—	—	£425
1888 Narrow date	131,899	£15	£30	£85	£200
1888 Wide date	incl above	£25	£60	£300	—
1889	1,807,224	£10	£20	£50	£110
1890	997,862	£12	£25	£60	£170
1891	556,394	£12	£25	£60	£170
1892	451,334	£12	£25	£70	£200

OLD HEAD ISSUES (Regnal date on edge in Roman numerals)

DATE	MINTAGE	F	VF	EF	UNC
1893 LVI	497,845	£12	£30	£130	£350
1893 LVII	incl. above	£15	£40	£200	£425
1893 Proof	1,312	—	—	—	£500
1894 LVII	144,906	£14	£45	£150	£375
1894 LVIII	incl. above	£14	£45	£150	£375
1895 LVIII	252,862	£12	£35	£130	£375
1895 LIX	incl. above	£12	£35	£130	£375
1896 LIX	317,599	£14	£35	£140	£400
1896 LX	incl. above	£12	£35	£130	£350
1897 LX	262,118	£12	£35	£130	£350
1897 LXI	incl. above	£12	£35	£130	£400
1898 LXI	166,150	£15	£40	£130	£500
1898 LXII	incl. above	£12	£35	£130	£350
1899 LXII	166,300	£12	£35	£130	£350
1899 LXIII	incl. above	£12	£35	£130	£350
1900 LXIII	353,356	£12	£35	£130	£350
1900 LXIV	incl. above	£12	£52	£130	£350

Victoria, Jubilee head

EDWARD VII (1901–10)

DATE	MINTAGE	F	VF	EF	UNC
1902	256,020	£40	£65	£120	£185
1902 "Matt Proof"	15,123	—	—	—	£175

GEORGE V (1910–36)

DATE	MINTAGE	F	VF	EF	UNC
1927 Proof only	15,030	—	£80	£140	£225
1928	9,034	£70	£110	£220	£420
1929	4,994	£70	£110	£220	£420
1930	4,847	£70	£110	£220	£425
1931	4,056	£70	£110	£220	£400
1932	2,395	£140	£300	£600	£900
1933	7,132	£70	£110	£220	£425
1934	932	£500	£1100	£2000	£4000
1935 Jubilee issue. Incuse edge inscription	714,769	£8	£12	£16	£25
1935 — — error edge inscription	incl. above	—	—	—	£1500
1935 — Specimen in box	incl. above	—	—	—	£45
1935 — Proof	incl. above	—	—	—	£150
1935 — Proof. Raised edge inscription	2,500	—	—	£175	£300
1935 — — fine lettering	incl. above	—	—	—	£1000
1935 — — error edge inscription	incl. above	—	—	—	£1500
1935 — Gold proof	30	—	—	Extremely rare	
1936	2,473	£110	£275	£400	£800

GEORGE VI (1936–52)

DATE	MINTAGE	F	VF	EF	UNC
1937 Coronation	418,699	£9	£15	£25	£35
1937 Proof	26,402	—	—	—	£40
1951 Festival of Britain, Proof-like	1,983,540	—	—	£3	£6

ELIZABETH II (1952–)

Pre-Decimal issues (Five Shillings)

DATE	MINTAGE	F	VF	EF	UNC
1953	5,962,621	—	—	£3	£6
1953 Proof	40,000	—	—	—	£20
1960	1,024,038	—	—	£3	£6
1960 Polished dies	70,000	—	—	—	£8
1965 Churchill	19,640,000	—	—	—	£1

Later issues are listed in the Decimal section.

DOUBLE FLORINS

VICTORIA (1837–1901)

DATE	MINTAGE	F	VF	EF	UNC
1887 Roman I	483,347	£10	£20	£40	£80
1887 Roman I Proof	incl. above	—	—	—	£300
1887 Arabic 1	incl. above	£10	£20	£40	£80
1887 Arabic 1 Proof	incl. above	—	—	—	£300
1888	243,340	£12	£32	£80	£120
1888 Second I in VICTORIA an inverted 1	incl. above	£20	£35	£80	£250
1889	1,185,111	£15	£23	£40	£100
1889 inverted 1	incl. above	£20	£35	£80	£300
1890	782,146	£12	£33	£55	£110

Patterns were also produced in 1911, 1914 and 1950 and are all extremely rare.

HALFCROWNS

OLIVER CROMWELL

DATE	MINTAGE	F	VF	EF	UNC
1656				Extremely rare	
1658		£850	£1800	£3250	—
1658 Proof in Gold				Extremely rare	

CHARLES II (1660–1685)

DATE	MINTAGE	F	VF	EF	UNC
1663 First bust		£100	£400	£2000	—
1663 — no stops on obv.		£130	£600	—	—
1664 Second bust		£130	£500	£2200	—
1666 Third bust		£900	—	—	—
1666 — Elephant		£700	£2000	—	—
1667/4 — 7 over 4				Extremely rare	
1668/4 — 8 over 4		£200	—	—	—
1669 —		£400	£1600	—	—
1669/4 — 9 over 4		£200	£800	—	—
1670 —		£80	£400	£2000	—
1670 — MRG for MAG		£300	£1000	—	—
1671 —		£80	£300	£2200	—
1671/0 — 1 over 0		£100	£500	£2400	—
1672 —		£90	£500	£2200	—
1672 Fourth bust		£100	£500	£2200	—
1673 —		£80	£300	£2000	—
1673 — Plumes both sides				Extremely rare	
1673 — Plume below bust		£2000	—	—	—
1674 —		£100	£600	—	—
1675 —		£95	£325	£1800	—
1676 —		£90	£300	£1500	—
1676 — inverted 1 in date		£100	£350	£1600	—
1677 —		£90	£350	£1200	—
1678 —		£200	£800	—	—
1679 — GRATTA error				Extremely rare	
1679 —		£100	£350	£1800	—
1680 —		£150	£700	—	—
1681/0 — 1 over 0		£160	—	—	—
1681 —		£110	£400	£900	—
1681 — Elephant & Castle		£2000	—	—	—
1682 —		£110	£400	£2500	—
1683 —		£110	£375	£2200	—
1683 — Plume below bust				Extremely rare	
1684/3 — 4 over 3		£200	£700	£3500	—

JAMES II (1685–1688)

DATE	MINTAGE	F	VF	EF	UNC
1685 First bust		£175	£550	£2250	—
1686 —		£175	£550	£2250	—
1686/5 — 6 over 5		£200	£650	—	—
1686 — V over S		£220	£600	—	—
1687 —		£170	£600	£1900	—
1687/6 — 7 over 6		£200	£700	—	—
1687 Second bust		£170	£500	£1900	—
1688 —		£150	£500	£1900	—

WILLIAM AND MARY (1688–1694)

DATE	MINTAGE	F	VF	EF	UNC
1689 First busts; first shield		£70	£300	£1300	—
1689 — — no pearls in crown		£70	£300	£1300	—
1689 — — FRA for FR		£120	£400	£1500	—
1689 — — No stop on obv		£70	£300	£1300	—
1689 — Second shield		£70	£300	£1300	—
1689 — — no pearls in crown		£70	£325	£1300	—

DATE	MINTAGE	F	VF	EF	UNC
1690 — —		£125	£650	£2500	—
1690 — — error GRETIA for GRATIA		£300	£1500	£4000	—
1691 Second busts		£120	£450	£2000	—
1692 —		£120	£450	£2000	—
1693 —		£120	£450	£2000	—
1693 — 3 over inverted 3		£130	£475	£2200	—

WILLIAM III (1694–1702)

DATE	MINTAGE	F	VF	EF	UNC
1696 First bust, large shields, early harp		£60	£220	£800	—
1696 — — — B (Bristol) below bust		£60	£240	£1000	—
1696 — — — C (Chester)		£70	£300	£1000	—
1696 — — — E (Exeter)		£100	£400	£1300	—
1696 — — — N (Norwich)		£80	£400	£1200	—
1696 — — — y (York)		£80	£350	£1200	—
1696 — — — — Scottish arms at date				Extremely rare	
1696 — — ordinary harp		£65	£250	£1200	—
1696 — — — C		£100	£500	£800	
1696 — — — E		£90	£500	£800	—
1696 — — — N		£125	£550	£2000	—
1696 — Small shields, ordinary harp		£55	£225	£700	—
1696 — — — B		£70	£300	£1000	—
1696 — — — C		£75	£300	£1050	—
1696 — — — E		£90	£350	—	—
1696 — — — N		£80	£350	£1250	—
1696 — — — y		£80	£350	£1250	—
1696 Second bust				Only one known	
1697 First bust, large shields, ordinary harp		£60	£250	£700	—
1697 — — — GRR for GRA				Extremely rare	
1697 — — — B		£60	£300	£1000	—
1697 — — — C		£60	£350	£1100	
1697 — — — E		£75	£350	£1100	—
1697 — — — N		£75	£350	£1100	—
1697 — — — y		£75	£350	£1100	—
1698 — —		£80	£300	£1100	—
1698/7 — — 8 over 7				Extremely rare	
1699 — —		£100	£300	£1200	—
1699 — — Scottish arms at date				Extremely rare	
1700 — —		£80	£300	£1000	—
1701 — —		£90	£325	£1050	—
1701 — — No stops on rev		£100	£350	—	—
1701 — — Elephant & Castle below				Fair	£1150
1701 — — Plumes in angles on rev.		£175	£550	£1700	—

ANNE (1702–1714)

DATE	MINTAGE	F	VF	EF	UNC
1703 Plain (pre-Union)		£500	£2200	—	—
1703 VIGO below bust		£100	£300	£1000	—
1704 Plumes in angles on rev.		£150	£500	£1600	—
1705 —		£100	£450	£1500	—
1706 Roses & Plumes in angles on rev.		£75	£300	£1000	—
1707 —		£75	£300	£900	—
1707 Plain (post-Union)		£70	£200	£700	—
1707 E below bust		£70	£200	£700	—
1707 — SEPTIMO edge				Extremely rare	
1708 Plain		£70	£250	£800	—
1708 E below bust		£70	£250	£800	—
1708 Plumes in angles on rev.		£70	£250	£900	—
1709 Plain		£75	£250	£700	—
1709 E below bust		£220	£800	—	—
1710 Roses & Plumes in angles on rev.		£75	£300	£950	—
1712 —		£75	£300	£950	—
1713 Plain		£75	£300	£950	—
1713 Roses & Plumes in angles on rev.		£75	£300	£950	—
1714 —		£75	£300	£950	—
1714/3 4 over 3		£100	£425	—	—

DATE	MINTAGE	F	VF	EF	UNC

GEORGE I (1714–1727)

DATE	MINTAGE	F	VF	EF	UNC
1715 Roses & Plumes in angles on rev.		£300	£700	£2500	–
1715 Plain edge				Extremely rare	
1717 —		£300	£700	£2500	–
1720 —		£300	£700	£2500	–
1720/17 20 over 17		£300	£750	–	–
1723 SSC in angles on rev.		£250	£700	£2350	–
1726 Small Roses & Plumes in angles on rev.		£3250	£20000	–	–

GEORGE II (1727–1760)

DATE	MINTAGE	F	VF	EF	UNC
1731 Young head, Plain, proof only		–	–	£4500	–
1731 — Roses & Plumes in angles on rev.		£85	£400	£1000	–
1732 — —		£85	£400	£1000	–
1734 — —		£85	£400	£1000	–
1735 — —		£85	£400	£1000	–
1736 — —		£80	£400	£1000	–
1739 — Roses in angles on rev.		£80	£350	£900	–
1741/39 — — 41 over 30		£125	£400	–	–
1741 — —		£80	£325	£900	–
1743 Old head, Roses in angles on rev.		£65	£160	£650	–
1745 — —		£65	£160	£650	–
1745 — LIMA below bust		£65	£150	£625	–
1746 — —		£65	£150	£625	–
1746/5 — — 6 over 5		£75	£180	£700	–
1746 — Plain, Proof		–	–	£1800	–
1750 — —		£120	£500	£1500	–
1751 — —		£140	£550	£1600	–

GEORGE III (1760–1820)

DATE	MINTAGE	F	VF	EF	UNC
1816 "Bull head"	–	£15	£60	£175	£400
1817 —	8,092,656	£15	£60	£175	£400
1817 "Small head"	incl. above	£15	£60	£175	£400
1818 —	2,905,056	£15	£60	£175	£400
1819/8 — 9 over 8	incl. above			Extremely rare	
1819 —	4,790,016	£15	£60	£175	£400
1820 —	2,396,592	£30	£110	£325	£800

GEORGE IV (1820–30)

DATE	MINTAGE	F	VF	EF	UNC
1820 First bust, first reverse	incl. above	£20	£50	£200	£450
1821 — —	1,435,104	£20	£50	£200	£450
1821 — — Proof	incl. above	–	–	–	£1400
1823 — —	2,003,760	£800	£2500	–	–
1823 — Second reverse	incl. above	£20	£50	£180	£450
1824 — —	465,696	£25	£65	£200	£550
1824 Second bust, third reverse	incl. above			Extremely rare	
1825 — —	2,258,784	£20	£50	£150	£350
1826 — —	2,189,088	£18	£50	£150	£350
1826 — — Proof	incl. above	–	–	–	£1200
1828 — —	49,890	£45	£110	£325	£800
1829 — —	508,464	£50	£110	£325	£800

WILLIAM IV (1830–37)

DATE	MINTAGE	F	VF	EF	UNC
1831	–			Extremely rare	
1831 Proof (W.W. in script & block)	–	–	–	–	£1000
1834 W.W. in block	993,168	£20	£60	£200	£500
1834 W.W. in script	incl. above	£20	£60	£200	£500
1835	281,952	£25	£70	£220	£550
1836	1,588,752	£20	£50	£200	£550
1836/5 6 over 5	incl. above	£40	£100	£400	–
1837	150,526	£30	£100	£375	£900

VICTORIA (1837–1901)

YOUNG HEAD ISSUES

DATE	MINTAGE	F	VF	EF	UNC
1839 (two varieties)	—	£500	£1500	£4500	—
1839 Proof	—	—	—	—	£3000
1840	386,496	£40	£180	£500	£1200
1841	42,768	£300	£600	£1500	£3000
1842	486,288	£35	£100	£400	£1000
1843	454,608	£70	£200	£700	£1500
1844	1,999,008	£25	£50	£300	£800
1845	2,231,856	£25	£50	£300	£800
1846	1,539,668	£30	£60	£300	£800
1848 Plain 8	367,488	£70	£200	£600	£2000
1848/6	incl. above	£60	£175	£500	£1800
1849	261,360	£50	£100	£400	£1000
1849 Small date	incl. above	£60	£150	£600	£1100
1850	484,613	£35	£90	£400	£1000
1853 Proof only	—	—	—	—	£2000
1874	2,188,599	£18	£40	£180	£350
1875	1,113,483	£18	£40	£180	£350
1876	633,221	£18	£40	£180	£350
1876/5 6 over 5	incl. above	£20	£45	£200	£350
1877	447,059	£18	£40	£180	£350
1878	1,466,323	£18	£40	£180	£350
1879	901,356	£20	£45	£200	£350
1880	1,346,350	£16	£45	£150	£350
1881	2,301,495	£16	£45	£150	£325
1882	808,227	£16	£45	£150	£325
1883	2,982,779	£16	£45	£150	£325
1884	1,569,175	£16	£45	£150	£325
1885	1,628,438	£16	£45	£150	£325
1886	891,767	£16	£45	£150	£325
1887	1,438,046	£16	£45	£150	£325

JUBILEE HEAD ISSUES

DATE	MINTAGE	F	VF	EF	UNC
1887	incl. above	£5	£8	£16	£40
1887 Proof	1,084	—	—	—	£175
1888	1,428,787	£8	£15	£35	£80
1889	4,811,954	£8	£14	£35	£80
1890	3,228,111	£8	£14	£45	£100
1891	2,284,632	£8	£15	£45	£100
1892	1,710,946	£8	£14	£50	£110

OLD HEAD ISSUES

DATE	MINTAGE	F	VF	EF	UNC
1893	1,792,600	£7	£15	£40	£85
1893 Proof	1,312	—	—	—	£175
1894	1,524,960	£10	£25	£60	£150
1895	1,772,662	£8	£18	£50	£130
1896	2,148,505	£7	£15	£45	£130
1897	1,678,643	£7	£15	£40	£120
1898	1,870,055	£7	£15	£40	£120
1899	2,865,872	£7	£15	£40	£120
1900	4,479,128	£7	£15	£40	£120
1901	1,516,570	£7	£15	£40	£120

EDWARD VII (1901–10)

DATE	MINTAGE	F	VF	EF	UNC
1902	1,316,008	£8	£22	£60	£90
1902 "Matt Proof"	15,123	—	—	—	£160
1903	274,840	£80	£350	£900	£2000
1904	709,652	£50	£200	£400	£1000
1905	166,008	£200	£600	£1500	£4000
1906	2,886,206	£10	£35	£150	£600
1907	3,693,930	£10	£35	£150	£600
1908	1,758,889	£15	£50	£300	£800
1909	3,051,592	£10	£50	£250	£600
1910	2,557,685	£8	£30	£85	£350

GEORGE V (1910–36)

First issue

DATE	MINTAGE	F	VF	EF	UNC
1911	2,914,573	£7	£20	£50	£120
1911 Proof	6,007	—	—	—	£95
1912	4,700,789	£6	£14	£40	£140

George V first type reverse

DATE	MINTAGE	F	VF	EF	UNC
1913	4,090,169	£6	£12	£50	£150
1914	18,333,003	£3	£8	£30	£60
1915	32,433,066	£3	£8	£25	£55
1916	29,530,020	£3	£8	£25	£50
1917	11,172,052	£3	£8	£30	£70
1918	29,079,592	£3	£8	£20	£50
1919	10,266,737	£4	£10	£30	£70
Second issue—debased silver					
1920	17,982,077	£3	£7	£20	£60
1921	23,677,889	£3	£7	£18	£55
1922	16,396,724	£3	£7	£18	£55
1923	26,308,526	£6	£7	£15	£40
1924	5,866,294	£8	£15	£60	£110
1925	1,413,461	£15	£45	£175	£600
1926	4,473,516	£5	£15	£40	£120
Third issue —Modified effigy					
1926	incl. above	£4	£10	£30	£75
1927	6,837,872	£4	£8	£25	£50
Fourth issue—New shield reverse					
1927 Proof	15,000	—	—	—	£65
1928	18,762,727	£3	£6	£15	£35
1929	17,632,636	£3	£6	£15	£35
1930	809,051	£8	£35	£200	£500
1931	11,264,468	£3	£6	£15	£35
1932	4,793,643	£3	£6	£20	£75
1933	10,311,494	£3	£6	£15	£40
1934	2,422,399	£3	£6	£40	£130
1935	7,022,216	£3	£6	£12	£20
1936	7,039,423	£3	£6	£10	£18

George V, fourth issue, new shield reverse

GEORGE VI (1936–52)

DATE	MINTAGE	F	VF	EF	UNC
1937	9,106,440	—	£3	£6	£12
1937 Proof	26,402	—	—	—	£15
1938	6,426,478	£2	£4	£11	£20
1939	15,478,635	£2	£3	£6	£10
1940	17,948,439	£2	£3	£6	£8
1941	15,773,984	£2	£3	£6	£8
1942	31,220,090	£2	£3	£6	£7
1943	15,462,875	£2	£3	£6	£7
1944	15,255,165	£2	£3	£6	£7
1945	19,849,242	£2	£3	£6	£7
1946	22,724,873	£2	£3	£6	£7
Cupro-nickel					
1947	21,911,484	—	£1	£2	£4
1948	71,164,703	—	£1	£2	£4
1949	28,272,512	—	£1	£2	£6
1950	28,335,500	—	£1	£2	£6
1950 Proof	17,513	—	£1	£2	£9
1951	9,003,520	—	£1	£2	£6
1951 Proof	20,000	—	—	—	£9
1952			Only one known		

ELIZABETH II (1952–)

DATE	MINTAGE	F	VF	EF	UNC
1953	4,333,214	—	—	£1	£3
1953 Proof	40,000	—	—	—	£5
1954	11,614,953	—	£1	£4	£20
1955	23,628,726	—	—	£1	£6
1956	33,934,909	—	—	£1	£6
1957	34,200,563	—	—	£1	£6
1958	15,745,668	—	£1	£3	£20
1959	9,028,844	—	£1	£5	£22
1960	19,929,191	—	—	£1	£2
1961	25,887,897	—	—	—	£2
1961 Polished dies	incl. above	—	—	£1	£2
1962	24,013,312	—	—	—	£1
1963	17,625,200	—	—	—	£1
1964	5,973,600	—	—	—	£1
1965	9,778,440	—	—	—	£1
1966	13,375,200	—	—	—	£1
1967	33,058,400	—	—	—	—

FLORINS

VICTORIA (1837–1901)

YOUNG (CROWNED) HEAD ISSUES

"Godless" type (without D.G.—"Dei Gratia")

DATE	MINTAGE	F	VF	EF	UNC
1848 "Godless" Pattern only plain edge	—			Very rare	
1848 "Godless" Pattern only milled edge	—			Extremely rare	
1849	413,820	£20	£50	£135	£300

(Beware of recent forgeries)

"Gothic" type i.e. date in Roman numerals in obverse legend

"brit." in legend. No die no.

DATE	MINTAGE	F	VF	EF	UNC
1851 mdcccli Proof	1,540			Extremely rare	
1852 mdccclii	1,014,552	£22	£55	£200	£425
1853 mdcccliii	3,919,950	£22	£55	£200	£425
1853 — Proof	incl. above	—	—	—	£2000
1854 mdcccliv	550,413	£500	—	—	—
1855 mdccclv	831,017	£22	£55	£200	£500
1856 mdccclvi	2,201,760	£22	£55	£200	£500
1857 mdccclvii	1,671,120	£22	£55	£120	£500
1858 mdccclviii	2,239,380	£22	£55	£200	£500
1859 mdccclix	2,568,060	£22	£55	£200	£500
1860 mdccclx	1,475,100	£28	£75	£250	£525
1862 mdccclxii	594,000	£90	£270	£700	£2200
1863 mdccclxiii	938,520	£500	£1000	£2500	£5000

"brit" in legend. Die no. below bust

DATE	MINTAGE	F	VF	EF	UNC
1864 mdccclxiv	1,861,200	£22	£55	£200	£450
1864 Gothic Piedfort flan	incl. above			Extremely rare	
1865 mdccclxv	1,580,044	£22	£55	£200	£500
1866 mdccclxvi	914,760	£22	£55	£200	£500
1867 mdccclxvii	423,720	£40	£100	£350	£700
1867—only 42 arcs in border	incl. above			Extremely rare	

"britt" in legend. Die no. below bust

DATE	MINTAGE	F	VF	EF	UNC
1868 mdccclxviii	896,940	£22	£55	£200	£450
1869 mdccclxix	297,000	£30	£70	£250	£650
1870 mdccclxx	1,080,648	£20	£55	£200	£400
1871 mdccclxxi	3,425,605	£22	£55	£200	£400
1872 mdccclxxii	7,199,690	£22	£55	£175	£375
1873 mdccclxxiii	5,921,839	£22	£55	£200	£375
1874 mdccclxxiv	1,642,630	£22	£55	£200	£375
1874 — iv over iii in date	incl. above	£25	£60	£200	£350
1875 mdccclxxv	1,117,030	£20	£55	£190	£375
1876 mdccclxxvi	580,034	£25	£70	£200	£400
1877 mdccclxxvii	682,292	£22	£55	£180	£375
1877 — 48 arcs in border no W.W.	incl. above	£22	£55	£180	£425
1877 — 42 arcs	incl. above	£22	£55	£180	£425
1877 — — no die number	incl. above			Extremely rare	
1878 mdccclxxviii with die number	1,786,680	£20	£55	£180	£400
1879 mdccclxxix no die no	1,512,247			Extremely rare	
1879 — 48 arcs in border	incl. above	£20	£55	£180	£400
1879 — no die number	incl. above			Extremely rare	

"Gothic" florin

DATE	MINTAGE	F	VF	EF	UNC
1879 — 38 arcs, no W.W..	incl. above	£20	£55	£180	£400
1880 mdccclxxx Younger portrait	—			Extremely rare	
1880 — 34 arcs, Older portrait....	2,167,170	£20	£55	£180	£375
1881 mdccclxxxi — —	2,570,337	£20	£55	£190	£370
1881 — xx! i broken puncheon...	incl. above	£25	£70	£200	£425
1883 mdccclxxxiii — —..............	3,555,667	£18	£50	£170	£375
1884 mdccclxxxiv — —	1,447,379	£18	£50	£170	£375
1885 mdccclxxxv — —	1,758,210	£18	£50	£170	£375
1886 mdccclxxxvi — —	591,773	£18	£50	£170	£375
1887 mdccclxxxvii — —.............	1,776,903	£40	£110	£275	£600
1887 — 46 arcs	incl. above	£40	£110	£325	£650

JUBILEE HEAD ISSUES

DATE	MINTAGE	F	VF	EF	UNC
1887	incl. above	£5	£10	£22	£45
1887 Proof..................................	1,084	—	—	—	£200
1888	1,547,540	£6	£12	£40	£100
1889..	2,973,561	£6	£14	£40	£100
1890..	1,684,737	£8	£22	£70	£200
1891..	836,438	£15	£50	£150	£350
1892..	283,401	£25	£70	£220	£550

VICTORIA—OLD HEAD ISSUES

DATE	MINTAGE	F	VF	EF	UNC
1893..	1,666,103	£6	£15	£35	£80
1893 Proof..................................	1,312	—	—	—	£175
1894..	1,952,842	£8	£22	£55	£175
1895	2,182,968	£7	£20	£55	£150
1896..	2,944,416	£6	£16	£45	£120
1897..	1,699,921	£6	£16	£45	£120
1898..	3,061,343	£6	£16	£45	£120
1899..	3,966,953	£6	£16	£45	£120
1900..	5,528,630	£6	£16	£45	£120
1901..	2,648,870	£6	£16	£45	£120

EDWARD VII (1901–10)

DATE	MINTAGE	F	VF	EF	UNC
1902..	2,189,575	£7	£15	£40	£80
1902 "Matt Proof"	15,123	—	—	—	£110
1903..	1,995,298	£10	£35	£120	£500
1904..	2,769,932	£10	£35	£120	£400
1905..	1,187,596	£50	£150	£500	£1100
1906..	6,910,128	£10	£35	£130	£450
1907..	5,947,895	£11	£35	£130	£450
1908..	3,280,010	£12	£50	£300	£700
1909..	3,482,829	£10	£45	£220	£550
1910..	5,650,713	£8	£30	£100	£275

GEORGE V (1910–36)

First issue

DATE	MINTAGE	F	VF	EF	UNC
1911..	5,951,284	£4	£10	£30	£75
1911 Proof..................................	6,007	—	—	—	£100
1912	8,571,731	£4	£14	£30	£90
1913..	4,545,278	£6	£18	£35	£110
1914..	21,252,701	£4	£15	£22	£45
1915..	12,367,939	£5	£16	£24	£50
1916..	21,064,337	£4	£15	£22	£45
1917..	11,181,617	£5	£16	£28	£65
1918..	29,211,792	£4	£15	£22	£45
1919..	9,469,292	£5	£15	£30	£70

***Second issue** —debased silver*

DATE	MINTAGE	F	VF	EF	UNC
1920..	15,387,833	£2	£12	£32	£70
1921..	34,863,895	£2	£12	£30	£50
1922..	23,861,044	£2	£12	£30	£50
1923..	21,546,533	£2	£10	£25	£55
1924..	4,582,372	£6	£18	£60	£160
1925..	1,404,136	£14	£40	£180	£500
1926..	5,125,410	£5	£15	£40	£90

***Fourth issue**—new reverse*

DATE	MINTAGE	F	VF	EF	UNC
1927 Proof only	101,497	—	—	—	£65
1928..	11,087,186	£2	£4	£12	£28
1929..	16,397,279	£2	£4	£12	£28

DATE	MINTAGE	F	VF	EF	UNC
1930	5,753,568	£2	£5	£15	£40
1931	6,556,331	£2	£5	£12	£30
1932	717,041	£8	£20	£150	£500
1933	8,685,303	£2	£5	£15	£35
1935	7,540,546	£2	£5	£10	£20
1936	9,897,448	£2	£4	£9	£20

GEORGE VI (1936–52)

DATE	MINTAGE	F	VF	EF	UNC
1937	13,006,781	—	£3	£3	£6
1937 Proof	26,402	—	—	—	£8
1938	7,909,388	£2	£4	£10	£20
1939	20,850,607	£2	£3	£5	£8
1940	18,700,338	£2	£3	£5	£10
1941	24,451,079	£2	£3	£5	£8
1942	39,895,243	£2	£3	£5	£8
1943	26,711,987	£2	£3	£5	£8
1944	27,560,005	£2	£3	£5	£8
1945	25,858,049	£2	£3	£5	£8
1946	22,300,254	£2	£3	£5	£8
Cupro-nickel					
1947	22,910,085	—	—	£1	£3
1948	67,553,636	—	—	£1	£3
1949	28,614,939	—	—	£1	£5
1950	24,357,490	—	—	£2	£7
1950 Proof	17,513	—	—	£1	£8
1951	27,411,747	—	—	£2	£8
1951 Proof	20,000	—	—	—	£8

ELIZABETH II (1952–)

DATE	MINTAGE	F	VF	EF	UNC
1953	11,958,710	—	—	—	£2
1953 Proof	40,000	—	—	—	£6
1954	13,085,422	—	—	£5	£25
1955	25,887,253	—	—	£1	£3
1956	47,824,500	—	—	£1	£3
1957	33,071,282	—	—	£4	£25
1958	9,564,580	—	—	£3	£18
1959	14,080,319	—	—	£4	£25
1960	13,831,782	—	—	£1	£4
1961	37,735,315	—	—	£1	£2
1962	35,147,903	—	—	£1	£2
1963	26,471,000	—	—	£1	£2
1964	16,539,000	—	—	£1	£2
1965	48,163,000	—	—	—	£1.50
1966	83,999,000	—	—	—	£1.50
1967	39,718,000	—	—	—	£1.50

SHILLINGS

OLIVER CROMWELL

	F	VF	EF	UNC
1658	£650	£1150	£2400	—
1658 Dutch Copy			Extremely rare	

CHARLES II (1660–85)

	F	VF	EF	UNC
1663 First bust	£75	£275	£900	—
1663 — GARTIA error			Extremely rare	
1663 — Irish & Scottish shields transposed	£200	—	—	—
1666 — Elephant below bust	£400	£1250	£4000	—
1666 "Guinea" head, elephant	£1800	£3700	—	—
1666 Second bust			Extremely rare	
1668 —	£75	£220	£850	—
1668/7 — 8 over 7	£85	£300	—	—
1668 Second bust	£75	£250	£850	—
1669/6 First bust variety			Extremely rare	
1669			Extremely rare	
1669 Second bust			Extremely rare	

DATE	F	VF	EF	UNC
1670 —	£85	£325	£1000	—
1671 —	£100	£350	£1200	—
1671 — Plume below, plume in centre rev.	£400	£800	£2800	—
1672 —	£80	£225	£900	—
1673 —	£90	£350	£900	—
1673 — Plume below, plume in centre rev.	£350	£750	£2800	—
1673/2 — 3 over 2	£120	£500	—	—
1674/3 — 4 over 3	£120	£500	—	—
1674 —	£90	£300	£1000	—
1674 — Plume below bust, plume in centre rev.	£350	£750	£2800	—
1674 — Plume rev. only	£320	£750	£2800	—
1674 Third bust	£250	£750	—	—
1675 Second bust	£110	£400	—	—
1675/4 — 5 over 4	£150	£600	—	—
1675 — Plume below bust, plume in centre rev.	£300	£750	£3000	—
1675 Third bust	£225	£600	—	—
1675/3 — 5 over 3	£225	£600	—	—
1676 Second bust	£90	£250	£900	—
1676/5 — 6 over 5	£100	£400	—	—
1676 — Plume below bust, plume in centre rev.	£350	£750	£3000	—
1677 —	£75	£275	£1000	—
1677 — Plume below bust	£300	£750	£3000	—
1678 —	£90	£300	£1000	—
1678/7 — 8 over 7	£100	£600	—	—
1679 —	£80	£275	£950	—
1679 — Plume below bust, plume in centre rev.	£350	£800	£3000	—
1679 — Plume below bust	£350	£750	£3000	—
1679 — 9 over 7	£100	£500	—	—
1680 —			Extremely rare	
1680 — Plume below bust, plume in centre rev.	£350	£900	£3250	—
1680/79 — — 80 over 79	£325	£1000	—	—
1681 —	£150	£500	£1500	—
1681 — 1 over 0	£140	£500	£1500	—
1681/0 Elephant & Castle below bust	£2500	—	—	—
1682/1 — 2 over 1	£500	£1500	—	—
1683 —			Extremely rare	
1683 Fourth (Larger) bust	£200	£600	£2200	—
1684 —	£150	£500	£1800	—

JAMES II (1685–88)

DATE	F	VF	EF	UNC
1685	£110	£400	£1500	—
1685 Plume in centre rev. rev			Extremely rare	
1685 No stops on rev.	£160	£650	—	—
1686	£170	£400	£1500	—
1686/5 6 over 5	£170	£400	£1500	—
1687	£150	£400	£1600	—
1687/6 7 over 6	£130	£400	£1600	—
1688	£130	£400	£1600	—
1688/7 last 8 over 7	£140	£400	£1600	—

WILLIAM & MARY (1688–94)

DATE	F	VF	EF	UNC
1692	£140	£425	£1800	—
1692 inverted 1	£170	£425	£1850	—
1693	£140	£425	£1800	—

WILLIAM III (1694–1702)

Provincially produced shillings carry privy marks or initials below the bust: B: Bristol. C: Chester. E: Exeter. N: Norwich. Y or y: York.

DATE	F	VF	EF	UNC
1695 First bust	£35	£100	£500	—
1696 —	£35	£80	£375	—
1696 — no stops on rev.	£50	£120	£650	—
1696 — MAB for MAG			Extremely rare	
1696 — 1669 error			Extremely rare	
1696 — 1669 various GVLELMVS errors			Extremely rare	
1696 — B below bust	£40	£120	£600	—
1696 — C	£40	£120	£600	—
1696 — E	£45	£140	£700	—
1696 — N	£40	£120	£600	—

DATE	F	VF	EF	UNC
1696 — y	£40	£110	£600	—
1696 — Y	£40	£110	£600	—
1696 Second bust		Only one known		
1696 Third bust C below	£160	£400	£1000	—
1696 — Y			Extremely rare	
1697 First bust	£40	£90	£350	—
1697 — GRI for GRA error			Extremely rare	
1697 — Scottish & Irish shields transposed			Extremely rare	
1697 — Irish arms at date			Extremely rare	
1697 — no stops on rev	£45	£150	£600	—
1697 — GVLELMVS error			Extremely rare	
1697 — B	£45	£130	£625	—
1697 — C	£45	£120	£625	—
1697 — E	£45	£120	£625	—
1697 — N	£45	£110	£625	—
1697 — — no stops on obv.			Extremely rare	
1697 — y	£45	£120	£550	—
1697 — — arms of France & Ireland transposed			Extremely rare	
1697 — Y	£45	£120	£550	—
1697 Third bust	£40	£110	£500	—
1697 — B	£45	£110	£500	—
1697 — C	£45	£110	£500	—
1697 — — Fr.a error	£100	£300	—	—
1697 — — no stops on obv.	£70	£200	—	—
1697 — — arms of Scotland at date			Extremely rare	
1697 — E	£45	£110	£600	—
1697 — N	£45	£110	£600	—
1697 — y	£50	£120	£500	—
1697 Third bust variety	£45	£100	£350	—
1697 — B	£45	£120	£600	—
1697 — C	£90	£400	—	—
1698 —	£70	£200	£750	—
1698 — Plumes in angles of rev.	£200	£500	£1200	—
1698 Fourth bust "Flaming hair"	£140	£400	£1400	—
1699 —	£90	£300	£1000	—
1699 Fifth bust	£80	£200	£700	—
1699 — Plumes in angles on rev.	£100	£325	£1000	—
1699 — Roses in angles on rev.	£95	£275	£900	—
1700 —	£45	£100	£400	—
1700 — Small round oo in date	£45	£100	£400	—
1700 — no stop after DEI			Extremely rare	
1700 — Plume below bust	£1500	£3000	—	—
1701 —	£80	£220	£525	—
1701 — Plumes in angles on rev.	£100	£300	£1000	—

William III First bust

ANNE (1702–14)

DATE	F	VF	EF	UNC
1702 First bust (pre-Union with Scotland)	£60	£300	£600	—
1702 — Plumes in angles on rev.	£70	£275	£600	—
1702 — VIGO below bust	£70	£220	£600	—
1702 — — colon before ANNA			Extremely rare	
1703 Second bust, VIGO below	£55	£170	£500	—
1704 — Plain	£500	£1400	—	—
1704 — Plumes in angles on rev.	£70	£175	£700	—
1705 — Plain	£65	£175	£600	—
1705 — Plumes in angles on rev.	£60	£175	£600	—
1705 — Roses & Plumes in angles on rev.	£60	£175	£600	—
1707 — —	£50	£170	£550	—
1707 Second bust (post-Union) E below bust	£40	£100	£450	—
1707 — E* below bust	£70	£200	£650	—
1707 Third bust, Plain	£35	£90	£350	—
1707 — Plumes in angles on rev.	£40	£150	£700	—
1707 — E below bust	£35	£80	£400	—
1707 "Edinburgh" bust, E* below			Extremely rare	
1708 Second bust, E below	£40	£80	£400	—
1708 — E* below bust	£45	£150	£600	—
1708/7 — — 8 over 7			Extremely rare	
1708 — Roses & Plumes in angles on rev.	£80	£250	£600	—

Anne, VIGO below bust

DATE	MINTAGE	F	VF	EF	UNC
1708 Third bust, Plain		£35	£85	£325	—
1708 — Plumes in angles on rev.		£50	£150	£450	—
1708 Third bust, E below bust		£50	£160	£500	—
1708/7 — — 8 over 7		£80	£240	—	—
1708 — Roses & Plumes in angles on rev.		£60	£170	£500	—
1708 "Edinburgh" bust, E* below		£50	£150	£500	—
1709 Third bust, Plain		£40	£100	£450	—
1709 "Edinburgh" bust, E* below		£45	£150	£550	—
1709 — E no star (filled in die?)		£70	£160	£500	—
1710 Third bust, Roses & Plumes in angles		£50	£120	£550	—
1710 Fourth bust, Roses & Plumes in angles		£50	£140	£550	—
1711 Third bust, Plain		£60	£120	£375	—
1711 Fourth bust, Plain		£25	£55	£160	—
1712 — Roses & Plumes in angles on rev.		£50	£100	£350	—
1713 — —		£50	£100	£300	—
1713/2 — 3 over 2		£50	£160	—	—
1714 — —		£55	£85	£300	—
1714/3 —				Extremely rare	

GEORGE I (1714–27)

DATE	MINTAGE	F	VF	EF	UNC
1715 First bust, Roses & Plumes in angles on rev.		£70	£200	£700	—
1716 — —		£80	£300	£1000	—
1717 — —		£55	£200	£900	—
1718 — —		£50	£120	£650	—
1719 — —		£110	£300	£1100	—
1720 — —		£40	£110	£400	—
1720/18 — —		£100	£300	£1000	—
1720 — Plain		£35	£100	£400	—
1721 — Roses & Plumes in angles on rev.		£50	£160	£800	—
1721/0 — — 1 over 0		£50	£160	£600	—
1721 — Plain		£100	£350	£1000	—
1721/19 — — 21 over 19		£125	£250	—	—
1722 — Roses & Plumes in angles on rev.		£70	£200	£800	—
1723 — —		£70	£200	£800	—
1723 — SSC rev., Arms of France at date		£70	£170	£700	
1723 — SSC in angles on rev		£20	£100	£180	—
1723 Second bust, SSC in angles on rev.		£40	£120	£400	—
1723 — Roses & Plumes in angles		£60	£180	£750	—
1723 — WCC (Welsh Copper Co) below bust		£400	£900	£3500	—
1724 — Roses & Plumes in angles on rev.		£60	£175	£550	—
1724 — WCC below bust		£400	£900	£3500	—
1725 — Roses & Plumes in angles on rev.		£50	£175	£750	—
1725 — — no stops on obv.		£70	£200	£700	—
1725 — WCC below bust		£400	£1100	£4000	—
1726 — —.		£350	£1000	£4000	—
1726 — Roses & Plumes in angles on rev.		£300	£1500	—	—
1727 — —				Extremely rare	
1727 — — no stops on obv.				Extremely rare	

GEORGE II (1727–60)

George II Young head

DATE	MINTAGE	F	VF	EF	UNC
1727 Young head, Plumes in angles on rev.		£55	£250	£500	—
1727 — Roses & Plumes in angles on rev.		£55	£150	£500	—
1728 — —		£55	£150	£500	—
1728 — Plain		£60	£200	£625	—
1729 — Roses & Plumes in angles on rev.		£50	£150	£500	—
1731 — —		£60	£150	£500	—
1731 — Plumes in angles on rev.		£60	£300	£800	—
1732 — Roses & Plumes in angles on rev.		£50	£150	£500	—
1734 — —		£50	£150	£500	—
1735 — —		£50	£150	£500	—
1736 — —		£50	£150	£500	—
1736/5 — — 6 over 5		£60	£200	£650	—
1737 — —		£50	£150	£550	—
1739 — Roses in angles on rev.		£40	£110	£375	—
1739/7 — — 9 over 7				Extremely rare	
1741 — —		£40	£110	£375	—
1741/39 — — 41 over 39				Extremely rare	
1743 Old head, Roses in angles on rev.		£25	£75	£300	—
1745 — —		£25	£75	£300	—
1745 — — LIMA beow bust		£20	£75	£275	—

George II Old head

DATE	MINTAGE	F	VF	EF	UNC
1745/3 — — — 5 over 3		£50	£150	£400	—
1746 — — —		£50	£150	£600	—
1746/5 — — — 6 over 5		£100	£275	—	—
1746 — Plain, Proof		—	—	£1400	—
1747 — Roses in angles on rev.		£40	£90	£350	—
1750 — Plain		£35	£120	£350	—
1750/6 — — 0 over 6		£60	£150	£500	—
1751 — —		£100	£275	£650	—
1758 — —		£15	£40	£110	—

GEORGE III (1760–1820)

DATE	MINTAGE	F	VF	EF	UNC
1763 "Northumberland" bust		£400	£675	£1350	—
1787 rev. no semée of hearts in 4th shield		£15	£30	£80	—
1787 — No stop over head		£15	£30	£80	—
1787 — No stop at date		£15	£30	£80	—
1787 — No stops on obv		£18	£35	£85	—
1787 rev. with semée of hearts in shield		£15	£30	£80	—
1798 "Dorrien Magens" bust		—	—	£8000	—

NEW COINAGE—shield in garter reverse

DATE	MINTAGE	F	VF	EF	UNC
1816	—	£8	£20	£50	£100
1817	3,031,360	£8	£20	£50	£100
1817 GEOE for GEOR	incl. above	£110	£225	£450	—
1818	1,342,440	£8	£20	£80	£150
1819	7,595,280	£8	£20	£50	£100
1819/8 9 over 8	incl. above	£10	£30	£70	—
1820	7,975,440	£8	£20	£50	£100

GEORGE IV (1820–30)

DATE	MINTAGE	F	VF	EF	UNC
1821 First bust, first reverse	2,463,120	£10	£40	£140	£325
1821 — — Proof	incl. above	—	—	—	£750
1823 — Second reverse	693,000	£20	£55	£200	£375
1824 — —	4,158,000	£10	£40	£125	£350
1825 — —	2,459,160	£20	£40	£125	£475
1825/3 — — 5 over 3	incl. above			Extremely rare	
1825 Second bust, third reverse	incl. above	£4	£14	£50	£130
1825 — — Roman I	incl. above			Extremely rare	
1826 — —	6,351,840	£4	£14	£45	£130
1826 — — Proof	incl. above	—	—	—	£400
1827 — —	574,200	£20	£50	£140	£400
1829 — —	879,120	£15	£50	£140	£400

WILLIAM IV (1830–37)

DATE	MINTAGE	F	VF	EF	UNC
1831 Proof only	—	—	—	—	£550
1834	3,223,440	£12	£35	£130	£350
1835	1,449,360	£12	£35	£130	£350
1836	3,567,960	£12	£35	£130	£350
1837	478,160	£15	£40	£130	£450

VICTORIA (1837–1901)

YOUNG HEAD ISSUES

First head

DATE	MINTAGE	F	VF	EF	UNC
1838 WW on truncation	1,956,240	£10	£30	£140	£300
1839 —	5,666,760	£10	£30	£140	£300

Second head

DATE	MINTAGE	F	VF	EF	UNC
1839 WW on truncation, Proof only	incl. above	—	—	—	£500
1839 no WW	incl. above	£10	£30	£110	£300
1840	1,639,440	£10	£30	£110	£300
1841	875,160	£10	£30	£110	£300
1842	2,094,840	£10	£30	£110	£300
1843	1,465,200	£10	£35	£120	£300
1844	4,466,880	£8	£30	£100	£275
1845	4,082,760	£8	£30	£100	£275
1846	4,031,280	£8	£30	£100	£275
1848 last 8 of date over 6	1,041,480	£45	£100	£500	£800
1849	845,480	£15	£45	£150	£425

DATE	MINTAGE	F	VF	EF	UNC
1850	685,080	£500	£900	£2000	£4500
1851	470,071	£25	£110	£250	£550
1851/49 51 over 49	incl. above	£125	£600	—	—
1852	1,306,574	£10	£30	£100	£275
1853	4,256,188	£10	£30	£100	£275
1853 Proof	incl. above	—	—	—	£400
1854	552,414	£115	£200	£900	£2000
1854/1 4 over 1	incl. above	£140	£500	—	—
1855	1,368,400	£8	£30	£100	£220
1856	3,168,000	£8	£30	£100	£220
1857	2,562,120	£8	£30	£100	£220
1857 error F:G with inverted G ...	incl. above	£110	£325	—	—
1858	3,108,600	£8	£30	£110	£220
1859	4,561,920	£8	£30	£110	£220
1860	1,671,120	£8	£30	£110	£260
1861	1,382,040	£9	£35	£125	£350
1862	954,360	£40	£120	£275	£800
1863	859,320	£100	£250	£600	£1500
1863/1 3 over 1				Extremely rare	
Die no. added above date up to 1879					
1864	4,518,360	£8	£25	£80	£180
1865	5,619,240	£8	£25	£80	£200
1866	4,984,600	£8	£25	£80	£200
1866 error BBITANNIAR	incl. above	£80	£220	—	—
1867	2,166,120	£8	£30	£90	£200
Third head—with die no					
1867	incl. above	£50	£100	—	—
1868	3,330,360	£8	£30	£80	£200
1869	736,560	£8	£30	£80	£200
1870	1,467,471	£8	£30	£80	£200
1871	4,910,010	£8	£30	£80	£200
1872	8,897,781	£8	£30	£80	£200
1873	6,489,598	£8	£30	£80	£200
1874	5,503,747	£8	£30	£80	£200
1875	4,353,983	£8	£30	£80	£200
1876	1,057,487	£8	£30	£80	£200
1877	2,989,703	£8	£30	£80	£200
1878	3,127,131	£8	£30	£80	£200
1879	3,611,507	£20	£55	£200	£450
Fourth head—no die no					
1879 no Die no.	incl. above	£7	£22	£65	£175
1880	4,842,786	£7	£22	£65	£175
1881	5,255,332	£7	£22	£65	£175
1882	1,611,786	£12	£50	£170	£350
1883	7,281,450	£6	£22	£55	£140
1884	3,923,993	£6	£22	£55	£140
1885	3,336,526	£6	£22	£55	£140
1886	2,086,819	£6	£22	£55	£140
1887	4,034,133	£7	£24	£55	£140
JUBILEE HEAD ISSUES					
1887	incl. above	£2	£6	£11	£28
1887 Proof	1,084	—	—	—	£80
1888	4,526,856	£4	£9	£20	£50
1889	7,039,628	£25	£80	£275	—
1889 Large bust (until 1892)	incl. above	£5	£10	£40	£70
1890	8,794,042	£5	£10	£40	£70
1891	5,665,348	£5	£10	£40	£75
1892	4,591,622	£5	£10	£40	£80
OLD HEAD ISSUES					
1893	7,039,074	£4	£8	£25	£55
1893 small lettering	incl. above	£3	£8	£25	£55
1893 Proof	1,312	—	—	—	£100
1894	5,953,152	£7	£20	£50	£100
1895	8,880,651	£6	£18	£40	£100
1896	9,264,551	£6	£15	£40	£75
1897	6,270,364	£5	£10	£40	£75
1898	9,768,703	£5	£10	£40	£65
1899	10,965,382	£5	£10	£40	£65
1900	10,937,590	£5	£10	£40	£75
1901	3,426,294	£5	£10	£40	£65

Victoria Jubilee head

Victoria Old or Veiled head

EDWARD VII (1901–10)

DATE	MINTAGE	F	VF	EF	UNC
1902	7,809,481	£3	£12	£45	£65
1902 Proof matt	13,123	—	—	—	£75
1903	2,061,823	£10	£35	£100	£400
1904	2,040,161	£1	£35	£100	£400
1905	488,390	£55	£150	£600	£1600
1906	10,791,025	£4	£10	£40	£100
1907	14,083,418	£4	£10	£40	£110
1908	3,806,969	£8	£20	£130	£400
1909	5,664,982	£8	£20	£100	£320
1910	26,547,236	£3	£8	£40	£85

GEORGE V (1910–36)

DATE	MINTAGE	F	VF	EF	UNC
First issue					
1911	20,065,901	£2	£6	£16	£40
1911 Proof	6,007	—	—	—	£65
1912	15,594,009	£2	£7	£22	£60
1913	9,011,509	£4	£15	£40	£90
1914	23,415,843	£2	£5	£20	£40
1915	39,279,024	£2	£5	£20	£40
1916	35,862,015	£2	£5	£20	£40
1917	22,202,608	£2	£5	£20	£40
1918	34,915,934	£2	£5	£20	£40
1919	10,823,824	£2	£6	£25	£45
Second issue—debased silver					
1920	22,825,142	—	£2	£15	£35
1921	22,648,763	—	£2	£15	£35
1922	27,215,738	—	£2	£15	£35
1923	14,575,243	—	£2	£15	£30
1924	9,250,095	£4	£7	£35	£90
1925	5,418,764	£3	£6	£30	£90
1926	22,516,453	—	£5	£20	£85
Third issue—Modified bust					
1926	incl. above	—	£3	£20	£40
1927 —	9,247,344	£1	£3	£20	£40
Fourth issue—large lion and crown on rev., date in legend					
1927	incl. above	£1	£2	£15	£35
1927 Proof	15,000	—	—	—	£45
1928	18,136,778	—	£2	£10	£30
1929	19,343,006	—	£2	£12	£30
1930	3,172,092	—	£2	£15	£40
1931	6,993,926	—	£2	£10	£30
1932	12,168,101	—	£2	£10	£35
1933	11,511,624	—	£2	£10	£30
1934	6,138,463	—	£2	£12	£40
1935	9,183,462	—	£2	£6	£16
1936	11,910,613	—	£2	£4	£12

George V First obverse

George V Second obverse

GEORGE VI (1936–52)

E = England rev. (lion standing on large crown). S = Scotland rev. (lion seated on small crown holding sword and mace)

DATE	MINTAGE	F	VF	EF	UNC
1937 E	8,359,122	—	£2	£3	£6
1937 E Proof	26,402	—	—	—	£12
1937 S	6,748,875	—	£2	£3	£5
1937 S Proof	26,402	—	—	—	£12
1938 E	4,833,436	—	£2	£8	£14
1938 S	4,797,852	—	£2	£8	£14
1939 E	11,052,677	—	£2	£3	£6
1939 S	10,263,892	—	£2	£3	£6
1940 E	11,099,126	—	—	£3	£7
1940 S	9,913,089	—	—	£3	£7

DATE	MINTAGE	F	VF	EF	UNC
1941 E	11,391,883	—	—	£3	£6
1941 S	8,086,030	—	—	£3	£5
1942 E	17,453,643	—	—	£3	£4
1942 S	13,676,759	—	—	£3	£4
1943 E	11,404,213	—	—	£3	£5
1943 S	9,824,214	—	—	£3	£5
1944 E	11,586,751	—	—	£3	£4
1944 S	10,990,167	—	—	£3	£4
1945 E	15,143,404	—	—	£3	£5
1945 S	15,106,270	—	—	£3	£5
1946 E	16,663,797	—	—	£3	£5
1946 S	16,381,501	—	—	£3	£5
Cupro-nickel					
1947 E	12,120,611	—	—	—	£2
1947 S	12,283,223	—	—	—	£2
1948 E	45,576,923	—	—	—	£2
1948 S	45,351,937	—	—	—	£2
1949 E	19,328,405	—	—	—	£5
1949 S	21,243,074	—	—	—	£5
1950 E	19,243,872	—	—	—	£5
1950 E Proof	17,513	—	—	—	£15
1950 S	14,299,601	—	—	—	£5
1950 S Proof	17,513	—	—	—	£15
1951 E	9,956,930	—	—	—	£5
1951 E Proof	20,000	—	—	—	£15
1951 S	10,961,174	—	—	—	£5
1951 S Proof	20,000	—	—	—	£15

English reverse

Scottish reverse

ELIZABETH II (1952–)

E = England rev. (shield with three lions). S = Scotland rev. (shield with one lion).

DATE	MINTAGE	F	VF	EF	UNC
1953 E	41,942,894	—	—	—	£1
1953 E Proof	40,000	—	—	—	£3
1953 S	20,663,528	—	—	—	£1
1953 S Proof	40,000	—	—	—	£3
1954 E	30,262,032	—	—	—	£2
1954 S	26,771,735	—	—	—	£2
1955 E	45,259,908	—	—	—	£2
1955 S	27,950,906	—	—	—	£2
1956 E	44,907,008	—	—	—	£10
1956 S	42,853,639	—	—	—	£10
1957 E	42,774,217	—	—	—	£1
1957 S	17,959,988	—	—	—	£10
1958 E	14,392,305	—	—	—	£10
1958 S	40,822,557	—	—	—	£1
1959 E	19,442,778	—	—	—	£1
1959 S	1,012,988	£1	£2	£6	£22
1960 E	27,027,914	—	—	—	£1
1960 S	14,376,932	—	—	—	£1
1961 E	39,816,907	—	—	—	£1
1961 S	2,762,558	—	—	—	£3
1962 E	36,704,379	—	—	—	£1
1962 S	17,475,310	—	—	—	£1
1963 E	49,433,607	—	—	—	£1
1963 S	32,300,000	—	—	—	£1
1964 E	8,590,900	—	—	—	£1
1964 S	5,239,100	—	—	—	£1
1965 E	9,216,000	—	—	—	£1
1965 S	2,774,000	—	—	—	£2
1966 E	15,002,000	—	—	—	£1
1966 S	15,604,000	—	—	—	£1

English reverse

Scottish reverse

SIXPENCES

DATE	F	VF	EF	UNC

OLIVER CROMWELL

DATE	F	VF	EF	UNC
1658 Patterns by Thos. Simon & Tanner Four varieties		Extremely rare		

CHARLES II (1660–85)

DATE	F	VF	EF	UNC
1674	£70	£300	£900	—
1675	£70	£300	£900	—
1675/4 5 over 4	£80	£300	£925	—
1676	£70	£300	£900	—
1676/5 6 over 5	£80	£300	£900	—
1677	£70	£300	£900	—
1678/7	£65	£280	£900	—
1679	£60	£300	£900	—
1680	£90	£500	£1000	—
1681	£65	£300	£900	—
1682/1	£700	£300	£1000	—
1682	£75	£300	£950	—
1683	£65	£300	£925	—
1684	£65	£300	£900	—

JAMES II (1685–88)

DATE	F	VF	EF	UNC
1686 Early shields	£110	£400	£1000	—
1687/6 — 7 over 6	£110	£400	£1000	—
1687 Late shields	£110	£400	£950	—
1687/6 — 7 over 6	£100	£400	£1000	—
1688 —	£105	£400	£1000	—

WILLIAM & MARY (1688–94)

DATE	F	VF	EF	UNC
1693	£100	£425	£900	—
1693 error inverted 3	£110	£425	£900	—
1694	£110	£450	£1000	—

WILLIAM III (1694–1702)

Provincially produced sixpences carry privy marks or initials below the bust: B: Bristol. C: Chester. E: Exeter. N: Norwich. Y or y: York.

DATE	F	VF	EF	UNC
1695 First bust, early harp in 4th shield on rev.	£35	£100	£400	—
1696 — —	£35	£100	£325	—
1696 — — French arms at date		Extremely rare		
1696 — — Scottish arms at date		Extremely rare		
1696 — — DFI for DEI		Extremely rare		
1696 — — No stops on obv.	£30	£100	£375	—
1696 — — B	£40	£100	£400	—
1696 — — — B over E		Extremely rare		
1696 — — C	£35	£100	£425	—
1696 — — E	£40	£100	£425	—
1696 — — N	£40	£100	£425	—
1696 — — y	£40	£110	£475	—
1696 — — Y	£45	£200	£500	—
1696 — Later harp	£45	£175	£400	—
1696 — — B	£60	£225	£500	—
1696 — — — no stops on obv	£60	£225	£500	—
1696 — — C	£70	£350	£850	—
1696 — — N	£70	£325	—	—
1696 Second bust	£200	£600	—	—
1697 First bust, later harp	£30	£75	£300	—
1697 — — Arms of France & Ireland transposed		Extremely rare		

DATE	MINTAGE	F	VF	EF	UNC
1697 — — B		£40	£100	£400	—
1697 — — C		£40	£100	£425	—
1697 — — — Irish shield at date			Extremely rare		
1697 — — E		£40	£100	£400	—
1697 — — N		£40	£100	£400	—
1697 — — — error GVLIEMVS			Extremely rare		
1697 — — y		£40	£110	£425	—
1697 — — — Irish shield at date			Extremely rare		
1697 Second bust		£100	£400	£1200	—
1697 Third bust		£25	£70	£275	—
1697 — error GVLIEIMVS			Extremely rare		
1697 — B		£40	£100	£450	—
1697 — — IRA for FRA			Extremely rare		
1697 — C		£40	£200	£500	—
1697 — E		£40	£200	£500	—
1697 — Y		£40	£200	£500	—
1698 —		£40	£170	£450	—
1698 — Plumes in angles on rev.		£50	£200	£650	—
1699 —		£60	£240	£700	—
1699 — Plumes in angles on rev.		£60	£250	£700	—
1699 — Roses in angles on rev.		£70	£250	£700	—
1699 — — error G LIELMVS			Extremely rare		
1700 —		£40	£90	£350	—
1700 — Plume below bust		£2000	—	—	—
1701 —		£55	£120	£425	—

ANNE (1702–14)

DATE	MINTAGE	F	VF	EF	UNC
1703 VIGO below bust Before Union with Scotland		£40	£130	£400	—
1705 Plain		£50	£170	£500	—
1705 Plumes in angles on rev.		£45	£150	£425	—
1705 Roses & Plumes in angles on rev.		£60	£150	£425	—
1707 Roses & Plumes in angles on rev.		£40	£140	£350	—
1707 (Post-Union), Plain		£30	£70	£275	—
1707 E (Edinburgh) below bust		£30	£80	£300	—
1707 Plumes in angles on rev.		£40	£100	£300	—
1708 Plain		£30	£80	£300	—
1708 E below bust		£30	£80	£300	—
1708 E* below bust		£40	£100	£350	—
1708 "Edinburgh" bust E* below		£35	£100	£350	—
1708 Plumes in angles on rev.		£40	£110	£350	—
1710 Roses & Plumes in angles on rev.		£35	£110	£370	—
1711 Plain		£25	£60	£170	—

GEORGE I (1714–27)

DATE	MINTAGE	F	VF	EF	UNC
1717 Roses & Plumes in angles on rev.		£80	£225	£675	—
1717 Plain edge			Extremely rare		
1720 —		£80	£220	£600	—
1723 SSC in angles on rev.		£20	£50	£175	—
1723 Larger lettering		£20	£50	£175	—
1726 Small Roses & Plumes in angles on rev.		£80	£225	£650	—

GEORGE II (1727–60)

DATE	MINTAGE	F	VF	EF	UNC
1728 Young head, Plain		£70	£240	£525	—
1728 — Proof		—	—	£3000	—
1728 — Plumes in angles on rev.		£40	£140	£400	—
1728 — Roses & Plumes in angles on rev.		£35	£125	£300	—
1731 — —		£35	£125	£300	—
1732 — —		£35	£125	£300	—
1734 — —		£35	£140	£350	—
1735 — —		£35	£140	£350	
1735/4 5 over 4		£40	£150	£400	—
1736 — —		£35	£140	£350	—
1739 — Roses in angles on rev.		£30	£80	£225	—
1741 —		£28	£80	£225	—

DATE	MINTAGE	F	VF	EF	UNC
1743 Old head, Roses in angles on rev.		£20	£70	£225	—
1745 — —		£20	£70	£225	—
1745 — — 5 over 3		£30	£80	£250	—
1745 — Plain, LIMA below bust		£20	£70	£200	—
1746 — — —		£20	£70	£200	—
1746 — — Proof		—	—	£800	—
1750 — —		£30	£120	£325	—
1751 — —		£35	£150	£350	—
1757 — —		£14	£28	£65	—
1758 — —		£14	£28	£65	—

GEORGE III (1760–1820)

DATE	MINTAGE	F	VF	EF	UNC
1787 rev. no semée of hearts on 4th shield		£10	£25	£55	£80
1787 rev. with semée of hearts		£10	£25	£55	£80
NEW COINAGE					
1816	—	£6	£15	£40	£95
1817	10,921,680	£6	£15	£40	£95
1818	4,284,720	£8	£24	£80	£170
1819	4,712,400	£6	£15	£40	£75
1819 very small 8 in date	incl. above	£6	£15	£40	£100
1820	1,488,960	£6	£15	£40	£100

GEORGE IV (1820–30)

DATE	MINTAGE	F	VF	EF	UNC
1821 First bust, first reverse	863,280	£12	£25	£80	£275
1821 error BBRITANNIAR		£60	£220	£700	—
1821 — — Proof	incl. above	—	—	—	£600
1824 — Second (garter) reverse	633,600	£12	£25	£80	£250
1825 —	483,120	£12	£25	£75	£225
1826 — —	689,040	£20	£60	£200	£450
1826 Second bust, third (lion on crown) reverse	incl. above	£10	£25	£75	£160
1826 — — Proof	incl. above	—	—	—	£300
1827 — —	166,320	£18	£55	£200	£400
1828 — —	15,840	£16	£40	£125	£275
1829 — —	403,290	£12	£40	£110	£275

WILLIAM IV (1830–37)

DATE	MINTAGE	F	VF	EF	UNC
1831	1,340,195	£12	£30	£110	£275
1831 Proof	incl. above	—	—	—	£400
1834	5,892,480	£12	£30	£110	£275
1835	1,552,320	£12	£30	£110	£260
1836	1,987,920	£12	£35	£140	£300
1837	506,880	£15	£40	£160	£400

VICTORIA (1837–1901)

DATE	MINTAGE	F	VF	EF	UNC
YOUNG HEAD ISSUES					
First head					
1838	1,607,760	£8	£30	£80	£200
1839	3,310,560	£8	£30	£70	£200
1839 Proof	incl. above	—	—	—	£375
1840	2,098,800	£8	£30	£75	£200
1841	1,386,000	£8	£30	£80	£220
1842	601,920	£8	£30	£80	£220
1843	3,160,080	£8	£30	£70	£200
1844	3,975,840	£8	£25	£45	£200
1844 Large 44 in date	incl. above	£12	£40	£100	£270
1845	3,714,480	£8	£25	£60	£200
1846	4,226,880	£8	£25	£60	£200
1848	586,080	£30	£90	£275	£700
1848/6 final 8 over 6	incl. above	£40	£90	£300	—
1850	498,960	£8	£30	£70	£200
1850/3 0 over 3	incl. above	£15	£30	£80	£270

DATE	MINTAGE	F	VF	EF	UNC
1851	2,288,107	£8	£25	£70	£200
1852	904,586	£8	£25	£70	£200
1853	3,837,930	£8	£25	£70	£200
1853 Proof	incl above	—	—	—	£500
1854	840,116	£50	£150	£500	£1000
1855	1,129,684	£8	£24	£70	£175
1855/3 last 5 over 3	incl. above	£10	£35	£70	£200
1856	2,779,920	£8	£24	£70	£180
1857	2,233,440	£8	£24	£70	£180
1858	1,932,480	£8	£24	£70	£180
1859	4,688,640	£8	£24	£75	£180
1859/8 9 over 8	incl. above	£10	£30	£80	£220
1860	1,100,880	£9	£22	£80	£200
1862	990,000	£35	£100	£300	£700
1863	491,040	£35	£75	£300	£775
Die no. added above date from 1864 to 1879					
1864	4,253,040	£8	£25	£70	£180
1865	1,631,520	£8	£25	£70	£180
1866	4,140,080	£8	£25	£70	£180
1866 no Die no.	incl. above	£25	£100	—	—
Second head					
1867	1,362,240	£7	£20	£70	£200
1868	1,069,200	£7	£20	£60	£150
1869	388,080	£7	£20	£60	£150
1870	479,613	£7	£20	£60	£150
1871	3,662,684	£6	£20	£50	£140
1871 no Die no.	incl. above	£6	£20	£50	£140
1872	3,382,048	£6	£20	£50	£140
1873	4,594,733	£6	£20	£50	£140
1874	4,225,726	£6	£20	£50	£140
1875	3,256,545	£6	£20	£50	£140
1876	841,435	£6	£20	£55	£140
1877	4,066,486	£6	£20	£55	£140
1877 no Die no	incl. above	£6	£20	£55	£140
1878	2,624,525	£6	£20	£55	£130
1878 Dritanniar Error	incl. above	£60	£200	—	—
1879	3,326,313	£6	£18	£50	£140
1879 no Die no	incl. above	£5	£18	£50	£140
1880 no Die no	3,892,501	£5	£18	£50	£130
Third head					
1880	incl above	£6	£18	£50	£110
1881	6,239,447	£6	£18	£50	£110
1882	759,809	£10	£30	£100	£300
1883	4,986,558	£6	£16	£35	£90
1884	3,422,565	£6	£16	£35	£90
1885	4,652,771	£6	£16	£35	£90
1886	2,728,249	£6	£16	£35	£80
1887	3,675,607	£6	£16	£35	£80

JUBILEE HEAD ISSUES

DATE	MINTAGE	F	VF	EF	UNC
1887 Shield reverse	incl. above	£3	£5	£10	£25
1887 — Proof	incl. above	—	—	—	£75
1887 Six Pence in wreath reverse	incl. above	£3	£5	£10	£25
1888 —	4,197,698	£4	£7	£20	£40
1889 —	8,738,928	£4	£7	£25	£50
1890 —	9,386,955	£4	£7	£25	£50
1891 —	7,022,734	£4	£7	£25	£50
1892 —	6,245,746	£4	£8	£28	£60
1893 —	7,350,619	£400	£1000	£3000	—

OLD HEAD ISSUES

DATE	MINTAGE	F	VF	EF	UNC
1893	incl. above	£4	£8	£20	£45
1893 Proof	1,312	—	—	—	£75
1894	3,467,704	£7	£14	£40	£75
1895	7,024,631	£6	£14	£35	£65
1896	6,651,699	£4	£9	£30	£50
1897	5,031,498	£4	£9	£30	£50
1898	5,914,100	£4	£9	£30	£45
1899	7,996,80	£4	£9	£30	£45
1900	8,984,354	£4	£9	£30	£45
1901	5,108,757	£4	£9	£28	£45

Jubilee head, shield reverse

Jubilee head, wreath reverse

EDWARD VII (1901–10)

DATE	MINTAGE	F	VF	EF	UNC
1902	6,367,378	£3	£8	£25	£45
1902 "Matt Proof"	15,123	—	—	—	£50
1903	5,410,096	£6	£18	£50	£150
1904	4,487,098	£10	£40	£140	£350
1905	4,235,556	£7	£20	£60	£160
1906	7,641,146	£5	£10	£35	£90
1907	8,733,673	£5	£10	£40	£80
1908	6,739,491	£8	£25	£80	£275
1909	6,584,017	£6	£15	£45	£150
1910	12,490,724	£3	£5	£20	£40

Edward VII

GEORGE V (1910–36)

DATE	MINTAGE	F	VF	EF	UNC
First issue					
1911	9,155,310	£1	£3	£10	£35
1911 Proof	6,007	—	—	—	£45
1912	10,984,129	£1	£3	£20	£40
1913	7,499,833	£1	£6	£22	£50
1914	22,714,602	£1	£2	£10	£25
1915	15,694,597	£1	£3	£12	£35
1916	22,207,178	£1	£2	£8	£25
1917	7,725,475	£5	£15	£40	£85
1918	27,553,743	£1	£2	£12	£25
1919	13,375,447	£1	£3	£12	£35
1920	14,136,287	£1	£3	£10	£25
Second issue—debased silver					
1920	incl. above	£1	£3	£10	£28
1921	30,339,741	£1	£3	£10	£28
1922	16,878,890	£1	£2	£10	£28
1923	6,382,793	£3	£8	£40	£90
1924	17,444,218	£1	£5	£10	£25
1925	12,720,558	£1	£2	£10	£25
1925 Broad rim	incl. above	£1	£2	£10	£25
1926 —	21,809,621	£1	£2	£10	£25
Third issue—Modified bust					
1926	incl. above	£1	£2	£10	£30
1927	8,924,873	—	£1	£10	£30
Fourth issue—New design (oakleaves)					
1927 Proof only	15,000	—	—	—	£25
1928	23,123,384	—	£1	£7	£20
1929	28,319,326	—	£1	£7	£20
1930	16,990,289	—	£1	£8	£25
1931	16,873,268	—	£1	£7	£20
1932	9,406,117	—	£1	£8	£30
1933	22,185,083	—	£1	£7	£20
1934	9,304,009	£1	£2	£9	£25
1935	13,995,621	—	£1	£5	£10
1936	24,380,171	—	£1	£5	£10

George V, first reverse above and second reverse below

GEORGE VI (1936–52)

DATE	MINTAGE	F	VF	EF	UNC
First type					
1937	22,302,524	—	—	£1	£4
1937 Proof	26,402	—	—	—	£5
1938	13,402,701	—	£1	£3	£12
1939	28,670,304	—	—	£1	£5
1940	20,875,196	—	—	£1	£5
1941	23,086,616	—	—	£1	£5
1942	44,942,785	—	—	£1	£4
1943	46,927,111	—	—	£1	£4
1944	36,952,600	—	—	£1	£4
1945	39,939,259	—	—	£1	£3
1946	43,466,407	—	—	£1	£3
Cupro-nickel					
1947	29,993,263	—	—	£1	£3
1948	88,323,540	—	—	£1	£3
Second type—new cypher on rev.					
1949	41,335,515	—	—	£1	£3

George VI first reverse

George VI second reverse

DATE	MINTAGE	F	VF	EF	UNC
1950	32,741,955	—	—	£1	£3
1950 Proof	17,513	—	—	—	£6
1951	40,399,491	—	—	£1	£3
1951 Proof	20,000	—	—	—	£6
1952	1,013,477	£4	£12	£30	£70

ELIZABETH II (1952–)

DATE	MINTAGE	F	VF	EF	UNC
1953	70,323,876	—	—	—	£2
1953 Proof	40,000	—	—	—	£4
1954	105,241,150	—	—	—	£3
1955	109,929,554	—	—	—	£1
1956	109,841,555	—	—	—	£1
1957	105,654,290	—	—	—	£1
1958	123,518,527	—	—	—	£3
1959	93,089,441	—	—	—	£1
1960	103,283,346	—	—	—	£3
1961	115,052,017	—	—	—	£3
1962	166,483,637	—	—	—	25p
1963	120,056,000	—	—	—	25p
1964	152,336,000	—	—	—	25p
1965	129,644,000	—	—	—	25p
1966	175,676,000	—	—	—	25p
1967	240,788,000	—	—	—	25p

GROATS OR FOURPENCES

DATE	MINTAGE	F	VF	EF	UNC

The earlier fourpences are included in the Maundy oddments section as they are generally considered to have been issued for the Maundy ceremony.

WILLIAM IV (1831–37)

DATE	MINTAGE	F	VF	EF	UNC
1836	—	£8	£16	£40	£85
1837	962,280	£8	£16	£40	£85

VICTORIA (1838–1901)

DATE	MINTAGE	F	VF	EF	UNC
1837	Extremely Rare Proofs or Patterns only				
1837 over last 8 on its side		£10	£18	£50	£100
1838	2,150,280	£7	£15	£30	£80
1839	1,461,240	£7	£16	£35	£80
1839 Proof	incl. above				Rare
1840	1,496,880	£7	£15	£35	£80
1840 Small 0 in date	incl. above	£7	£16	£40	£90
1841	344,520	£7	£15	£35	£80
1842/1 2 over 1	incl. above	£7	£15	£35	£80
1842	724,680	£7	£15	£35	£80
1843	1,817640	£8	£16	£40	£100
1843 4 over 5	incl. above	£7	£15	£35	£80
1844	855,360	£7	£15	£35	£90
1845	914,760	£7	£15	£35	£90
1846	1,366,200	£7	£15	£35	£90
1847 7 over 6	225,720	£12	£30	£100	—
1848	712,800	£7	£15	£30	£80
1848/6 8 over 6	incl. above	£25	£100	—	—
1848/7 8 over 7	incl. above	£8	£20	£50	£100
1849	380,160	£7	£15	£35	£80
1849/8 9 over 8	incl. above	£8	£20	£60	£125
1851	594,000	£25	£70	£175	£350
1852	31,300	£50	£120	£350	—
1853	11,880	£40	£100	£375	—
1853 Proof Milled Rim	incl. above	—	—	—	£500
1853 Plain edge Proof				Extremely rare	
1854	1,096,613	£7	£14	£35	£80
1855	646,041	£7	£14	£35	£80
1857 Proofs only				Extremely rare	
1862 Proofs only				Extremely rare	
1888 Jubilee Head	—	£7	£15	£35	£75

THREEPENCES

DATE	MINTAGE	F	VF	EF	UNC

The earlier threepences are included in the Maundy oddments section.

WILLIAM IV (1830–37)

(issued for use in the West Indies)

1834		£6	£12	£60	£120
1835		£6	£12	£60	£120
1836		£6	£12	£60	£120
1837		£8	£15	£75	£140

VICTORIA (1837–1901)

YOUNG HEAD ISSUES

1838 BRITANNIAB error				Extremely rare	
1838	–	£7	£18	£50	£120
1839	–	£7	£18	£50	£120
18t40	–	£7	£18	£50	£120
1841	–	£7	£18	£55	£140
1842	–	£7	£18	£55	£140
1843	–	£7	£18	£45	£120
1843/34 43 over 34	–	£7	£18	£70	£160
1844	–	£10	£20	£60	£140
1845	1,319,208	£8	£18	£50	£135
1846	52,008	£8	£22	£70	£180
1847	4,488			Extremely rare	
1848	incl. above			Extremely rare	
1849	131,208	£8	£20	£70	£170
1850	954,888	£8	£18	£40	£100
1851	479,065	£8	£20	£50	£130
1851 5 over 8	incl. above	£10	£25	£100	–
1852	4,488			Extremely rare	
1853	36,168	£20	£50	£100	£275
1854	1,467,246	£6	£18	£50	£120
1855	383,350	£6	£18	£50	£130
1856	1,013,760	£6	£18	£55	£120
1857	1,758,240	£6	£18	£60	£140
1858	1,441,440	£6	£18	£50	£120
1858 BRITANNIAB error	incl. above			Extremely rare	
1858/6 final 8 over 6	incl. above	£8	£25	£100	–
1858/5 final 8 over 5	incl. above	£8	£25	£100	–
1859	3,579,840	£6	£18	£50	£110
1860	3,405,600	£6	£18	£50	£120
1861	3,294,720	£6	£18	£50	£110
1862	1,156,320	£6	£18	£45	£110
1863	950,400	£10	£30	£80	£200
1864	1,330,560	£6	£18	£45	£110
1865	1,742,400	£6	£18	£45	£100
1866	1,900,800	£6	£18	£45	£100
1867	712,800	£6	£18	£45	£100
1868	1,457,280	£6	£18	£45	£100
1868 RRITANNIAR error	incl. above			Extremely rare	
1869	–	£35	£70	£175	£300
1870	1,283,218	£5	£16	£45	£80
1871	999,633	£5	£16	£40	£80
1872	1,293,271	£5	£16	£40	£80
1873	4,055,550	£5	£16	£40	£80
1874	4,427,031	£5	£16	£40	£80
1875	3,306,500	£5	£16	£40	£80
1876	1,834,389	£5	£16	£40	£80
1877	2,622,393	£5	£16	£40	£80
1878	2,419,975	£5	£16	£40	£80
1879	3,140,265	£5	£16	£40	£80
1880	1,610,069	£5	£16	£40	£70
1881	3,248,265	£5	£16	£40	£70
1882	472,965	£6	£20	£60	£125
1883	4,369,971	£5	£10	£30	£50

Victoria first type

DATE	MINTAGE	F	VF	EF	UNC
1884	3,322,424	£5	£10	£30	£50
1885	5,183,653	£5	£10	£30	£50
1886	6,152,669	£5	£10	£30	£50
1887	2,780,761	£5	£10	£30	£50
JUBILEE HEAD ISSUES					
1887	incl. above	£1	£3	£9	£20
1887 Proof	incl. above	—	—	—	£45
1888	518,199	£2	£5	£18	£35
1889	4,587,010	£2	£5	£18	£35
1890	4,465,834	£2	£5	£18	£35
1891	6,323,027	£2	£5	£18	£35
1892	2,578,226	£2	£5	£18	£40
1893	3,067,243	£8	£25	£100	£220
OLD HEAD ISSUES					
1893	incl. above	£1	£3	£15	£30
1893 Proof	incl. above	—	—	—	£45
1894	1,608,603	£2	£6	£24	£50
1895	4,788,609	£1	£5	£22	£50
1896	4,598,442	£1	£5	£18	£35
1897	4,541,294	£1	£5	£18	£35
1898	4,567,177	£1	£5	£18	£35
1899	6,246,281	£1	£5	£18	£35
1900	10,644,480	£1	£5	£18	£35
1901	6,098,400	£1	£5	£14	£30

Victoria Jubilee head

Victoria Old or Veiled head

EDWARD VII (1901–10)

DATE	MINTAGE	F	VF	EF	UNC
1902	8,268,480	£1	£2	£7	£15
1902 "Matt Proof"	incl. above	—	—	—	£20
1903	5,227,200	£1	£4	£20	£45
1904	3,627,360	£2	£8	£40	£80
1905	3,548,160	£1	£4	£25	£60
1906	3,152,160	£1	£5	£22	£55
1907	4,831,200	£1	£4	£20	£50
1908	8,157,600	£1	£3	£20	£50
1909	4,055,040	£1	£4	£20	£50
1910	4,563,380	£1	£4	£18	£35

GEORGE V (1910–36)

DATE	MINTAGE	F	VF	EF	UNC
First issue					
1911	5,841,084	—	—	£3	£10
1911 Proof	incl. above	—	—	—	£30
1912	8,932,825	—	—	£3	£12
1913	7,143,242	—	—	£3	£12
1914	6,733,584	—	—	£3	£12
1915	5,450,617	—	—	£3	£12
1916	18,555,201	—	—	£3	£10
1917	21,662,490	—	—	£3	£10
1918	20,630,909	—	—	£3	£10
1919	16,845,687	—	—	£3	£10
1920	16,703,597	—	—	£3	£10
Second issue—debased silver					
1920	incl. above	—	—	£3	£12
1921	8,749,301	—	—	£3	£12
1922	7,979,998	—	—	£3	£40
1925	3,731,859	—	—	£5	£25
1926	4,107,910	—	—	£7	£28
Third issue—Modified bust					
1926	incl. above	—	—	£8	£22
Fourth issue—new design (oakleaves)					
1927 Proof only	15,022	—	—	—	£65
1928	1,302,106	£3	£8	£25	£60
1930	1,319,412	£2	£4	£10	£40
1931	6,251,936	—	—	£2	£7
1932	5,887,325	—	—	£2	£7
1933	5,578,541	—	—	£2	£7
1934	7,405,954	—	—	£2	£7
1935	7,027,654	—	—	£2	£7
1936	3,328,670	—	—	£2	£7

George V, fourth issue oak leaves design reverse

GEORGE VI (1936–52)

George VI "Thrift" design of the brass 3d

DATE	MINTAGE	F	VF	EF	UNC
Silver					
1937	8,148,156	—	—	£1	£4
1937 Proof	26,402	—	—	—	£10
1938	6,402,473	—	—	£1	£4
1939	1,355,860	—	—	£4	£12
1940	7,914,401	—	—	£1	£3
1941	7,979,411	—	—	£1	£3
1942	4,144,051	£2	£5	£12	£35
1943	1,397,220	£2	£5	£12	£35
1944	2,005,553	£5	£12	£35	£80
1945	Only one known				
Brass—larger size, 12 sided, "Thrift" design					
1937	45,707,957	—	—	£1	£4
1937 Proof	26,402	—	—	—	£8
1938	14,532,332	—	—	£1	£15
1939	5,603,021	—	—	£3	£40
1940	12,636,018	—	—	£3	£25
1941	60,239,489	—	—	£1	£8
1942	103,214,400	—	—	£1	£8
1943	101,702,400	—	—	£1	£8
1944	69,760,000	—	—	£1	£8
1945	33,942,466	—	—	£2	£18
1946	620,734	£6	£25	£125	£400
1948	4,230,400	—	—	£5	£40
1949	464,000	£5	£25	£150	£475
1950	1,600,000	—	£2	£20	£110
1950 Proof	17,513	—	—	—	£15
1951	1,184,000	—	£2	£20	£100
1951 Proof	20,000	—	—	—	£15
1952	25,494,400	—	—	—	£10

ELIZABETH II (1952–)

DATE	MINTAGE	F	VF	EF	UNC
1953	30,618,000	—	—	—	£1
1953 Proof	40,000	—	—	—	£6
1954	41,720,000	—	—	—	£5
1955	41,075,200	—	—	—	£5
1956	36,801,600	—	—	—	£6
1957	24,294,500	—	—	—	£5
1958	20,504,000	—	—	—	£9
1959	28,499,200	—	—	—	£6
1960	83,078,400	—	—	—	£2
1961	41,102,400	—	—	—	£1
1962	51,545,600	—	—	—	£1
1963	39,482,866	—	—	—	£1
1964	44,867,200	—	—	—	—
1965	27,160,000	—	—	—	—
1966	53,160,000	—	—	—	—
1967	151,780,800	—	—	—	—

TWO PENCES

It is generally accepted that earlier issues of the small silver twopences were only produced for inclusion with the Maundy sets, q.v., except for those listed below.

DATE	F	VF	EF	UNC
1797 "Cartwheel"	£22	£45	£280	£800
1797 Copper Proofs	Many varieties from £500+			

VICTORIA (1837–1901)

For use in the Colonies

DATE	F	VF	EF	UNC
1838	£4	£10	£18	£35
1848	£4	£12	£20	£40

THREE-HALFPENCES

WILLIAM IV (1830–37)

For use in the Colonies

DATE	F	VF	EF	UNC
1834	£6	£16	£32	£75
1835	£8	£20	£60	£200
1835 over 4	£6	£16	£32	£75
1836	£8	£18	£35	£85
1837	£12	£35	£100	£250

VICTORIA (1837–1901)

For use in the Colonies

DATE	F	VF	EF	UNC
1838	£6	£15	£35	£75
1839	£6	£15	£35	£75
1840	£7	£18	£40	£80
1841	£6	£15	£30	£70
1842	£6	£18	£35	£75
1843	£6	£15	£30	£70
1860	£9	£20	£70	£140
1862	£9	£20	£70	£140

PENNIES

The earlier small silver pennies are included in the Maundy oddments section.

GEORGE III (1760–1820)

DATE	MINTAGE	F	VF	EF	UNC
1797 "Cartwheel", 10 laurel leaves	8,601,600	£15	£35	£180	£550
1797 — 11 laurel leaves	incl. above	£15	£35	£180	£550
1806 Third type	—	£6	£15	£55	£150
1807	—	£5	£15	£55	£150
1808					Unique

GEORGE IV (1820–30)

DATE	MINTAGE	F	VF	EF	UNC
1825	1,075,200	£10	£35	£130	£400
1826 (varieties)	5,913,600	£10	£35	£130	£400
1826 Proof	—	—	—	—	£450
1827	1,451,520	£125	£400	£1500	—

WILLIAM IV (1830–37)

DATE	MINTAGE	F	VF	EF	UNC
1831 (varieties)	806,400	£14	£60	£250	£700
1831 Proof	—	—	—	£240	£700
1834	322,560	£25	£55	£240	£675
1837	174,720	£40	£100	£400	£1300

VICTORIA (1837–1901)

YOUNG HEAD ISSUES

Copper

DATE	MINTAGE	F	VF	EF	UNC
1839 Proof	unrecorded	—	—	—	£1000
1841	913,920	£7	£15	£100	£250
1841 No colon after REG	incl. above	£7	£15	£100	£250
1843	483,840	£60	£160	£800	£2000
1844	215,040	£10	£25	£90	£250
1845	322,560	£15	£35	£150	£450

"Cartwheel" penny

DATE	MINTAGE	F	VF	EF	UNC
1846	483,840	£15	£25	£120	£425
1846 FID: DEF colon spaced	incl. above	£15	£25	£120	£425
1846 FID:DEF colon close	incl. above	£15	£20	£120	£425
1847	430,080	£8	£20	£100	£275
1848	161,280	£8	£20	£100	£275
1848/7 final 8 over 7	incl. above	£7	£20	£100	£275
1848/6 final 8 over 6	incl. above	£15	£50	£200	—
1849	268,800	£130	£400	£1500	—
1851	268,800	£10	£30	£120	£400
1853	1,021,440	£5	£10	£50	£110
1853 Proof	—	—	—	—	£500
1854	6,720,000	£6	£15	£60	£110
1854/3 4 over 3	incl. above	£10	£30	£120	—
1855	5,273,856	£6	£15	£60	£140
1856	1,212,288	£50	£150	£300	£1200
1857 Plain trident	752,640	£6	£16	£65	£175
1857 Ornamental trident	incl. above	£5	£16	£65	£175
1858/7 final 8 over 7	incl. above	£5	£14	£65	£175
1858/3 final 8 over 3	incl. above	£25	£80	£250	—
1858	1,599,040	£5	£15	£60	£150
1859	1,075,200	£8	£25	£80	£250
1860/59	32,256	£350	£900	£2700	—
Bronze					
1860 Beaded border	5,053,440	£25	£45	£150	£600
1860 Toothed border	incl. above	£5	£15	£50	£200
1860 — Piedfort flan	—			Extremely rare	
1861	36,449,280	£4	£10	£45	£175
1862	50,534,400	£4	£10	£45	£160
1862 8 over 6	incl. above			Extremely rare	
1863	28,062,720	£4	£8	£40	£160
1863 Die no below date	incl. above			Extremely rare	
1864 Plain 4	3,440,640	£20	£100	£500	£1200
1864 Crosslet 4	incl. above	£20	£90	£500	£1200
1865	8,601,600	£6	£15	£50	£280
1865/3 5 over 3	incl. above	£20	£70	£300	—
1866	9,999,360	£5	£15	£55	£300
1867	5,483,520	£5	£15	£75	£600
1868	1,182,720	£10	£60	£200	£550
1869	2,580,480	£100	£300	£1000	£3000
1870	5,695,022	£8	£30	£110	£350
1871	1,290,318	£30	£100	£400	£1500
1872	8,494,572	£6	£20	£50	£175
1873	8,494,200	£6	£20	£50	£175
1874	5,621,865	£6	£20	£50	£175
1874 H	6,666,240	£6	£20	£50	£175
1874 Later (older) bust	incl. above	£10	£25	£70	£275
1875	10,691,040	£6	£20	£65	£240
1875 H	752,640	£35	£110	£600	£1750
1876 H	11,074,560	£5	£12	£55	£180
1877	9,624,747	£5	£14	£55	£180
1878	2,764,470	£5	£14	£50	£180
1879	7,666,476	£4	£12	£50	£170
1880	3,000,831	£4	£12	£50	£180
1881	2,302,362	£5	£12	£50	£180
1881 H	3,763,200	£5	£12	£50	£170
1882 H	7,526,400	£5	£12	£50	£170
1882 no H	—			Extremely Rare	
1883	6,237,438	£5	£14	£50	£160
1884	11,702,802	£5	£14	£50	£160
1885	7,145,862	£4	£14	£50	£160
1886	6,087,759	£4	£14	£50	£160
1887	5,315,085	£4	£14	£50	£160
1888	5,125,020	£4	£14	£50	£160

Victoria copper penny

(N.B. Prices for Victoria Bun head coins will be considerably higher in mint with full lustre)

DATE	MINTAGE	F	VF	EF	UNC
1889	12,559,737	£4	£14	£50	£150
1890	15,330,840	£4	£14	£50	£140
1891	17,885,961	£4	£12	£50	£140
1892	10,501,671	£4	£12	£60	£160
1893	8,161,737	£4	£12	£45	£140
1894	3,883,452	£8	£30	£100	£275
OLD HEAD ISSUES					
1895 Trident 2mm from P(ENNY)	5,395,830	£6	£24	£80	£300
1895 Trident 1mm from P	incl. above	—	£2	£15	£60
1896	24,147,156	—	£2	£15	£60
1897	20,756,620	—	£2	£15	£55
1897 Raised dot after One (O·NE)		£75	£150	£400	—
1898	14,296,836	—	£2	£16	£55
1899	26,441,069	—	£2	£14	£45
1900	31,778,109	—	£2	£13	£35
1901	22,205,568	—	£2	£7	£25

EDWARD VII (1901–10)

1902	26,976,768	—	£1	£8	£25
1902 "Low tide" to sea line	incl. above	£2	£8	£35	£125
1903	21,415,296	—	£3	£15	£70
1904	12,913,152	—	£4	£20	£100
1905	17,783,808	—	£3	£15	£70
1906	37,989,504	—	£3	£15	£60
1907	47,322,240	—	£3	£15	£60
1908	31,506,048	—	£3	£18	£70
1909	19,617,024	—	£3	£20	£100
1910	29,549,184	—	£3	£15	£50

GEORGE V (1910–36)

1911	23,079,168	—	£3	£12	£35
1912	48,306,048	—	£3	£12	£35
1912 H	16,800,000	—	£3	£30	£160
1913	65,497,812	—	£3	£15	£60
1914	50,820,997	—	£3	£15	£55
1915	47,310,807	—	£3	£15	£60
1916	86,411,165	—	£3	£15	£45
1917	107,905,436	—	£3	£15	£40
1918	84,227,372	—	£3	£12	£40
1918 H	3,660,800	£1	£8	£80	£400
1918 KN	incl. above	£7	£70	£500	£1800
1919	113,761,090	—	£2	£15	£40
1919 H	5,209,600	£1	£10	£175	£600
1919 KN	incl. above	£8	£75	£600	£2000
1920	124,693,485	—	£2	£12	£30
1921	129,717,693	—	£2	£12	£30
1922	16,346,711	—	£2	£18	£70
1922 with reverse of 1927		£1000	£2500	—	—
1926	4,498,519	—	£6	£20	£90
1926 Modified effigy	incl above	£20	£90	£400	£1500
1927	60,989,561	—	£2	£8	£32
1928	50,178,00	—	£2	£8	£30
1929	49,132,800	—	£2	£8	£30
1930	29,097,600	—	£2	£15	£50
1931	19,843,200	—	£2	£8	£35
1932	8,277,600	—	£2	£10	£70
1933	Only 7 examples known				
1934	13,965,600	—	£2	£20	£50
1935	56,070,000	—	—	£2	£9
1936	154,296,000	—	—	£2	£8

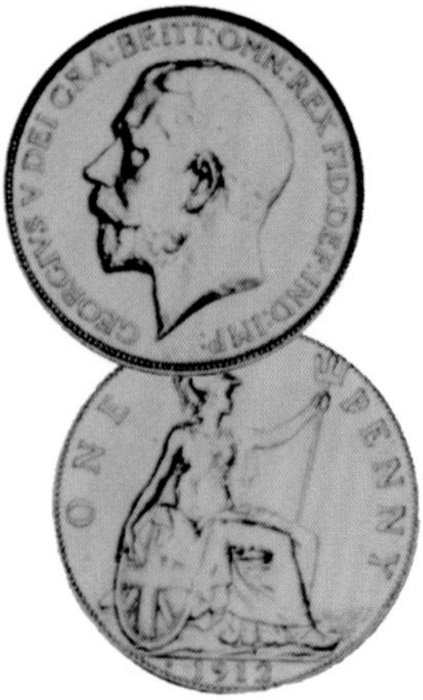

GEORGE VI (1936–52)

DATE	MINTAGE	F	VF	EF	UNC
1937	88,896,000	–	–	–	£3
1937 Proof	26,402	–	–	–	£6
1938	121,560,000	–	–	–	£3
1939	55,560,000	–	–	–	£4
1940	42,284,400	–	–	–	£12
1944 Mint Dark	42,600,000	–	–	–	£7
1945 Mint Dark	79,531,200	–	–	–	£7
1946 Mint Dark	66,855,600	–	–	–	£5
1947	52,220,400	–	–	–	£3
1948	63,961,200	–	–	–	£3
1949	14,324,400	–	–	–	£5
1950	240,000	£5	£12	£28	£45
1950 Proof	17,513	–	–	–	£25
1951	120,000	£18	£25	£45	£60
1951 Proof	20,000	–	–	–	£30

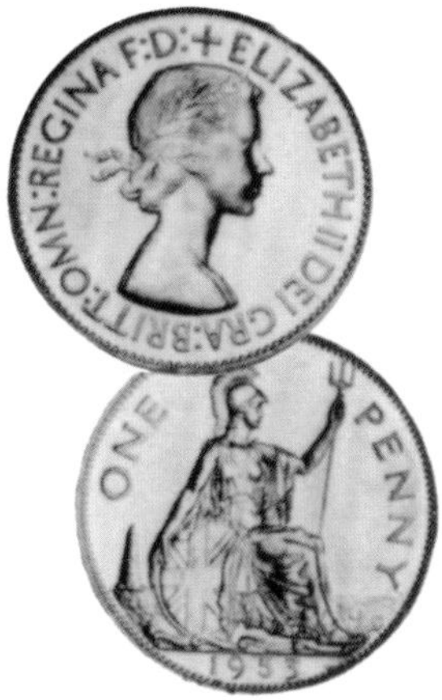

ELIZABETH II (1952–)

DATE	MINTAGE	F	VF	EF	UNC
1953	1,308,400	–	–	£1	£4
1953 Proof	40,000	–	–	–	£6
1954	Only one known				
1961	48,313,400	–	–	–	£1
1962	143,308,600	–	–	–	50p
1963	125,235,600	–	–	–	50p
1964	153,294,000	–	–	–	50p
1965	121,310,400	–	–	–	50p
1966	165,739,200	–	–	–	50p
1967	654,564,000	–	–	–	–

Later issues are included in the Decimal section.

HALFPENNIES

CHARLES II (1660–85)

DATE	F	VF	EF	UNC
1672	£60	£300	£1000	–
1672 CRAOLVS error		Extremely rare		
1673	£60	£300	£1000	–
1673 CRAOLVS error		Extremely rare		
1673 No rev. stop	£90	£500	–	–
1673 No stops on obv.		Extremely rare		
1675	£60	£500	£1050	–
1675 No stops on obv.	£70	£550	–	–
1675/3 5 over 3	£175	£600	–	–

JAMES II (1685–88)

DATE	F	VF	EF	UNC
1685 (tin)	£125	£600	£2750	–
1686 (tin)	£140	£600	£2750	–
1687 (tin)	£125	£600	£2750	–

WILLIAM & MARY (1688–94)

Tin

DATE	F	VF	EF	UNC
1689 Small draped busts, edge dated	£600	–	–	–
1690 Large cuirassed busts, edge dated	£150	£500	£2500	–
1691 — date on edge and in exergue	£150	£500	£2500	–
1692 — —	£150	£500	£2500	–

DATE	F	VF	EF	UNC
Copper				
1694 Large cuirassed busts, date in exergue ..	£50	£225	£1000	–
1694 – – GVLIEMVS error		Extremely rare		
1694 – – M! RI! error		Extremely rare		
1694 – – No stops on rev.		Extremely rare		

WILLIAM III (1694–1702)

DATE	F	VF	EF	UNC
1695 First issue (date in exergue).....................	£40	£130	£600	–
1695 – No stop after BRITANNIA on rev.........		Extremely rare		
1696 –	£35	£140	£600	–
1696 – TERTVS error		Extremely rare		
1697 –	£35	£125	£650	–
1697 – No stop after TERTIVS on obv.	£50	£200	–	–
1698 –	£40	£150	£700	–
1698 Second issue (date in legend)	£45	£180	–	–
1698 – No stop after date..............................	£45	£180	–	–
1699 –	£40	£140	£700	–
1699 – No stop after date..............................	£200	–	–	–
1699 Third issue (date in exergue) (Britannia with right hand on knee)......................................	£40	£150	£700	–
1699 – No stop after date..............................		Extremely rare		
1699 – BRIT! NNI! error	£200	–	–	–
1699 – TERTVS error		Extremely rare		
1699 – No stop on rev.		Extremely rare		
1699 – No stops on obv.................................	£90	£300	–	–
1700 –	£40	£140	£700	–
1700 – No stops on obv.................................	£100	£300	–	–
1700 – No stops after GVLIELMUS	£100	£300	–	–
1700 – BRITVANNIA error.............................		Extremely rare		
1700 – GVIELMS error..................................	£100	£300	–	–
1700 – GVLIEEMVS error	£100	£300	–	–
*1701 –	£40	£175	£650	–
1701 – BRIT! NNI! error	£70	£275	–	–
1701 – No stops on obv.................................		Extremely rare		
1701 – inverted As for Vs..............................	£70	£300	–	–

GEORGE I (1714–27)

DATE	F	VF	EF	UNC
1717 "Dump" issue	£40	£130	£600	
1718 –	£35	£130	£500	–
1719 Second issue..	£30	£130	£425	–
1720 –	£25	£130	£425	–
1721 –	£25	£100	£425	–
1721 – Stop after date...................................	£40	£140	–	–
1722 –	£30	£120	£425	–
1722 –inverted A for V on obv.		Extremely rare		
1723 –	£30	£120	£425	–
1723 –No stop on rev.	£80	£330	–	–
1724 –	£25	£120	£450	–

GEORGE II (1727–60)

DATE	F	VF	EF	UNC
1729 Young head	£25	£75	£325	–
1729 – No stop on rev.	£25	£75	£325	–
1730 –	£20	£75	£325	–
1730 – GEOGIVS error....................................	£60	£200	£600	–
1730 – Stop after date....................................	£25	£100	£350	–
1730 – No stop after REX on obv.	£30	£120	£400	–
1731 –	£20	£100	£300	–
1731 – No rev. stop..	£25	£100	£325	–
1732 –	£20	£90	£300	–
1732 – No rev. stop..	£25	£100	£325	–
1733 –	£20	£70	£300	–

DATE	MINTAGE	F	VF	EF	UNC
1734/3 — 4 over 3		£35	£190	—	—
1734 — No stop on obv.		£35	£190	—	—
1735 —		£20	£80	£300	—
1736 —		£20	£70	£300	—
1737 —		£20	£80	£300	—
1738 —		£20	£80	£300	—
1739 —		£18	£70	£250	—
1740 Old head		£15	£60	£220	—
1742 —		£15	£60	£220	—
1742/0 — 2 over 0		£22	£110	£325	—
1743 —		£15	£70	£225	—
1744 —		£15	£70	£225	—
1745 —		£15	£70	£225	—
1746 —		£15	£70	£225	—
1747 —		£15	£70	£225	—
1748 —		£15	£70	£225	—
1749 —		£15	£70	£225	—
1750 —		£15	£70	£225	—
1751 —		£15	£70	£225	—
1752 —		£15	£70	£225	—
1753 —		£15	£70	£225	—
1754 —		£15	£70	£225	—

GEORGE III (1760–1820)

DATE	MINTAGE	F	VF	EF	UNC
First type—Royal Mint					
1770		£18	£50	£250	—
1770 No stop on rev.		£25	£65	£300	—
1771		£10	£45	£250	—
1771 No stop on rev.		£20	£60	£260	—
1772 Error GEORIVS		£50	£150	£550	
1772		£10	£40	£175	—
1772 No stop on rev		£20	£60	£220	—
1773		£10	£35	£220	—
1773 No stop after REX		£25	£70	—	—
1773 No stop on rev.		£20	£60	£200	—
1774		£10	£30	£180	—
1775		£10	£30	£180	—
Second type—Soho Mint					
1799		£2	£7	£30	£80
Third type					
1806		£2	£7	£30	£80
1807		£2	£7	£30	£80

George III second type

GEORGE IV (1820–30)

DATE	MINTAGE	F	VF	EF	UNC
1825	215,040	£10	£35	£120	£250
1826 (varieties)	9,031,630	£10	£35	£120	£250
1826 Proof	—	—	—	—	£400
1827	5,376,000	£10	£25	£100	£200

WILLIAM IV (1830–37)

DATE	MINTAGE	F	VF	EF	UNC
1831	806,400	£8	£25	£80	£250
1831 Proof	—	—	—	—	£300
1834	537,600	£8	£25	£80	£250
1837	349,440	£8	£25	£80	£250

VICTORIA (1837–1901)

YOUNG HEAD ISSUES

Copper

DATE	MINTAGE	F	VF	EF	UNC
1838	456,960	£5	£16	£50	£150
1839 Proof	268,800	—	—	—	£300

DATE	MINTAGE	F	VF	EF	UNC
1841	1,075,200	£5	£16	£40	£130
1843	967,680	£25	£45	£140	£325
1844	1,075,200	£6	£18	£45	£160
1845	1,075,200	£50	£130	£650	—
1846	860,160	£8	£18	£60	£180
1847	725,640	£8	£18	£50	£170
1848	322,560	£8	£18	£50	£170
1848/7 final 8 OVER 7	incl. above	£8	£17	£50	£170
1851	215,040	£5	£15	£50	£165
1852	637,056	£7	£16	£50	£165
1853	1,559,040	£4	£8	£20	£60
1853/2 3 over 2	incl. above	£15	£25	£50	£160
1853 Proof	—	—	—	—	£225
1854	12,354,048	£4	£8	£30	£65
1855	1,455,837	£4	£8	£30	£65
1856	1,942,080	£8	£20	£55	£175
1857	1,820,720	£5	£14	£40	£80
1858	2,472,960	£4	£10	£30	£80
1858/7 final 8 over 7	incl. above	£4	£10	£30	£80
1858/6 final 8 over 6	incl. above	£4	£10	£30	£80
1859	1,290,240	£6	£16	£50	£150
1859/8 9 over 8	incl. above	£5	£15	£45	£140
1860	unrecorded	£750	£2000	£4000	£6500
Bronze					
1860 Beaded border	6,630,400	£3	£9	£35	£145
1860 Toothed border		£4	£12	£45	£175
1861	54,118,400	£3	£9	£35	£140
1862 Die letter A, B or C to left of lighthouse				Extremely rare	
1862	61,107,200	£3	£9	£35	£120
1863	15,948,800	£3	£9	£30	£120
1864	537,600	£3	£10	£40	£120
1865	8,064,000	£4	£18	£60	£160
1865/3 5 over 3	incl. above	£30	£75	£300	—
1866	2,508,800	£5	£15	£50	£150
1867	2,508,800	£5	£15	£45	£150
1868	3,046,400	£5	£12	£50	£160
1869	3,225,600	£8	£40	£100	£340
1870	4,350,739	£5	£15	£50	£200
1871	1,075,280	£75	£100	£300	£700
1872	4,659,410	£4	£10	£35	£120
1873	3,404,880	£4	£10	£35	£120
1874	1,347,655	£5	£25	£90	£230
1874 H	5,017,600	£3	£10	£50	£210
1875	5,430,815	£3	£8	£50	£160
1875 H	1,254,400	£4	£10	£40	£140
1876 H	5,809,600	£4	£10	£40	£140
1877	5,209,505	£3	£10	£40	£150
1878	1,425,535	£5	£20	£60	£140
1879	3,582,545	£3	£10	£35	£125
1880	2,423,465	£4	£12	£50	£160
1881	2,007,515	£4	£12	£35	£125
1881 H	1,792,000	£3	£10	£35	£125
1882 H	4,480,000	£3	£10	£35	£125
1883	3,000,725	£3	£10	£35	£120
1884	6,989,580	£3	£10	£35	£120
1885	8,600,574	£3	£10	£35	£120
1886	8,586,155	£3	£10	£35	£120
1887	10,701,305	£3	£10	£35	£120
1888	6,814,670	£3	£10	£35	£120
1889	7,748,234	£3	£10	£35	£120
1889/8 9 over 8	incl. above	£10	£30	£80	—
1890	11,254,235	£3	£10	£30	£120

Victoria copper halfpenny

Victoria bronze halfpenny

DATE	MINTAGE	F	VF	EF	UNC
1891	13,192,260	£3	£10	£30	£100
1892	2,478,335	£3	£10	£40	£125
1893	7,229,344	£3	£10	£30	£100
1894	1,767,635	£5	£10	£55	£190
OLD HEAD ISSUES					
1895	3,032,154	£1	£4	£15	£45
1896	9,142,500	£1	£4	£10	£40
1897	8,690,315	£1	£4	£10	£40
1898	8,595,180	£1	£4	£10	£40
1899	12,108,001	£1	£4	£10	£40
1900	13,805,190	£1	£4	£10	£35
1901	11,127,360	£1	£2	£8	£20

EDWARD VII (1901–10)

1902	13,672,960	£2	£4	£8	£25
1902 "Low tide"	incl. above	£8	£35	£100	£260
1903	11,450,880	£2	£5	£20	£45
1904	8,131,200	£2	£5	£20	£45
1905	10,124,800	£2	£5	£20	£45
1906	16,849,280	£2	£5	£20	£45
1907	16,849,280	£2	£5	£20	£45
1908	16,620,800	£2	£5	£20	£45
1909	8,279,040	£2	£5	£20	£45
1910	10,769,920	£2	£5	£20	£45

GEORGE V (1910–36)

1911	12,570,880	—	£3	£12	£30
1912	21,185,920	—	£2	£12	£30
1913	17,476,480	—	£2	£14	£35
1914	20,289,111	—	£2	£12	£35
1915	21,563,040	£1	£3	£15	£45
1916	39,386,143	—	£2	£12	£35
1917	38,245,436	—	£2	£12	£30
1918	22,321,072	—	£2	£12	£30
1919	28,104,001	—	£2	£12	£30
1920	35,146,793	—	£2	£12	£30
1921	28,027,293	—	£2	£12	£35
1922	10,734,964	—	£2	£15	£40
1923	12,266,282	—	£2	£12	£35
1924	13,971,038	—	£2	£10	£30
1925	12,216,123	—	£2	£10	£30
1925 Modified effigy	incl. above	£2	£5	£25	£65
1926	6,172,306	—	£2	£10	£35
1927	15,589,622	—	£2	£10	£30
1928	20,935,200	—	£2	£8	£25
1929	25,680,000	—	£2	£8	£25
1930	12,532,800	—	£2	£8	£25
1931	16,137,600	—	£2	£8	£25
1932	14,448,000	—	£2	£8	£25
1933	10,560,000	—	£2	£8	£25
1934	7,704,000	—	£2	£12	£32
1935	12,180,000	—	£1	£6	£16
1936	23,008,800	—	£1	£5	£10

GEORGE VI (1936–52)

1937	24,504,000	—	—	£1	£3
1937 Proof	26,402	—	—	£1	£10
1938	40,320,000	—	—	£1	£5
1939	28,924,800	—	—	£1	£5

DATE	MINTAGE	F	VF	EF	UNC
1940	32,162,400	—	—	£1	£8
1941	45,120,000	—	—	£1	£7
1942	71,908,800	—	—	£1	£4
1943	76,200,000	—	—	£1	£4
1944	81,840,000	—	—	£1	£4
1945	57,000,000	—	—	£1	£4
1946	22,725,600	—	—	£1	£5
1947	21,266,400	—	—	£1	£4
1948	26,947,200	—	—	£1	£3
1949	24,744,000	—	—	£1	£3
1950	24,153,600	—	—	£1	£4
1950 Proof	17,513	—	—	£1	£6
1951	14,868,000	—	—	£1	£5
1951 Proof	20,000	—	—	£1	£6
1952	33,78,400	—	—	£1	£3

ELIZABETH II (1952–)

DATE	MINTAGE	F	VF	EF	UNC
1953	8,926,366	—	—	—	£1
1953 Proof	40,000	—	—	—	£3
1954	19,375,000	—	—	—	£3
1955	18,799,200	—	—	—	£3
1956	21,799,200	—	—	—	£3
1957	43,684,800	—	—	—	£1
1958	62,318,400	—	—	—	£1
1959	79,176,000	—	—	—	£1
1960	41,340,000	—	—	—	£1
1962	41,779,200	—	—	—	£1
1963	45,036,000	—	—	—	20p
1964	78,583,200	—	—	—	20p
1965	98,083,200	—	—	—	20p
1966	95,289,600	—	—	—	20p
1967	146,491,200	—	—	—	10p

Later issues are included in the Decimal section.

FARTHINGS

OLIVER CROMWELL

DATE	F	VF	EF	UNC
Undated (copper) Draped bust, shield rev. Variations			Extremely rare	

CHARLES II (1660–85)

DATE	F	VF	EF	UNC
Copper				
1672	£40	£200	£700	—
1673	£40	£200	£650	—
1673 CAROLA for CAROLO error	£75	£375	—	—
1673 No stops on obv.			Extremely rare	
1673 No stop on rev.			Extremely rare	
1674	£40	£200	£650	—
1675	£40	£175	£650	—
1675 No stop after CAROLVS			Extremely rare	
1679	£55	£250	£750	—
1679 No stop on rev.	£60	£300	—	—
Tin				
1684 with date on edge	£200	£500	—	—
1685 —			Extremely rare	

DATE	F	VF	EF	UNC
JAMES II (1685–88)				
1684 (tin) Cuirassed bust			Extremely rare	
1685 (tin) —	£150	£550	£1800	—
1686 (tin) —	£150	£550	£1800	—
1687 (tin) —			Extremely rare	
1687 (tin) Draped bust	£200	£750	—	—
WILLIAM & MARY (1688–94)				
1689 (tin) Small draped busts	£600	—	—	—
1689 (tin) — with edge date 1690			Extremely rare	
1690 (tin) Large cuirassed busts	£150	£500	£2400	—
1690 (tin) — with edge date 1689			Extremely rare	
1691 (tin) —	£160	£550	—	—
1692 (tin) —	£150	£500	£2400	—
1694 (copper) —	£50	£200	£700	—
1694 No stop after MARI!			Extremely rare	
1694 No stop on obv.			Extremely rare	
1694 No stop on rev.			Extremely rare	
1694 Unbarred As in BRITANNIA			Extremely rare	
WILLIAM III (1694–1702)				
1695 First issue (date in exergue)	£40	£175	£650	—
1695 — GVLIELMV error			Extremely rare	
1696 —	£40	£175	£650	—
1697 —	£40	£175	£600	—
1697 — GVLIELMS error			Extremely rare	
1698 —	£200	£650	—	—
1698 Second issue (date in legend)	£50	£250	£750	—
1699 First issue	£40	£200	£650	—
1699 Second issue	£40	£200	£650	—
1699 — No stop after date	£50	£250	—	—
1700 First issue	£35	£125	£575	—
1700 — error RRITANNIA			Extremely rare	
ANNE (1702–14)				
1714	£300	£525	£925	—
GEORGE I (1714–27)				
1717 First small "Dump" issue	£125	£400	£900	—
1718 1 Known				—
1719 Second issue	£30	£120	£425	—
1719 — No stop on rev.	£70	£350	—	—
1719 — No stops on obv.	£70	£350	—	—
1720 —	£30	£120	£450	—
1721 —	£25	£120	£450	—
1721/0 — Last 1 over 0	£40	£130	—	—
1722 —	£30	£110	£425	—
1723 —	£30	£110	£450	—
1723 — R over sideways R in REX			Extremely rare	
1724 —	£30	£120	£450	—
GEORGE II (1727–60)				
1730 Young head	£15	£60	£275	—
1731 —	£15	£60	£275	—
1732 —	£15	£75	£300	—
1733 —	£15	£65	£300	—
1734 —	£15	£60	£300	—
1734 — No stop on obv.	£30	£100	£350	—

George I, first type

George I second type

DATE	MINTAGE	F	VF	EF	UNC
1735 —		£15	£60	£275	—
1735 — 3 over 5		£20	£90	£325	—
1736 —		£12	£60	£275	—
1737 —		£12	£55	£275	—
1739 —		£12	£55	£275	—
1741 Old Head		£12	£50	£260	—
1744 —		£11	£50	£275	—
1746 —		£11	£50	£275	—
1746 — V over LL in GEORGIVS			Extremely rare		
1749 —		£15	£50	£225	—
1750 —		£15	£45	£210	—
1754 —		£9	£30	£175	—
1754 — 4 over 0		£25	£80	£300	—

GEORGE III (1760–1820)

DATE	MINTAGE	F	VF	EF	UNC
1771 First (London) issue		£20	£60	£250	—
1773 —		£11	£40	£170	—
1773 — No stop on rev.		£18	£50	£200	—
1773 — No stop after REX		£25	£70	£200	
1774 —		£10	£40	£175	
1775 —		£10	£40	£175	—
1797 Second (Soho Mint) issue				Patterns only	
1799 Third (Soho Mint) issue		£2	£8	£40	£85
1806 Fourth (Soho Mint) issue		£2	£8	£40	£85
1807 —		£2	£8	£40	£85

George III, third (Soho Mint) issue

GEORGE IV (1820–30)

DATE	MINTAGE	F	VF	EF	UNC
1821 First bust (laureate, draped), first reverse (date in exergue)	2,688,000	£3	£10	£60	£110
1822 —	5,924,350	£3	£10	£60	£110
1823 —	2,365,440	£4	£10	£60	£110
1823 I for 1 in date	incl. above	£15	£70	£250	£110
1825 —	4,300.800	£4	£10	£60	£110
1826 —	6,666,240	£4	£10	£60	£110
1826 Second bust (couped, date below), second reverse (ornament in exergue)	incl. above	£4	£10	£60	£110
1826 — Proof	—	—	—	—	£250
1827 —	2,365,440	£4	£10	£55	£140
1828 —	2,365,440	£4	£11	£60	£140
1829 —	1,505,280	£4	£11	£60	£140
1830 —	2,365,440	£4	£10	£55	£140

George III, fourth (Soho Mint) issue

WILLIAM IV (1830–37)

DATE	MINTAGE	F	VF	EF	UNC
1831	2,688,000	£5	£12	£45	£120
1831 Proof	—	—	—	—	£300
1834	1,935,360	£5	£12	£45	£120
1835	1.720,320	£5	£12	£45	£120
1836	1,290.240	£5	£12	£50	£120
1837	3.010,560	£5	£12	£45	£135

VICTORIA (1837–1901)

FIRST YOUNG HEAD (COPPER) ISSUES

DATE	MINTAGE	F	VF	EF	UNC
1838	591,360	£4	£15	£40	£125
1839	4,300,800	£4	£15	£40	£125
1839 Proof	—	—	—	—	£300
1840	3,010,560	£4	£15	£40	£100
1841	1,720,320	£4	£15	£40	£125
1841 Proof				Extremely rare	
1842	1,290,240	£8	£25	£90	£275

DATE	MINTAGE	F	VF	EF	UNC
1843..	4,085,760	£5	£12	£40	£125
1843 I for 1 in date		£50	£275	—	—
1844..	430,080	£50	£110	£500	£1500
1845..	3,225,600	£6	£10	£40	£100
1846..	2,580,480	£6	£18	£50	£140
1847..	3,879,720	£5	£10	£45	£100
1848..	1,290,240	£5	£10	£45	£100
1849..	645,120	£25	£70	£260	£550
1850..	430,080	£5	£10	£35	£90
1851..	1,935,360	£6	£20	£60	£200
1851 D over sideways D in DEI ...	incl. above	£25	£50	£200	—
1852..	822,528	£7	£20	£50	£150
1853..	1,028,628	£4	£7	£30	£60
1853 Proof.................................	—	—	—	—	£450
1854..	6,504,960	£4	£10	£35	£55
1855..	3,440,640	£4	£10	£35	£55
1856..	1,771,392	£8	£20	£60	£180
1856 R over E in VICTORIA.........	incl. above	£20	£50	£140	—
1857..	1,075,200	£4	£10	£35	£70
1858..	1,720,320	£4	£10	£35	£70
1859..	1,290,240	£10	£25	£65	£200
1860..	unrecorded	£800	£2000	£5000	—
SECOND YOUNG OR "BUN" HEAD (BRONZE) ISSUES					
1860 Toothed border...................	2,867,200	£2	£5	£40	£100
1860 Beaded border	incl. above	£3	£7	£40	£110
1860 Toothed/Beaded border mule	incl. above			Extremely rare	
1861..	8,601,600	£2	£5	£35	£100
1862..	14,336,000	£1	£5	£35	£100
1862 Large 8 in date....................	incl. above			Extremely rare	
1863..	1,433,600	£20	£50	£175	£450
1864..	2,508,800	£1	£5	£30	£90
1865..	4,659,200	£1	£5	£30	£80
1865 5 over 2.............................	incl. above	£10	£18	£40	—
1866..	3,584,000	£1	£5	£25	£85
1867..	5,017,600	£1	£5	£25	£85
1868..	4,851,210	£1	£5	£25	£85
1869..	3,225,600	£1	£8	£35	£120
1872..	2,150,400	£1	£5	£25	£70
1873..	3,225,620	£1	£5	£25	£70
1874 H.....................................	3,584,000	£1	£5	£25	£100
1874 H both Gs over sideways G	incl. above	£150	£275	£800	—
1875..	712,760	£3	£10	£35	£100
1875 H.....................................	6,092,800	£1	£5	£20	£70
1876 H.....................................	1,175,200	£3	£12	£50	£130
1878..	4,008,540	£1	£4	£20	£70
1879..	3,977,180	£1	£4	£20	£70
1880..	1,842,710	£1	£4	£20	£70
1881..	3,494,670	£1	£4	£20	£70
1881 H.....................................	1,792,000	£1	£4	£20	£70
1882 H.....................................	1,792,000	£1	£5	£20	£70
1883..	1,128,680	£4	£15	£55	£125
1884..	5,782,000	£1	£4	£20	£40
1885..	5,442,308	£1	£4	£20	£40
1886..	7.707,790	£1	£4	£20	£40
1887..	1,340,800	£1	£4	£20	£40
1888..	1,887,250	£1	£4	£20	£40
1890..	2,133,070	£1	£4	£20	£40
1891..	4,959,690	£1	£4	£20	£40
1892..	887,240	£2	£10	£50	£110
1893..	3,904,320	£1	£4	£20	£40

Victoria Young Head first (copper) issue

Victoria Young Head second (bronze) issue

DATE	MINTAGE	F	VF	EF	UNC
1894	2,396,770	£1	£4	£20	£40
1895	2,852,852	£10	£25	£70	£175

OLD HEAD ISSUES

DATE	MINTAGE	F	VF	EF	UNC
1895 Bright finish	incl. above	£1	£2	£16	£35
1896 —	3,668,610	£1	£2	£16	£25
1897 —	4,579,800	£1	£2	£16	£25
1897 Dark finish	incl. above	£1	£2	£16	£25
1898 —	4,010,080	£1	£2	£16	£25
1899 —	3,864,616	£1	£2	£16	£25
1900 —	5,969,317	£1	£2	£16	£25
1901 —	8,016,460	£1	£2	£10	£20

EDWARD VII (1901–10)

DATE	MINTAGE	F	VF	EF	UNC
1902	5,125,120	50p	£1	£10	£15
1903	5,331,200	50p	£1	£12	£20
1904	3,628,800	£2	£5	£18	£40
1905	4,076,800	£1	£2	£12	£30
1906	5,340,160	50p	£1	£12	£25
1907	4,399,360	50p	£1	£10	£20
1908	4,264,960	50p	£1	£10	£20
1909	8,852,480	50p	£1	£10	£20
1910	2,298,400	£2	£8	£20	£60

GEORGE V (1910–36)

DATE	MINTAGE	F	VF	EF	UNC
1911	5,196,800	25p	50p	£5	£10
1912	7,669,760	25p	50p	£8	£10
1913	4,184,320	25p	50p	£5	£10
1914	6,126,988	25p	50p	£4	£10
1915	7,129,255	25p	50p	£4	£12
1916	10,993,325	25p	50p	£4	£10
1917	21,434,844	25p	50p	£4	£10
1918	19,362,818	25p	50p	£4	£10
1919	15,089,425	25p	50p	£4	£10
1920	11,480,536	25p	50p	£4	£8
1921	9,469,097	25p	50p	£4	£8
1922	9,956,983	25p	50p	£4	£8
1923	8,034,457	25p	50p	£4	£8
1924	8,733,414	25p	50p	£4	£8
1925	12,634,697	25p	50p	£4	£8
1926 Modified effigy	9,792,397	25p	50p	£4	£8
1927	7,868,355	25p	50p	£4	£8
1928	11,625,600	25p	50p	£4	£8
1929	8,419,200	25p	50p	£4	£8
1930	4,195,200	25p	50p	£4	£8
1931	6,595,200	25p	50p	£4	£8
1932	9,292,800	25p	50p	£4	£8
1933	4,560,000	25p	50p	£4	£8
1934	3,052,800	25p	50p	£4	£8
1935	2.227,200	£1	£3	£10	£22
1936	9,734,400	25p	50p	£3	£6

GEORGE VI (1936–52)

DATE	MINTAGE	F	VF	EF	UNC
1937	8,131,200	—	—	50p	£1
1937 Proof	26,402	—	—	£1	£4
1938	7,449,600	—	—	£1	£6
1939	31,440,000	—	—	50p	£1
1940	18,360,000	—	—	50p	£1
1941	27,312,000	—	—	50p	£1
1942	28,857,600	—	—	50p	£1
1943	33,345,600	—	—	50p	£1

DATE	MINTAGE	F	VF	EF	UNC
1944	25,137,600	—	—	50p	£1
1945	23,736,000	—	—	50p	£1
1946	24,364,800	—	—	50p	£1
1947	14,745,600	—	—	50p	£1
1948	16,622,400	—	—	50p	£1
1949	8,424,000	—	—	50p	£1
1950	10,324,800	—	—	50p	£1
1950 Proof	17,513	—	—	50p	£8
1951	14,016,000	—	—	50p	£1
1951 Proof	20,000	—	—	50p	£8
1952	5,251,200	—	—	50p	£1

ELIZABETH II (1952–)

DATE	MINTAGE	F	VF	EF	UNC
1953	6,131,037	—	—	—	£1
1953 Proof	40,000	—	—	—	£5
1954	6,566,400	—	—	—	£1
1955	5,779,200	—	—	—	£1
1956	1,996,800	—	50p	£1	£3

HALF FARTHINGS

GEORGE IV (1820–30)

DATE	MINTAGE	F	VF	EF	UNC
1828 (two different obverses) (issued for Ceylon)	7,680,000	£9	£20	£50	£130
1830 (large or small date) (issued for Ceylon)	8,766,320	£9	£20	£45	£125

WILLIAM IV (1830–37)

DATE	MINTAGE	F	VF	EF	UNC
1837 (issued for Ceylon)	1,935,360	£20	£55	£140	£225

VICTORIA (1837–1901)

DATE	MINTAGE	F	VF	EF	UNC
1839	2,042,880	£5	£10	£30	£75
1842	unrecorded	£4	£8	£25	£75
1843	3,440,640	£3	£6	£20	£45
1844	6,451,200	£3	£6	£15	£45
1844 E over N in REGINA	incl. above	£10	£45	£100	—
1847	3,010,560	£6	£12	£30	£65
1851	unrecorded	£5	£12	£35	£90
1851 5 over 0	unrecorded	£8	£20	£60	£135
1852	989,184	£5	£12	£40	£90
1853	955,224	£5	£15	£50	£110
1853 Proof	incl. above	—	—	—	£200
1854	677,376	£8	£25	£70	£150
1856	913,920	£8	£25	£70	£150
1868	unrecorded	—	—	—	Rare
1868	unrecorded	—	—	—	Rare

THIRD FARTHINGS

GEORGE IV (1820–30)

DATE	MINTAGE	F	VF	EF	UNC
1827 (issued for Malta)	unrecorded	£7	£15	£45	£110

WILLIAM IV (1830–37)

DATE	MINTAGE	F	VF	EF	UNC
1835 (issued for Malta)	unrecorded	£7	£16	£45	£125

VICTORIA (1837–1901)

DATE	MINTAGE	F	VF	EF	UNC
1844 (issued for Malta)	1,301,040	£10	£24	£70	£170
1844 RE for REG	incl. above	£30	£60	£250	—
1866	576,000	£6	£14	£30	£60
1868	144,000	£6	£14	£30	£60
1876	162,000	£6	£14	£30	£60
1878	288,000	£6	£14	£30	£60
1881	144,000	£6	£14	£30	£60
1884	144,000	£6	£14	£30	£60
1885	288,000	£6	£14	£30	£60

EDWARD VII (1902–10)

DATE	MINTAGE	F	VF	EF	UNC
1902 (issued for Malta)	288,000	£3	£7	£20	£35

GEORGE V (1911–36)

DATE	MINTAGE	F	VF	EF	UNC
1913 (issued for Malta)	288,000	£3	£7	£20	£35

QUARTER FARTHINGS

VICTORIA (1837–1901)

DATE	MINTAGE	F	VF	EF	UNC
1839 (issued for Ceylon)	3,840,000	£25	£40	£80	£160
1851 (issued for Ceylon)	2,215,680	£25	£40	£80	£160
1852 (issued for Ceylon)	incl. above	£25	£40	£80	£160
1853 (issued for Ceylon)	incl. above	£25	£40	£80	£160
1853 Proof	—	—	—	—	£450

EMERGENCY ISSUES

GEORGE III (1760–1820)

To alleviate the shortage of circulating coinage during the Napoleonic Wars the Bank of England firstly authorised the countermarking of other countries' coins, enabling them to pass as English currency. The coins, countermarked with punches depicting the head of George III, were mostly Spanish American 8 reales of Charles III. Although this had limited success it was later decided to completely overstrike the coins with a new English design on both sides—specimens that still show traces of the original host coin's date are avidly sought after by collectors. This overstriking continued for a number of years although all the known coins are dated 1804. Finally, in 1811 the Bank of England issued silver tokens which continued up to 1816 when a completely new regal coinage was introduced.

DATE	F	VF	EF	UNC
DOLLAR				
Oval countermark of George III				
On "Pillar" type 8 reales	£175	£650	£1000	–
*On "Portrait" type............	£200	£350	£750	–
Octagonal countermark of George III				
On "Portrait" type.............	£200	£600	£850	–
HALF DOLLAR				
Oval countermark of George III				
On "Portrait" type 4 reales	£200	£400	£850	–
FIVE SHILLINGS OR ONE DOLLAR				
These coins were overstruck on Spanish-American coins				
1804..................................	£100	£250	£450	–

— With details of original coin still visible add from 10%.

BANK OF ENGLAND TOKENS

DATE	F	VF	EF	UNC
THREE SHILLINGS				
1811 Draped bust..............	£35	£50	£100	–
1812 –.............................	£35	£50	£125	–
1812 Laureate bust	£35	£50	£100	–
1813 –.............................	£35	£50	£100	–
1814 –.............................	£35	£50	£100	–
1815 –.............................	£35	£50	£100	–
1816 –.............................	£125	£250	£850	–
ONE SHILLING AND SIXPENCE				
1811 Draped bust..............	£20	£45	£75	£145
1812 –.............................	£20	£45	£75	£145
1812 Laureate bust	£20	£45	£75	£145
1812 Proof in platinum				Unique
1813 –.............................	£20	£35	£65	£130
1813 Proof in platinum				Unique
1814 –.............................	£20	£35	£65	£130
1815 –.............................	£20	£35	£65	£130
1816 –.............................	£20	£35	£65	£130
NINEPENCE				
1812 Pattern only	–	–	Very Rare	

MAUNDY SETS

CHARLES II (1660–85)

DATE	F	VF	EF	UNC
Undated	£175	£300	£650	–
1670	£160	£285	£625	–
1671	£150	£260	£600	–
1672	£150	£260	£625	–
1673	£150	£250	£600	–
1674	£155	£260	£615	–
1675	£150	£260	£600	–
1676	£170	£285	£625	–
1677	£140	£250	£575	–
1678	£210	£400	£725	–
1679	£170	£280	£625	–
1680	£160	£255	£600	–
1681	£185	£275	£650	–
1682	£165	£275	£600	–
1683	£165	£275	£625	–
1684	£200	£350	£675	–

JAMES II (1685–88)

DATE	F	VF	EF	UNC
1686	£175	£3000	£625	–
1687	£175	£300	£640	–
1688	£190	£330	£650	–

WILLIAM & MARY (1688–94)

DATE	F	VF	EF	UNC
1689	£600	£800	£1400	–
1691	£575	£775	£1300	–
1692	£485	£700	£1200	–
1693	£350	£575	£1000	–
1694	£315	£475	£850	–

WILLIAM III (1694–1702)

DATE	F	VF	EF	UNC
1698	£200	£360	£745	–
1699	£425	£625	£1150	–
1700	£220	£375	£775	–
1701	£195	£360	£750	–

ANNE (1702–14)

DATE	F	VF	EF	UNC
1703	£165	£320	£600	–
1705	£150	£290	£575	–
1706	£140	£275	£550	–
1708	£475	£650	£1200	–
1709	£195	£325	£700	–
1710	£200	£360	£675	–
1713	£160	£325	£600	–

Sets in contemporary dated boxes are usually worth a higher premium. For example approximately £20 can be added to sets from Victoria to George VI in contemporary undated boxes and above £25 for dated boxes.

GEORGE I (1714–27)

DATE	MINTAGE	F	VF	EF	UNC
1723		£170	£340	£675	–
1727		£165	£325	£650	–

GEORGE II (1727–60)

DATE	MINTAGE	F	VF	EF	UNC
1729		£140	£245	£525	–
1731		£140	£250	£525	–
1732		£135	£240	£500	–
1735		£130	£235	£500	–
1737		£135	£245	£515	–
1739		£130	£235	£490	–
1740		£125	£230	£475	–
1743		£200	£330	£700	–
1746		£120	£220	£450	–
1760		£140	£235	£475	–

GEORGE III (1760–1820)

DATE	MINTAGE	F	VF	EF	UNC
1763		£120	£220	£385	–
1763 Proof		–		Extremely rare	
1766		£130	£220	£425	–
1772		£130	£230	£425	–
1780		£125	£225	£400	–
1784		£130	£225	£410	–
1786		£130	£230	£410	–
1792 Wire		£175	£300	£495	£675
1795		£90	£140	£215	£325
1800		£85	£125	£200	£310
New Coinage					
1817		£110	£155	£220	£360
1818		£105	£140	£215	£345
1820		£110	£150	£215	£355

GEORGE IV (1820–30)

DATE	MINTAGE	F	VF	EF	UNC
1822		–	£115	£190	£325
1823		–	£105	£190	£315
1824		–	£110	£190	£315
1825		–	£105	£180	£315
1826		–	£105	£180	£315
1827		–	£105	£180	£315
1828		–	£105	£180	£315
1828 Proof		–	–	–	£2700
1829		–	£105	£180	£315
1830		–	£110	£180	£315

WILLIAM IV (1830–37)

DATE	MINTAGE	F	VF	EF	UNC
1831		–	£120	£200	£350
1831 Proof		–	–	–	£850
1831 Proof Gold		–	–		£26000
1832		–	£120	£210	£350
1833		–	£120	£200	£340
1834		–	£125	£210	£350
1835		–	£120	£200	£340
1836		–	£125	£210	£360
1837		–	£140	£220	£375

VICTORIA (1837–1901)

YOUNG HEAD ISSUES

DATE	MINTAGE	EF	UNC
1838	4,158	£145	£250
1838 Proof	unrecorded		£1700
1838 Proof Gold			£22,000
1839	4,125	£150	£275
1839 Proof	unrecorded	£350	£725
1840	4,125	£190	£295
1841	2,574	£210	£375
1842	4,125	£215	£400
1843	4,158	£150	£275
1844	4,158	£200	£350
1845	4,158	£130	£250
1846	4,158	£385	£700
1847	4,158	£385	£625
1848	4,158	£380	£625
1849	4,158	£225	£360
1850	4,158	£155	£275
1851	4,158	£165	£290
1852	4,158	£425	£625
1853	4,158	£450	£700
1853 Proof	unrecorded		£1000
1854	4,158	£160	£285
1855	4,158	£170	£315
1856	4,158	£140	£250
1857	4,158	£165	£300
1858	4,158	£145	£250
1859	4,158	£130	£235
1860	4,158	£150	£280
1861	4,158	£140	£255
1862	4,158	£155	£270
1863	4,158	£175	£335
1864	4,158	£155	£245
1865	4,158	£155	£260
1866	4,158	£150	£260
1867	4,158	£135	£255
1867 Proof	unrecorded	–	£1500
1868	4,158	£135	£230
1869	4,158	£175	£300
1870	4,458	£125	£210
1871	4,488	£125	£200
1871 Proof	unrecorded	–	£1600
1872	4,328	£115	£190
1873	4,162	£115	£180
1874	4,488	£115	£180
1875	4,154	£115	£180
1876	4,488	£115	£175
1877	4,488	£110	£170
1878	4,488	£110	£165
1878 Proof	unrecorded	–	£1500
1879	4,488	£110	£170
1879 Proof	unrecorded	–	£2100
1880	4,488	£110	£170
1881	4,488	£110	£175
1881 Proof	unrecorded	–	£1500
1882	4,146	£125	£205
1882 Proof	unrecorded	–	£1500
1883	4,488	£95	£160
1884	4,488	£95	£160
1885	4,488	£95	£160
1886	4,488	£95	£160
1887	4,488	£120	£185

JUBILEE HEAD ISSUES

DATE	MINTAGE	EF	UNC
1888	4,488	£105	£160
1888 Proof	unrecorded	–	£1400
1889	4,488	£100	£155
1890	4,488	£105	£160
1891	4,488	£100	£155
1892	4,488	£110	£165

OLD HEAD ISSUES

DATE	MINTAGE	EF	UNC
1893	8,976	£65	£110
1894	8,976	£80	£115
1895	8,976	£70	£110
1896	8,976	£70	£110
1897	8,976	£70	£110
1898	8,976	£70	£110
1899	8,976	£70	£110
1900	8,976	£65	£105
1901	8,976	£65	£105

EDWARD VII (1902–110)

DATE	MINTAGE	EF	UNC
1902	8,976	£55	£100
1902 Matt proof	15,123	–	£105
1903	8,976	£60	£105
1904	8,976	£70	£110
1905	8,976	£70	£110
1906	8,800	£65	£105
1907	8,760	£60	£105
1908	8,769	£60	£105
1909	1,983	£105	£170
1910	1,440	£110	£180

GEORGE V (1911–136)

DATE	MINTAGE	EF	UNC
1911	1,786	£85	£135
1911 Proof	6,007	–	£145
1912	1,246	£90	£145
1913	1,228	£85	£145
1914	982	£110	£155
1915	1,293	£90	£145
1916	1,128	£90	£145
1917	1,237	£90	£145
1918	1,375	£90	£145
1919	1,258	£90	£145
1920	1,399	£90	£150
1921	1,386	£95	£150
1922	1,373	£90	£150
1923	1,430	£90	£145
1924	1,515	£95	£145
1925	1,438	£90	£145
1926	1,504	£90	£150
1927	1,647	£95	£145
1928	1,642	£95	£150
1929	1,761	£95	£150
1930	1,724	£90	£145
1931	1,759	£90	£145
1932	1,835	£90	£145
1933	1,872	£90	£145
1934	1,887	£90	£145
1935	1,928	£95	£150
1936	1,323	£110	£170

GEORGE VI (1936–52)

DATE	MINTAGE	EF	UNC
1937	1,325	£80	£125
1937 Proof	20,900	£80	£125
1938	1,275	£90	£145
1939	1,234	£90	£145
1940	1,277	£90	£145
1941	1,253	£90	£155
1942	1,231	£90	£145
1943	1,239	£90	£145
1944	1,259	£90	£145

DATE AND PLACE OF ISSUE	MINTAGE		UNC
1945	1,355	£90	£145
1946	1,365	£90	£145
1947	1,375	£90	£150
1948	1,385	£95	£155
1949	1,395	£95	£155
1950	1,405	£95	£155
1951	1,468	£95	£155
1952	1,012	£115	£165

ELIZABETH II (1952–)

DATE AND PLACE OF ISSUE	MINTAGE		UNC
1953 St. Paul's Cathedral	1,025	—	£600
1953 Proof in gold	unrecorded		Ex. rare
1953 Proof Matt			Very rare
1954 Westminster Abbey	1,020	—	£125
1955 Southwark Cathedral	1,036	—	£125
1955 Proof Matt		—	£1800
1956 Westminster Abbey	1,088	—	£125
1957 St. Albans Cathedral	1,094	—	£125
1958 Westminster Abbey	1,100	—	£125
1959 St. George's Chapel, Windsor	1,106	—	£125
1960 Westminster Abbey	1,112	—	£125
1961 Rochester Cathedral	1,118	—	£125
1962 Westminster Abbey	1,125	—	£125
1963 Chelmsford Cathedral	1,131	—	£125
1964 Westminster Abbey	1,137	—	£125
1965 Canterbury Cathedral	1,143	—	£125
1966 Westminster Abbey	1,206	—	£125
1967 Durham Cathedral	986	—	£130
1968 Westminster Abbey	964	—	£130
1969 Selby Cathedral	1,002	—	£125
1970 Westminster Abbey	980	—	£130
1971 Tewkesbury Abbey	1,018		£115
1972 York Minster	1,026		£125
1973 Westminster Abbey	1,004		£115
1974 Salisbury Cathedral	1,042		£115
1975 Peterborough Cathedral	1,050		£115
1976 Hereford Cathedral	1,158		£120
1977 Westminster Abbey	1,138		£130
1978 Carlisle Cathedral	1,178		£120
1979 Winchester Cathedral	1,188		£115
1980 Worcester Cathedral	1,198		£115
1981 Westminster Abbey	1,178		£115
1982 St David's Cathedral	1,218		£115
1983 Exeter Cathedral	1,228		£115
1984 Southwell Minster	1,238		£115
1985 Ripon Cathedral	1,248		£115
1986 Chichester Cathedral	1,378		£115
1987 Ely Cathedral	1,390		£125
1988 Lichfield Cathedral	1,402		£125
1989 Birmingham Cathedral	1,353		£125
1990 Newcastle Cathedral	1,523		£130
1991 Westminster Abbey	1,384		£130
1992 Chester Cathedral	1,424		£130
1993 Wells Cathedral	1,440		£130
1994 Truro Cathedral	1,433		£130
1995 Coventry Cathedral	1,466		£130
1996 Norwich Cathedral	1,629		£130
1997 Birmingham Cathedral	1,786		£130
1998 Portsmouth Cathedral	1,654		£130
1999 Bristol Cathedral	1,676		£130
2000 Lincoln Cathedral	1,686		£140
2000 Silver Proof	13,180		£140
2001 Westminster Abbey	1,132		£150
2002 Canterbury Cathedral	1,681		£150
2002 Gold Proof	2,000		£150
2003 Gloucester Cathedral	1,608		£150
2004 Liverpool Cathedral	1,613		£150
2005 Wakefield Cathedral	1,685		£160
2006 Guildford Cathedral	1,937		£160
2006 Silver Proof	—		£170
2007 Manchester Cathedral	1,822		£170
2008 St Patrick's Cathedral (Armagh)	1,833		£200
2009 St. Edmundsbury Cathedral	—		—

Despite the decimalisation of the coinage in 1971, in keeping with ancient tradition the Royal Maundy sets are still made up of four silver coins (4p, 3p, 2p and 1p). The designs for the reverse of the coins are a crowned numeral in a wreath of oak leaves—basically the same design that has been used for Maundy coins since Charles II.

MAUNDY ODDMENTS SINGLE COINS

It is nowadays considered that the early small denomination silver coins 4d–1d were originally struck for the Maundy ceremony although undoubtedly many subsequently circulated as small change—therefore they are listed here under "Maundy silver single coins".

FOUR PENCE

CHARLES II (1660–85)

DATE	F	VF	EF
Undated	£45	£70	£135
1670	£45	£75	£140
1671	£35	£65	£125
1672/1	£35	£65	£125
1673	£40	£70	£125
1674	£40	£70	£125
1674 7 over 6	£45	£75	£140
1675	£35	£65	£120
1675/4	£40	£75	£150
1676	£35	£65	£130
1676 7 over 6	£50	£80	£145
1677	£30	£65	£120
1678	£30	£60	£115
1678 8 over 7	£40	£70	£130
1679	£30	£50	£110
1680	£35	£60	£120
1681	£35	£60	£125
1682	£33	£60	£130
1682/1	£40	£70	£140
1683	£35	£65	£135
1684	£35	£70	£135
1684 4 over 3	£40	£70	£140

JAMES II (1685–88)

DATE	F	VF	EF
1686	£40	£75	£140
1686 Date over crown	£50	£80	£155
1687	£40	£70	£130
1687 7 over 6	£45	£75	£140
1688	£42	£80	£140
1688 1 over 8	£50	£75	£145

WILLIAM & MARY (1688–94)

DATE	F	VF	EF
1689	£40	£60	£135
1689 GV below bust	£45	£70	£150
1689 GVLEELMVS	£80	£160	£270
1690	£50	£75	£150
1690 6 over 5	£55	£85	£165
1691	£50	£85	£160
1691 1 over 0	£55	£90	£170
1692	£70	£100	£190
1692 Mar.ia	£125	£190	£280
1692 2 over 1	£70	£100	£200
1693	£70	£110	£200
1693 3 over 2	£70	£110	£200
1694	£60	£95	£170

WILLIAM III (1694–1702)

DATE	F	VF	EF
1698	£55	£90	£165
1699	£40	£80	£150
1700	£50	£90	£160
1701	£45	£85	£160
1702	£55	£105	£150

ANNE (1702–14)

DATE	F	VF	EF
1703	£45	£80	£145
1704	£40	£75	£130
1705 £55	£110	£165	—

DATE	F	VF	EF	UNC
1706	£40	£75	£140	–
1708	£45	£85	£150	–
1709	£40	£70	£125	–
1710	£40	£70	£120	–
1713	£40	£75	£135	–

GEORGE I (1714–27)

1717	£40	£75	£135	–
1721	£40	£80	£140	–
1723	£45	£80	£145	–
1727	£45	£75	£140	–

GEORGE II (1727–60)

1729	£40	£70	£115	–
1731	£40	£70	£115	–
1732	£35	£70	£105	–
1735	£35	£65	£105	–
1737	£40	£65	£105	–
1739	£40	£65	£105	–
1740	£35	£60	£100	–
1743	£70	£120	£200	–
1743 3 over 0	£75	£125	£215	
1746	£35	£55	£90	–
1760	£40	£65	£105	–

GEORGE III (1760–1820)

1763 Young head	£30	£65	£90	–
1763 Proof	–	–	Extremely rare	
1765	£360	£600	£925	–
1766	£35	£70	£105	–
1770	£100	£165	£250	–
1772	£50	£90	£135	–
1776	£50	£85	£130	–
1780	£35	£70	£100	–
1784	£35	£65	£95	–
1786	£35	£75	£110	–
1792 Older head, Thin 4	£55	£85	£150	£220
1795	–	£30	£60	£95
1800	–	£30	£55	£80
1817 New coinage	–	£30	£50	£85
1818	–	£30	£50	£75
1820	–	£35	£55	£85

GEORGE IV (1820–30)

1822	–	–	£45	£95
1823	–	–	£40	£80
1824	–	–	£40	£80
1826	–	–	£40	£75
1827	–	–	£40	£75
1828	–	–	£40	£75
1829	–	–	£40	£75
1830	–	–	£40	£75

WILLIAM IV (1830–37)

1831–37	–	–	£45	£90

VICTORIA (1837–1901)

1838–87 (Young Head)	–	–	£20	£35
1841 & 1857	–	–	£30	£45
1888–92 (Jubilee Head)	–	–	£20	£35
1893–1909 (Old Head	–	–	£17	£30

DATE	F	VF	EF	UNC
EDWARD VII (1901–10)				
1902–08	—	—	£15	£25
1909 & 1910	—	—	£25	£45
GEORGE V (1910–36)				
1911–36	—	—	£20	£30
GEORGE VI (1936–52)				
1937–52	—	—	£20	£35
ELIZABETH II (1952–)				
1953	—	—	£85	£150
1954–85	—	—	£25	£45
1986–2007	—	—	£35	£45
2002 in Gold Proof	—	—	£425	£650
2008	—	—	£35	£55
2009	—	—	£35	£35

THREEPENCE

DATE	F	VF	EF	UNC
CHARLES II (1660–85)				
Undated	£40	£75	£150	—
1670	£35	£65	£115	—
1671	£35	£60	£115	—
1671 GRVTIA	£50	£80	£190	—
1672	£35	£65	£120	—
1673	£35	£65	£115	—
1674	£35	£65	£120	—
1675	£40	£70	£120	—
1676	£50	£85	£170	—
1676 ERA for FRA	£50	£90	£185	—
1677	£35	£60	£120	—
1678	£25	£55	£105	—
1679	£25	£50	£100	—
1679 O/A in CAROLVS	£60	£90	£190	—
1680	£35	£70	£130	—
1681	£35	£70	£130	—
1682	£35	£70	£130	—
1683	£35	£70	£130	—
1684	£35	£75	£130	—
1684/3	£40	£75	£135	—
JAMES II (1685–88)				
1685	£40	£75	£150	—
1685 Struck on fourpence flan	£80	£115	£215	—
1686	£35	£65	£125	—
1687	£30	£65	£120	—
1687 7 over 6	£40	£65	£120	—
1688	£50	£85	£170	—
1688 8 over 7	£50	£90	£175	—
WILLIAM & MARY (1688–94)				
1689	£35	£65	£135	—
1689 No stop on reverse	£40	£80	£150	—
1689 LMV over MVS (obverse)	£60	£90	£185	—
1690	£50	£80	£145	—
1690 6 over 5	£55	£95	£160	—
1691 First bust	£350	£525	£750	—
1691 Second bust	£250	£410	£515	—
1692	£55	£95	£175	—
1692 G below bust	£60	£95	£180	—
1692 GV below bust	£60	£95	£160	—
1692 GVL below bust	£60	£95	£185	—
1693	£90	£155	£225	—
1693 3 over 2	£95	£165	£230	—

DATE	F	VF	EF	UNC
1694	£55	£85	£160	–
1694 M•RI•	£80	£115	£220	–

WILLIAM III (1694–1702)

DATE	F	VF	EF	UNC
1698	£45	£85	£140	–
1699	£40	£75	£130	–
1700	£50	£95	£150	–
1701	£40	£70	£125	–
1701 GBA instead of GRA	£45	£80	£145	–

ANNE (1702–14)

DATE	F	VF	EF	UNC
1703	£45	£70	£130	–
1703 7 of date above crown	£50	£80	£140	–
1704	£40	£60	£115	–
1705	£55	£80	£145	–
1706	£40	£65	£115	–
1707	£40	£70	£115	–
1708	£35	£65	£120	–
1709	£40	£70	£125	–
1710	£30	£60	£100	–
1713	£40	£75	£125	–

GEORGE I (1714–27)

DATE	F	VF	EF	UNC
1717	£40	£65	£115	–
1721	£45	£65	£125	–
1723	£45	£70	£135	–
1727	£50	£70	£130	–

GEORGE II (1727–60)

DATE	F	VF	EF	UNC
1729	£40	£65	£105	–
1731	£40	£65	£105	–
1731 Small lettering	£45	£70	£115	–
1732	£40	£65	£105	–
1731 Stop over head	£40	£65	£110	–
1735	£35	£60	£105	–
1737	£40	£65	£115	–
1739	£35	£60	£110	–
1740	£35	£60	£100	–
1743 Small and large lettering	£35	£55	£115	–
1743 Stop over head	£40	£65	£115	–
1746	£30	£50	£90	–
1746 6 over 3	£38	£55	£95	–
1760	£40	£60	£110	–

GEORGE III (1760–1820)

DATE	F	VF	EF	UNC
1762	£15	£30	£45	–
1763	£15	£30	£50	–
1763 Proof	–	–	Extremely rare	
1765	£275	£415	£675	–
1766	£35	£60	£100	–
1770	£40	£65	£110	–
1772	£30	£55	£85	–
1780	£35	£50	£85	–
1784	£35	£55	£100	–
1786	£35	£55	£90	–
1792	£45	£75	£160	£250
1795	–	£25	£50	£75
1800	–	£30	£55	£90
1817	–	£30	£55	£110
1818	–	£30	£50	£105
1820	–	£32	£55	£115

DATE	F	VF	EF	UNC
GEORGE IV (1820–30)				
1822	—	—	£50	£115
1823	—	—	£50	£105
1824	—	—	£50	£110
1825–30	—	—	£50	£105
WILLIAM IV (1830–37)				
1831–1836	—	—	£65	£130
1837	—	—	£75	£140
VICTORIA (1837–1901)				
1838	—	—	£70	£150
1839	—	—	£85	£175
1840	—	—	£90	£200
1841	—	—	£120	£220
1842	—	—	£130	£260
1843	—	—	£80	£155
1844	—	—	£115	£215
1845	—	—	£55	£125
1846	—	—	£275	£550
1847	—	—	£270	£485
1848	—	—	£270	£485
1849	—	—	£135	£260
1850	—	—	£85	£165
1851	—	—	£90	£180
1852	—	—	£325	£550
1853	—	—	£350	£570
1854	—	—	£95	£195
1855	—	—	£100	£205
1856	—	—	£70	£185
1857	—	—	£100	£210
1858	—	—	£80	£165
1859	—	—	£70	£130
1860	—	—	£90	£180
1861	—	—	£85	£170
1862	—	—	£85	£175
1863	—	—	£105	£210
1864	—	—	£85	£180
1865	—	—	£90	£180
1866	—	—	£85	£170
1867	—	—	£85	£170
1868	—	—	£70	£155
1869	—	—	£100	£200
1870	—	—	£70	£135
1871	—	—	£70	£140
1872	—	—	£65	£130
1873	—	—	£60	£120
1874	—	—	£60	£120
1875	—	—	£55	£110
1876	—	—	£50	£115
1877	—	—	£50	£110
1878	—	—	£55	£110
1879	—	—	£65	£115
1880	—	—	£55	£110
1881	—	—	£50	£110
1882	—	—	£85	£170
1883	—	—	£50	£100
1884	—	—	£50	£100
1885	—	—	£50	£95
1886	—	—	£40	£85
1887	—	—	£60	£120
1888–1892 (Jubilee Head)	—	—	£40	£75
1893–1901 (Old Head)	—	—	£25	£45

DATE	F	VF	EF	UNC

EDWARD VII (1901–10)

1902	—	—	£20	£40
1903	—	—	£30	£65
1904	—	—	£40	£80
1905	—	—	£40	£80
1906	—	—	£35	£70
1907	—	—	£35	£65
1908	—	—	£30	£60
1909	—	—	£40	£90
1910	—	—	£50	£95

GEORGE V (1910–36)

1911–34	—	—	£25	£45
1935	—	—	£30	£55
1936	—	—	£45	£75

GEORGE VI (1936–52)

1937–52	—	—	£35	£60

ELIZABETH II (1952–)

1953	—	—	£100	£175
1954–85	—	—	£30	£50
1986–2007	—	—	£37	£55
2002 In gold (proof)	—	—	—	£500
2008	—	—	—	£60
2009	—	—	—	£60

TWOPENCE

CHARLES II (1660–85)

Undated	£35	£60	£115	—
1668	£45	£65	£130	—
1670	£35	£60	£110	—
1671	£30	£55	£110	—
1672	£30	£55	£110	—
1672/1	£35	£55	£125	—
1673	£35	£55	£115	—
1674	£35	£60	£115	—
1675	£33	£60	£110	—
1676	£40	£65	£120	—
1677	£30	£55	£105	—
1678	£25	£50	£100	—
1679	£25	£45	£85	—
1680	£30	£55	£100	—
1681	£30	£50	£105	—
1682	£30	£50	£110	—
1682/1 ERA for FRA	£35	£65	£160	—
1683	£35	£60	£115	—
1684	£35	£60	£120	—

JAMES II (1685–88)

1686	£35	£60	£125	—
1686 reads IACOBVS	£40	£80	£160	—
1687	£40	£65	£125	—
1687 ERA for FRA	£45	£80	£160	—
1688	£30	£55	£115	—
1688/7	£35	£60	£125	—

WILLIAM & MARY (1688–94)

1689	£30	£65	£125	—
1691	£30	£55	£105	—
1692	£55	£100	£150	—
1693	£40	£70	£120	—
1693 GV below bust	£45	£75	£130	—
1693/2	£45	£75	£130	—
1694	£30	£55	£105	—
1694 MARLA error	£50	£90	£210	—

DATE	F	VF	EF	UNC
1694 HI for HIB	£40	£80	£155	–
1694 GVLI under bust	£40	£65	£135	–
1694 GVL under bust	£40	£65	£135	–

WILLIAM III (1694–1702)

1698	£40	£75	£120	–
1699	£30	£60	£100	–
1700	£35	£70	£125	–
1701	£40	£70	£120	–

ANNE (1702–14)

1703	£40	£65	£130	–
1704	£30	£50	£95	–
1704 No stops on obverse	£40	£60	£115	–
1705	£35	£65	£120	–
1706	£35	£65	£115	–
1707	£30	£50	£105	–
1708	£30	£50	£100	–
1709	£50	£80	£150	–
1710	£30	£50	£90	–
1713	£45	£70	£130	–

GEORGE I (1714–27)

1717	£30	£55	£90	–
1721	£30	£55	£85	–
1723	£35	£65	£115	–
1726	£30	£50	£95	–
1727	£30	£55	£95	–

GEORGE II (1727–60)

1729	£30	£50	£80	–
1731	£30	£50	£80	–
1732	£33	£55	£85	–
1735	£25	£50	£80	–
1737	£25	£50	£80	–
1739	£30	£55	£80	–
1740	£30	£50	£80	–
1743	£25	£50	£75	–
1743/0	£30	£55	£90	–
1746	£25	£45	£70	–
1756	£25	£45	£70	–
1759	£30	£50	£70	–
1760	£28	£45	£75	–

GEORGE III (1760–1820)

1763	£20	£40	£65	–
1763 Proof			Extremely rare	
1765	£280	£450	£675	–
1766	£25	£40	£65	–
1772	£25	£40	£60	–
1780	£25	£40	£60	–
1784	£25	£40	£60	–
1786	£25	£40	£55	–
1792	–	£50	£80	£135
1795	–	£20	£40	£55
1800	–	£20	£35	£45
1817	–	£25	£45	£65
1818	–	£20	£35	£50
1820	–	£20	£35	£50

DATE	F	VF	EF	UNC
GEORGE IV (1820–30)				
1822–30	–	–	£25	£40
1825 TRITANNIAR	–	–	£45	£80
WILLIAM IV (1830–37)				
1831–37	–	–	£30	£45
VICTORIA (1837–1901)				
1838–87 (Young Head)	–	–	£17	£30
1859 BEITANNIAR	–	–	£50	£85
1861 6 over 1	–	–	£25	£45
1888–92 (Jubilee Head)	–	–	£20	£30
1893–1901 (Old Head	–	–	£15	£25
EDWARD VII (1901–10)				
1902–08	–	–	£12	£20
1909	–	–	£25	£50
1910	–	–	£25	£45
GEORGE V (1910–36)				
1911–34	–	–	£15	£30
1935	–	–	£20	£35
1936	–	–	£25	£40
GEORGE VI (1936–52)				
1937–47	–	–	£20	£30
1948–52	–	–	£20	£35
ELIZABETH II (1952–)				
1953	–	–	£70	£125
1954–85	–	–	£20	£30
1986–2007	–	–	£20	£30
2002 Gold Proof	–	–	–	£400
2008	–	–	–	£40
2009	–	–	–	£40

PENNY

CHARLES II (1660–85)

DATE	F	VF	EF	UNC
Undated	£45	£75	£135	–
1670	£40	£75	£125	–
1671	£40	£75	£120	–
1672/1	£40	£75	£120	–
1673	£35	£75	£115	–
1674	£35	£75	£120	–
1674 Gratia (error)	£50	£90	£200	–
1675	£35	£75	£115	–
1675 Gratia (error)	£50	£90	£195	–
1676	£45	£75	£135	–
1676 Gratia (error)	£55	£100	£210	–
1677	£35	£65	£120	–
1677 Gratia (error)	£45	£85	£170	–
1678	£115	£215	£300	–
1678 Gratia (error)	£140	£225	£350	–
1679	£55	£85	£150	–
1680	£40	£70	£130	–
1681	£65	£100	£170	–
1682	£45	£70	£140	–
1682 ERA for FRA	£50	£100	£200	–
1683	£45	£75	£145	–
1683/1	£50	£90	£170	–
1684	£170	£230	£325	–
1684/3	£175	£245	£325	–

Charles II

DATE	F	VF	EF	UNC
JAMES II (1685–88)				
1685	£40	£70	£120	–
1686	£40	£70	£120	–
1687	£45	£75	£135	–
1687/8	£45	£80	£140	–
1688	£42	£65	£115	–
1688/7	£45	£75	£135	–
WILLIAM & MARY (1688–94)				
1689	£400	£550	£800	–
1689 M! RI!	£350	£550	£800	
1689 GVIELMVS (Error)	£375	£525	£755	–
1690	£55	£90	£140	–
1691	£50	£90	£145	–
1692	£150	£270	£450	–
1692/1	£155	£280	£460	–
1693	£60	£105	£170	–
1694	£50	£80	£145	–
1694 HI for HIB	£65	£110	£200	–
1694 No stops on obverse	£60	£105	£185	–
WILLIAM III (1694–1702)				
1698	£55	£90	£140	–
1698 HI. BREX (Error)	£60	£115	£200	–
1699	£235	£340	£550	–
1700	£60	£95	£155	–
1701	£60	£95	£135	–
ANNE (1702–14)				
1703	£45	£80	£135	–
1705	£40	£75	£120	–
1706	£40	£60	£110	–
1708	£300	£400	£600	–
1709	£40	£65	£110	–
1710	£100	£160	£250	–
1713/0	£50	£80	£130	–
GEORGE I (1714–27)				
1716	£30	£65	£85	–
1718	£30	£60	£85	–
1720	£35	£60	£90	–
1720 HIPEX (Error)	£45	£75	£160	–
1723	£45	£75	£120	–
1725	£40	£60	£90	–
1726	£40	£60	£85	–
1727	£40	£80	£125	–
GEORGE II (1727–60)				
1729	£35	£60	£95	–
1731	£35	£55	£90	–
1732	£25	£45	£70	–
1735	£25	£45	£65	–
1737	£30	£45	£70	–
1739	£30	£50	£70	–
1740	£25	£50	£75	–
1743	£35	£60	£80	–
1746	£35	£60	£80	–
1746/3	£38	£60	£80	–
1750	£25	£40	£55	–
1752	£25	£40	£55	–
1753	£25	£40	£55	–
1754	£25	£40	£55	–
1755	£25	£45	£60	–

James II

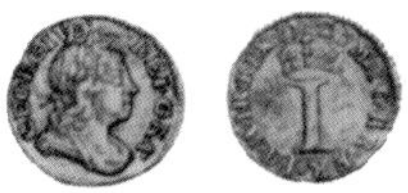

George II

DATE	F	VF	EF	UNC
1756	£25	£45	£55	–
1757	£25	£45	£55	–
1757 No colon after Gratia	£30	£55	£75	–
1758	£20	£40	£55	–
1759	£22	£35	£55	–
1760	£30	£50	£75	–

GEORGE III (1760–1820)

1763	£25	£45	£75	–
1763 Proof	–	–	Extremely rare	
1766	£25	£45	£60	–
1772	£25	£45	£55	–
1780	£27	£45	£65	–
1781	£20	£35	£55	–
1784	£20	£45	£65	–
1786	£20	£35	£60	–
1792	£25	£45	£65	£90
1795	–	£20	£35	£45
1800	–	£20	£30	£45
1817	–	£18	£25	£35
1818	–	£18	£25	£35
1820	–	£18	£25	£40

George III

GEORGE IV (1820–30)

1822–30	–	–	£18	£35

WILLIAM IV (1830–37)

1831–37	–	–	£20	£40

VICTORIA (1837–1901)

1838–87 (Young Head)	–	–	£15	£25
1888–92 (Jubilee Head)	–	–	£15	£25
1893–1901 (Old Head)	–	–	£13	£20

EDWARD VII (1901–10)

1902–08	–	–	£10	£16
1909	–	–	£20	£35
1910	–	–	£20	£50

GEORGE V (1910–36)

1911–14	–	–	£17	£35
1915	–	–	£18	£35
1916–19	–	–	£17	£30
1920	–	–	£20	£35
1921–28	–	–	£17	£30
1929	–	–	£20	£40
1930–34	–	–	£17	£30
1935	–	–	£20	£40
1936	–	–	£25	£45

GEORGE VI (1936–52)

1937–40	–	–	£22	£45
1941	–	–	£20	£45
1942–47	–	–	£20	£45
1948–52	–	–	£22	£50

ELIZABETH II (1952–)

1953	–	–	£200	£300
1965–85	–	–	£25	£40
1986–2007	–	–	£30	£45
2002 Proof in gold	–	–	–	£400
2008	–	–	£30	£50
2009	–	–	£30	£50

DECIMAL COINAGE

Since the introduction of the Decimal system in the UK, many coins have been issued for circulation purposes in vast quantities. In addition, from 1982 sets of coins to non-proof standard, and including examples of each denomination found in circulation, have been issued each year. For 1982 and 1983 they were to "circulation" standard and described as "Uncirculated". Individual coins from these sets are annotated "Unc" on the lists that follow. From 1984 to the present day they were described as "Brilliant Uncirculated" (BU on the lists), and from around 1986 these coins are generally distinguishable from coins intended for circulation. They were from then produced by the Proof Coin Division of the Royal Mint (rather than by the Coin Production Room which produces circulation-standard coins). For completeness however, we have included the annotations Unc and BU back to 1982, the start year for these sets.

It is emphasised that the abbreviations Unc and BU in the left-hand columns adjacent to the date refer to an advertising description or to an engineering production standard, not the preservation condition or grade of the coin concerned. Where no such annotation appears adjacent to the date, the coin is circulation-standard for issue as such.

We have included the "mintage" figures for circulation coins down to Twenty-five pence. Strictly speaking, these figures are for coins issued by the Royal Mint up to December 31, 2005. The figure given for the 1997 Two Pounds, for example, is considerably less than the actual quantity struck, because many were scrapped before issue due to failing an electrical conductivity test. Figures are not available for commemorative £5, £2 and 50p coins dated 2000 or since, their totals are included in the definitive version of the coins concerned. We have included the figures for non-circulation-standard coins where known. Where a coin is available in uncirculated grade at, or just above, face value no price has been quoted.

Base metal Proof issues of circulation coinage (£2 or £1 to one or half penny) of the decimal series were only issued, as with Unc or BU, as part of Year Sets, but many of these sets have been broken down into individual coins, hence the appearance of the latter on the market.

The lists do not attempt to give details of die varieties, except where there was an obvious intention to change the appearance of a coin, e.g. 1992 20p.

2008 saw new reverses and modified obverses for all circulation denominations from the One Pound to the One Penny. All seven denominations were put into circulation dated 2008, all with both the old and the new reverses, and it is assumed that all seven will appear with Shield reverses dated 2009.

HUNDRED POUNDS AND BELOW (Britannia Gold series)

In 1987 the gold £100 coin was introduced, known as the Britannia. It contained one Troy ounce of fine gold, alloyed to 22 carat, and this has continued to the present day. At the same time, and also continuing, coins of face value £50, £25 and £10 appeared, containing a half ounce, quarter ounce and one tenth of an ounce of fine gold respectively. From 1987 to 1989 the alloy was of equal weights of silver and copper, (Red Gold), whereas from 1990 to the present day the alloy has been silver only (yellow gold).

Proof sets of these coins are listed in the "Proof and Specimen Sets" section. In addition, non-proof coins have been minted, it is believed for each of the four coins for every year. The one ounce £100 Britannia is primarily issued as a bullion coin in the non-proof standard, originally in competition with the South African Krugerrand. Its price is quoted daily on the financial pages of some newspapers.

There were five reverse designs by Philip Nathan:- 1987-1996 Standing Britannia, 1997 Chariot, 1998-2000 Standing Britannia, 2001 Una and the Lion, 2002 Standing Britannia, 2003 Britannia's Helmeted Head, 2004 Standing Britannia, 2005 Britannia seated, 2006 Standing Britannia. For 2007 the design is a Seated Britannia with lion at her feet, by Christopher Le Brun. The 2008 design is of Britannia standing and facing left, by John Bergdahl. The 2009 reverse is similar to that of 1997, Britannia on a chariot.

In general the proof coins have reverse features frosted, The proofs with Standing Britannia and Una and the Lion reverses include P NATHAN on the reverse, whereas the equivalent bullion coins include NATHAN. The other three reverses have PN on both proofs and bullion coins.

HUNDRED POUNDS AND BELOW (Britannia Platinum series)

2007 saw the issue of four-coin proof sets in platinum, 0.9995 fine. The denomination and designs are similar to those of the Gold series of the same year. The issue was repeated in 2008, and again in 2009, above rule applies. It is understood that no bullion coins have been issued.

FIVE POUNDS (Sovereign series)

This series is all minted in gold, and, except where stated, have the Pistrucci St George and Dragon reverse. BU coins up to 2001 bear a U in a circle.

DATE	Mintage	UNC
1980 Proof	10,000	£650
1981 Proof	5,400	£650
1982 Proof	2,500	£675
1984 BU	15,104	£650
1984 Proof	8,000	£750
1985 New portrait BU	13,626	£650
1985 — Proof	6,130	£700
1986 BU	7,723	£650
1987 Uncouped portrait BU	5,694	£650
1988 BU	3,315	£650
1989 500th Anniversary of the Sovereign. Enthroned portrayal obverse and Crowned shield reverse BU	2,937	£750
1989 — Proof	5,000	£850
1990 Reverts to couped portrait BU	1,226	£650
1990 Proof	1,721	£750
1991 BU	976	£650
1991 Proof	1,336	£750
1992 BU	797	£650
1992 Proof	1,165	£750
1993 BU	906	£650
1993 Proof	1,078	£750
1994 BU	1,000	£650
1994 Proof	918	£750
1995 BU	1,000	£650

Pistrucci's famous rendering of St George and the Dragon.

DATE	Mintage	UNC
1995 Proof	1,250	£750
1996 BU	901	£650
1996 Proof	742	£750
1997 BU	802	£650
1997 Proof	860	£750
1998 New portrait BU	825	£675
1998 Proof	789	£850
1999 BU	991	£675
1999 Proof	1,000	£850
2000 ("Bullion")	10,000	£600
2000 BU	994	£650
2000 Proof	3,000	£850
2001 BU	1,000	£650
2001 Proof	3,500	£850
2002 Shield rev. ("Bullion")	—	£600
2002 BU	—	£650
2002 Proof	3,000	£850
2003 BU	—	£650
2003 Proof	—	£750
2004 BU	—	£650
2004 Proof	—	£750
2005 Noad's heraldic St George and Dragon BU	—	£750
2005 — Proof	—	£850
2006 BU	—	£800
2006 Proof	—	£850
2007 BU	—	£800
2007 Proof	—	£850
2008 BU	—	£850
2008 Proof	—	£900
2009 BU	—	—
2009 Proof	—	—

The obverse of the 1989 gold coins portray HM the Queen enthroned

NOTE: The prices quoted in this guide are set at August 2009 with the price of gold at £595 per ounce and silver £8.75 per ounce—market fluctuations will have a marked effect on the values of modern precious metal coins.

FIVE POUNDS (Crown series)

This series commenced in 1990 when the "Crown" was declared legal tender at £5, instead of 25p as all previous issues continued to be. Mintage is in cupro-nickel unless otherwise stated. BU includes those in individual presentation folders, and those in sets sold with stamp covers and/or banknotes.

DATE	Mintage	UNC
1990 Queen Mother's 90th Birthday.	2,761,431	£8
1990 — BU	48,477	£10
1990 — Silver Proof	56,800	£40
1990 — Gold Proof	2,500	£675
1993 Coronation 40th Anniversary	1,834,655	£8
1993 — BU	—	£10
1993 — Proof	—	£15
1993 — Silver Proof	100,000	£35
1993 — Gold Proof	2,500	£675
1996 HM the Queen's 70th Birthday	2,396,100	£8
1996 — BU	—	£10
1996 — Proof	—	£15
1996 — Silver Proof	70,000	£35
1996 — Gold Proof	2,127	£850
1997 Royal Golden Wedding	1,733,000	£10
1997 — BU	—	£12
1997 — — with £5 note	5,000	£75
1997 — Proof	—	£20
1997 — Silver Proof	75,000	£35
1997 — Gold Proof	2,750	£850
1998 Prince of Wales 50th birthday	1,407,300	£8
1998 — BU	—	£12
1998 — Proof	—	£20
1998 — Silver Proof	—	£45
1998 — Gold Proof	—	£850
1999 Princess of Wales Memorial.	1,600,000	£10
1999 — BU	—	£12
1999 — Proof	—	£20
1999 — Silver Proof	350,000	£45

DATE	Mintage	UNC
1999 — Gold Proof	7,500	£850
1999 Millennium	3,796,300	£8
1999 — BU	—	£15
1999 — Proof	—	£22
1999 — Silver Proof	100,000	£45
1999 — Gold Proof	2,500	£750
2000 —	3,147,092*	£8
2000 — BU	—	£15
2000 — — with special Millennium Dome mintmark	—	£12
2000 — Proof	—	£22
2000 — Silver Proof with gold highlight	50,000	£45
2000 — Gold Proof	2,500	£750
2000 Queen Mother's 100th Birthday	*incl. above**	£7
2000 — BU	—	£12
2000 — Silver Proof	100,000	£45
2000 — — — Piedfort	14,850	£175
2000 — Gold Proof	3,000	£700
2001 Victorian Era.	851,491	£7
2001 — BU	—	£12
2001 — Proof	—	£20
2001 — Silver Proof	100,000	£45
2001 — Gold Proof	3,000	£700
2001 — — with frosted relief	750	£950
2002 Golden Jubilee	3,687,882*	£7
2002 — BU	—	£12
2002 — Proof	—	£20
2002 — Silver Proof	75,000	£45
2002 — Gold Proof	5,502	£700
2002 Queen Mother Memorial	*incl. above**	£7
2002 — BU	—	£12
2002 — Silver Proof	25,000	£45
2002 — Gold Proof	3,000	£700
2003 Coronation Jubilee	1,307,010	£7
2003 — BU	—	£10
2003 — Proof	—	£20
2003 — Silver Proof	—	£45
2003 — Gold Proof	—	£700
2004 Entente Cordiale Centenary	—	£6
2004 — Proof Reverse Frosting	—	£15
2004 — Silver Proof	—	£35
2004 — — — Piedfort	—	£100
2004 — Gold Proof	—	£700
2004 — Platinum Proof Piedfort	501	£3500
2005 Trafalgar Bicentenary	—	£12
2005 — BU	—	£14
2005 — Proof	—	£20
2005 — Silver Proof	—	£45
2005 — — — Piedfort	—	£100
2005 — Gold Proof	—	£650
2005 Bicentenary of the Death of Nelson	—	£12
2005 — BU	—	£14
2005 — Proof	—	£22
2005 — Silver Proof	—	£50
2005 — — — Piedfort	—	£100
2005 — Gold Proof	—	£650
2005 — Platinum Proof Piedfort	200	£3750
2006 Queen's 80th birthday	—	£10
2006 — BU	—	£12
2006 — Proof	—	£20
2006 — Silver Proof	—	£45
2006 — — — Piedfort, selective gold plating on reverse	—	£100
2006 — Gold Proof	—	£750
2006 — Platinum Proof Piedfort	250	£3750
2007 Queen's Diamond Wedding	—	£10
2007 BU	—	£12
2007 — Proof	—	£20
2007 — Silver Proof	—	£45
2007 — — — Piedfort	—	£100
2007 — Gold Proof	—	£750
2007 — Platinum Proof Piedfort	—	£3650

DATE	Mintage	UNC
2008 Prince of Wales 60th Birthday	—	£10
2008 — BU	—	£12
2008 — Proof	—	£15
2008 — Silver Proof	—	£45
2008 — — — Piedfort	—	£85
2008 — Gold Proof	—	£750
2008 Elizabeth I 450th Anniversary of Accession	—	£12
2008 — BU	—	£15
2008 — Proof	—	£20
2008 — Silver Proof	—	£45
2008 — — — Piedfort	—	£100
2008 — Gold Proof	—	£800
2008 — Platinum Proof Piedfort	—	£3600
2009 500th Anniversary of Henry VIII accession	—	£10
2009 — BU	—	£15
2009 — Proof	—	£25
2009 — Silver Proof	—	£45
2009 — — — Piedfort	—	£100
2009 — Gold Proof	—	£1200
2009 — Platinum Proof Piedfort	100	£4500
2009 Olympic Countdown (3 years) BU	—	£12
2009 — Silver Proof	—	£55
2009 — — — Piedfort	—	£100
2009 — Gold Proof	—	£1295
2009 Celebration of Britain series:		
Stonehenge Silver Proof	—	£27
Palace of Westminster Silver Proof	—	£55
— CuNi Proof	—	£20
Angel of the North Silver Proof	—	£55
Flying Scotsman Silver Proof	—	£55
Globe Theatre Silver Proof	—	£55
Sir Isaac Newton Silver Proof	—	£55

DOUBLE SOVEREIGN

As with the Sovereign series Five Pound coins, those listed under this heading bear the Pistrucci St George and Dragon reverse, except where otherwise stated, and are minted in gold. They are, and always have been, legal tender at £2, and have a diameter indentical to that of the base metal Two Pound coins listed further below under a different heading. The denomination does not appear on Double Sovereigns.

DATE	Mintage	UNC
1980 Proof	10,000	£400
1982 Proof	2,500	£400
1983 Proof	12,500	£350
1985 New Portrait Proof	5,849	£400
1987 Proof	14,301	£350
1988 Proof	12,743	£350
1989 500th Anniversary of the Sovereign. Enthroned portrayal obverse and Crowned shield reverse Proof	14,936	£400
1990 Proof	4,374	£400
1991 Proof	3,108	£400
1992 Proof	2,608	£400
1993 Proof	2,155	£400
1996 Proof	3,167	£400
1998 New Portrait Proof	4,500	£425
2000 Proof	2,250	£400
2002 Shield reverse Proof	8,000	£450
2003 Proof	2,250	£450
2004 Proof	—	£450
2005 Noad heraldic St George and Dragon Proof	—	£500
2006 Proof	—	£475
2007 Proof	—	£450
2008 Proof	—	£450
2009 Proof	—	—

TWO POUNDS AND BELOW (Britannia Silver Series)

This series commenced in 1997, and, as with the Gold Britannia series, sets of the coins are listed in the "Proof and Specimen Sets" section. Coins contain one Troy ounce of fine silver (£2) alloyed to Britannia standard, i.e. 95.8 per cent fine silver, or fractions of one ounce as follows: half ounce (£1), quarter ounce (50 pence) and one tenth of an ounce (20 pence). Seven different reverses have been used, all four coins of any particular date being of the same design. The reverses by Philip Nathan appear as follows:
1997 Chariot, 1998 Standing Britannia, 1999 Chariot, 2000 Standing Britannia, 2001 Una and the Lion, 2002 Standing Britannia, 2003 Britannia's Helmeted Head, 2004 Standing Britannia, 2005 Britannia Seated, 2006 Standing Britannia, 2009 Chariot.
The 2007 design is by Christopher Le Brun, and features a seated Britannia with Lion at her feet. The 2008 is by John Bergdahl, and features a standing Britannia facing left.
Two pounds Britannia coins to BU or "bullion" standard have been issued as individual coins for each year from 1998 onwards.

TWO POUNDS

This series commenced in 1986 with nickel-brass commemorative coins, with their associated base metal and precious metal BU and proof coins. From 1997 (actually issued in 1998) a thinner bi-metal version commenced with a reverse theme of the advance of technology, and from this date the coin was specifically intended to circulate. This is true also for the parallel issues of anniversary and commemorative Two Pound issues in 1999 and onwards. All have their BU and proof versions, as listed below.

DATE	Mintage	UNC
1986 Commonwealth Games	8,212,184	£6
1986 — BU	—	£8
1986 — Proof	—	£12
1986 — Silver BU	—	£20
1986 — — Proof	—	£25
1986 — Gold Proof	—	£450
1989 Tercentenary of Bill of Rights.	4,392,825	£8
1989 — BU (issued in folder with Claim of Right)	—	£25
1989 — Proof (issued as pair with Claim of Right)	—	£35
1989 — Silver Proof (Pair as above)	—	£65
1989 — — — Piedfort (Pair as above)	—	£100
1989 Tercentenary of Claim of Right (issued in Scotland)	381,400	£15
1989 — BU (see above)	—	£25
1989 — Proof (see above)	—	£35
1989 — Silver Proof (see above)	—	£65
1989 — — — Piedfort (see above)	—	£100
1994 Tercentenary of the Bank of England	1,443,116	£5
1994 — BU	—	£8
1994 — Proof	—	£12
1994 — Silver Proof	—	£35
1994 — — — Piedfort	—	£85
1994 — Gold Proof	—	£550
1994 — — — with Double Sovereign obverse (no denomination)	—	£675
1995 50th Anniversary of End of WWII.	4,394,566	£5
1995 — BU	—	£8
1995 — Proof	—	£12
1995 — Silver Proof	—	£45
1995 — — — Piedfort	—	£85
1995 — Gold Proof	—	£650
1995 50th Anniversary of The United Nations	1,668,575	£5
1995 — BU	—	£6
1995 — Proof	—	£10
1995 — Silver Proof	—	£45
1995 — — — Piedfort	—	£85
1995 — Gold Proof	—	£600
1996 European Football Championships.	5,195,350	£6

DATE	Mintage	UNC
1996 — BU	—	£8
1996 — Proof	—	£10
1996 — Silver Proof	—	£35
1996 — — — Piedfort	—	£85
1996 — Gold Proof	—	£650
1997	13,734,625	£4
1997 BU	—	£8
1997 Proof	—	£12
1997 Silver Proof	—	£35
1997 — — Piedfort	—	£75
1997 Gold Proof (red (outer) and yellow (inner) 22ct)	—	£600
1998 New Portrait	—	£3
1998 BU	91,110,375	£8
1998 Proof	—	£12
1998 Silver Proof	—	£40
1998 — — Piedfort	—	£85
1999	33,719,000	£3
1999 Rugby World Cup	4,933,000	£5
1999 — BU	—	£6
1999 — Silver Proof (gold plated ring)	—	£40
1999 — — — Piedfort (Hologram)	—	£95
1999 — Gold Proof	—	£550
2000	25,770,000	£3
2000 BU	—	£5
2000 Proof	—	£10
2000 Silver Proof	—	£40
2000 Gold Proof	—	£550
2001	37,843,500*	—
2001 BU	—	£3
2001 Proof	—	£10
2001 Marconi	*Incl. in above**	£3
2001 — BU	—	£4
2001 — Proof	—	£10
2001 — Silver Proof (gold plated ring)	—	£35
2001 — — — Piedfort	—	£100
2001 — Gold Proof	—	£550
2002	15,521,000*	—
2002 BU	—	£3
2002 Proof	—	£10
2002 Commonwealth Games (4 versions)	*Incl. in above**	£3
2002 — BU (issued in set of 4)	—	£4
2002 — Proof (issued in set of 4)	—	£10
2002 — Silver Proof (issued in set of 4)	—	£32
2002 — — — Piedfort (painted) (issued in set of 4)	—	£150
2002 — Gold (issued in set of 4)	—	£550
2003	21,830,250*	—
2003 BU	—	£4
2003 Proof	—	£12
2003 DNA Double Helix	Incl in above*	£3
2003 — BU	—	£4
2003 — Proof	—	£10
2003 — Silver Proof (Gold-plated ring)	—	£35
2003 — — — Piedfort	—	£85
2003 — Gold Proof	—	£550
2004	13,904,500*	£3
2004 BU	—	£4
2004 Proof	—	£12
2004 Trevithick Steam Locomotive	Incl in above*	£3
2004 — BU	—	£4
2004 — Proof	—	£12
2004 — Silver BU	—	£35
2004 — — Proof (Gold-plated ring)	—	£45
2004 — — — Piedfort	—	£100
2004 — Gold Proof	—	£550
2005	—	£3
2005 BU	—	£4
2005 Proof	—	£5
2005 Gunpowder Plot	—	£3

DATE	Mintage	UNC
2005 — BU	—	£4
2005 — Proof	—	£6
2005 — Silver Proof	—	£35
2005 — — — Piedfort	—	£85
2005 — Gold Proof	—	£550
2005 End of World War II	—	£3
2005 — BU	—	£4
2005 — Silver Proof	—	£25
2005 — — — Piedfort	—	£95
2005 — Gold Proof	—	£550
2006	—	£3
2006 Proof	—	£6
2006 Brunel, The Man (Portrait)	—	£3
2006 — BU	—	£4
2006 — Proof	—	£6
2006 — Silver Proof	—	£25
2006 — — — Piedfort	—	£95
2006 —Gold Proof	—	£550
2006 Brunel, His Achievements (Paddington Station)	—	£3
2006 — BU	—	£4
2006 — Proof	—	£7
2006 — Silver Proof	—	£25
2006 — — — Piedfort	—	£85
2006 —Gold Proof	—	£550
2007	—	£3
2007 Proof	—	£8
2007 Tercentenary of the Act of Union	—	33
2007 BU	—	£4
2007 — Proof	—	£8
2007 — Silver Proof	—	£25
2007 — — — Piedfort	—	£85
2007 — Gold Proof	—	£550
2007 Bicentenary of the Abolition of the Slave Trade	—	£3
2007 — BU	—	£4
2007 — Proof	—	£7
2007 — Silver Proof	—	£30
2007 — — — Piedfort	—	£85
2007 — Gold Proof	—	£550
2008	—	33
2008 BU	—	£4
2008 Proof	—	£12
2008 Centenary of 4th Olympiad, London	—	£3
2008 — BU	—	£4
2008 — Proof	—	£12
2008 — Silver Proof	—	£30
2008 — — — Piedfort	—	£75
2008 — Gold proof	—	£550
2008 Olympic Games Handover Ceremony	—	£3
2008 — BU	—	£7
2008 — Silver Proof	—	£35
2008 — — — Piedfort	—	£100
2008 — Gold Proof	—	£600
2009	—	—
2009 BU	—	—
2009 Proof	—	—
2009 Silver Proof	—	—
2009 250th Anniversary of birth of Robert Burns	—	—
2009 — BU	—	£8
2009 — Proof	—	—
2009 — Silver Proof	—	£33
2009 — — — Piedfort	—	£55
2009 — Gold Proof	—	£525
2009 200th Anniversary of birth of Charles Darwin	—	—
2009 — BU	—	£8
2009 — Proof	—	—
2009 — Silver Proof	—	—
2009 — — — Piedfort	—	—
2009 Gold Proof	—	—

SOVEREIGN

All are minted in gold, bear the Pistrucci St George and Dragon reverse except where stated, and are legal tender at one pound.

DATE	Mintage	UNC
1974	5,002,566	£185
1976	4,150,000	£185
1978	6,550,000	£185
1979	9,100,000	£185
1979 Proof	50,000	£200
1980	5,100,000	£185
1980 Proof	91,200	£200
1981	5,000,000	£185
1981 Proof	32,960	£200
1982	2,950,000	£185
1982 Proof	22,500	£200
1983 Proof	21,250	£195
1984 Proof	19,975	£200
1985 New portrait Proof	17,242	£200
1986 Proof	17,579	£200
1987 Proof	22,479	£200
1988 Proof	18,862	£200
1989 500th Anniversary of the Sovereign—details as Five Pounds (Sov. Series). Proof	23,471	£500
1990 Proof	8,425	£220
1991 Proof	7,201	£220
1992 Proof	6,854	£230
1993 Proof	6,090	£230
1994 Proof	7,165	£230
1995 Proof	9,500	£230

NOTE: The prices quoted in this guide are set at August 2009 with the price of gold at £595 per ounce and silver £8.75 per ounce—market fluctuations will have a marked effect on the values of modern precious metal coins.

DATE	Mintage	UNC
1996 Proof	9,110	£235
1997 Proof	9,177	£245
1998 New Portrait Proof	11,349	£245
1999 Proof	11,903	£260
2000 (first Unc issue since 1982)	129,069	£160
2000 Proof	12,159	£210
2001	49,462	£160
2001 Proof	10,000	£210
2002 Shield Rev. ("bullion")	74,263	£160
2002 Proof	20,500	£200
2003 ("bullion")	43,208	£160
2003 Proof	—	£200
2004 ("bullion")	28,821	£160
2004 Proof	—	£210
2005 Noad heraldic St George and Dragon	—	£160
2005 — Proof	—	£200
2006 ("bullion")	—	£170
2006 Proof	—	£235
2007 ("bullion")	—	£160
2007 Proof	—	£135
2008 ("bullion")	—	£205
2008 Proof	—	£275
2009 ("bullion")	—	£270
2009 Proof	—	£190

HALF SOVEREIGN

Legal Tender at 50 pence, otherwise the notes for the Sovereign apply.

DATE	Mintage	UNC
1980 Proof only	86,700	£90
1982	2,500,000	£87
1982 Proof	21,590	£90
1983 Proof	19,710	£90
1984 Proof	19,505	£90
1985 New portrait Proof	15,800	£90
1986 Proof	17,075	£95
1987 Proof	20,687	£95
1988 Proof	18,266	£95
1989 500th Anniversary of the Sovereign—details as Five Pounds (Sov. Series) Proof	21,824	£180
1990 Proof	7,889	£95
1991 Proof	6,076	£95
1992 Proof	5,915	£105
1993 Proof	4,651	£105
1994 Proof	7,167	£105
1995 Proof	7,500	£105
1996 New Portrait Proof	7,340	£105
1997 Proof	9,177	£105
1998 Proof	7,496	£105
1999 Proof	9,403	£105
2000	146,822	£87
2000 Proof	9,708	£105
2001	98,763	£87
2001 Proof	7,500	£105
2002 Shield reverse ("bullion")	61,347	£90
2002 Proof	—	£90
2003 ("bullion")	47,805	£87
2003 Proof	—	£95
2004 ("bullion")	32,479	£87
2004 Proof	—	£95
2005 Noad heralldic St George and Dragon	—	£87
2005 — Proof	—	£95
2006 ("bullion")	—	£87
2006 Proof	—	£100
2006 ("bullion")	—	£87

DATE	Mintage	UNC
2007 Proof	–	£100
2008 ("bullion")	–	£110
2008 Proof	–	£145
2009 ("bullion")	–	£140
2009 Proof	–	£99

QUARTER SOVEREIGN

Minted in 22ct Gold, this new denomination was introduced in 2009, and follows on from two different patterns of 1853.

DATE	Mintage	UNC
2009 ("bullion")	–	£59
2009 Proof	–	£65

ONE POUND

Introduced into circulation in 1983 to replace the £1 note, all are minted in nickel-brass unless otherwise stated. The reverse changes yearly, the Royal Arms being the "definitive" version. Unc or BU may come either in a presentation folder or from a set. Collectors and others should be aware of the many different counterfeit £1 coin versions in circulation, a high proportion of which do not have matching obverses, although many, an increasing ratio, do.

DATE	Mintage	UNC
1983 Royal Arms	443,053,510	£5
1983 – Unc	1,134,000	£5
1983 – Proof	107,800	£6
1983 – Silver Proof	50,000	£32
1983 – – – Piedfort	10,000	£125
1984 Scottish Thistle	146,256,501	£4
1984 – BU	199,430	£5
1984 – Proof	106,520	£6
1984 – Silver Proof	44,855	£34
1984 – – – Piedfort	15,000	£65
1985 New portrait. Welsh Leek	228,430,749	£3
1985 – BU	213,679	£5
1985 – Proof	102,015	£6
1985 – Silver Proof	50,000	£34
1985 – – – Piedfort	15,000	£65
1986 Northern Ireland Flax	10,409,501	£3
1986 – BU	–	£5
1986 – Proof	–	£6
1986 – Silver Proof	–	£35
1986 – – – Piedfort	–	£65
1987 English Oak	39,298,502	£3
1987 – BU	–	£5
1987 – Proof	–	£6
1987 – Silver Proof	–	£35
1987 – – – Piedfort	–	£55
1988 Crowned Shield Of The Royal Arms	7,118,825	£2
1988 – BU	–	£5
1988 – Proof	–	£5
1988 – Silver Proof	–	£34
1988 – – – Piedfort	–	£60
1989 Scottish Thistle	70,580,501	£2
1989 – BU	–	£6
1989 – Proof	–	£9
1989 – Silver Proof	–	£30
1989 – – – Piedfort	–	£55
1990 Welsh Leek	–	£2
1990 – BU	97,269,302	£5

1983, 1993, 1998, 2003

1984, 1989

1985, 1990

1986, 1991

DATE	Mintage	UNC
1990 — Proof	—	£6
1990 — Silver Proof	—	£30
1991 Northern Ireland Flax	38,443,575	£2
1991 — BU	—	£5
1991 — Proof	—	£6
1991 — Silver Proof	—	£32
1992 English Oak	36,320,487	£2
1992 — BU	—	£5
1992 — Proof	—	£7
1992 — Silver Proof	—	£32
1993 Royal Arms	114,744,500	£2
1993 — BU	—	£5
1993 — Proof	—	£7
1993 — Silver Proof	—	£34
1993 — — — Piedfort	—	£65
1994 Scottish Lion	29,752,525	£2
1994 — BU	—	£5
1994 — Proof	—	£7
1994 — Silver Proof	—	£32
1994 — — — Piedfort	—	£65
1995 Welsh Dragon	34,503,501	£2
1995 — BU	—	£5
1995 — — (Welsh)	—	£5
1995 — Proof	—	£10
1995 — Silver Proof	—	£34
1995 — — — Piedfort	—	£70
1996 Northern Ireland Celtic-style Cross	89,886,000	£3
1996 — BU	—	£5
1996 — Proof	—	£7
1996 — Silver Proof	—	£35
1996 — — — Piedfort	—	£65
1997 English Lions	57,117,450	£3
1997 — BU	—	£5
1997 — Proof	—	£7
1997 — Silver Proof	—	£35
1997 — — — Piedfort	—	£70
1998 New portrait. Royal Arms. BU	—	£7
1998 — Proof	—	£8
1998 — Silver Proof	—	£30
1998 — — — Piedfort	—	£45
1999 Scottish Lion. BU	—	£6
1999 — Proof	—	£11
1999 — Silver Proof	—	£35
1999 — — — Reverse Frosting	—	£45
1999 — — — Piedfort	—	£75
2000 Welsh Dragon	109,496,500	£2
2000 — BU	—	£5
2000 — Proof	—	£7
2000 — Silver Proof	—	£35
2000 — — — Reverse Frosting	—	£45
2000 — — — Piedfort	—	£50
2001 Northern Ireland Celtic-style Cross.	—	£2
2001 — BU	58,093,731	£5
2001 — Proof	—	£6
2001 — Silver Proof	—	£35
2001 — — — Piedfort	—	£50
2002 English Lions	77,818,000	£2
2002 — BU	—	£5
2002 — Proof	—	£8
2002 — Silver Proof	—	£32
2002 — — — Piedfort	—	£55
2002 — Gold Proof	—	£250
2003 Royal Arms	61,596,500	£2
2003 — BU	—	£5
2003 — Proof	—	£10
2003 — Silver Proof	—	£40
2003 — — — Piedfort	—	£55

1987, 1992

1988

1994, 1999

1995, 2000

1996, 2001

1997, 2002

2004

DATE	Mintage	UNC
2004 Forth Railway Bridge	37,286,000	£3
2004 — BU	—	£5
2004 — Proof	—	£10
2004 — Silver Proof	—	£40
2004 — — — Piedfort	—	£55
2004 — Gold Proof	—	£250
2005 Menai Bridge	—	—
2005 — BU	—	£5
2005 — Proof	—	£10
2005 — Silver Proof	—	£55
2005 — — — Piedfort	—	£60
2005 — Gold Proof	—	£250
2006 Egyptian Arch	—	—
2006 — BU	—	£5
2006 — Proof	—	£10
2006 — Silver Proof	—	£35
2006 — — — Piedfort	—	£55
2006 — Gold Proof	—	£250
2007 Gateshead Millennium Bridge	—	—
2007 — BU	—	£6
2007 — Proof	—	£10
2007 — Silver Proof	—	£40
2007 — — — Piedfort	—	£55
2007 — Gold Proof	—	£300
2008 Royal Arms	—	—
2008 — BU	—	£6
2008 — Proof	—	£8
2008 — Silver Proof	—	£35
2008 — Gold Proof	—	£300
2008 — Platinum Proof	—	£425
2008 A series of 14 different reverses, the 25th Anniversary of the modern £1 coin, Silver Proof with selected gold highlighting on the reverses. the latter being all those used since 1983, the coins being with appropriate edge lettering	—	—
2008 The same as above, Gold Proof (the 2008 Royal Arms being already listed above)	—	—
2008 New Rev, Shield of the Royal Arms, no border beads on Obv.		—
2008 — BU	—	—
2008 — Proof	—	—
2008 — Silver Proof	—	—
2008 — Silver Proof Piedfort	—	—
2008 — Platinum Proof	—	—
2009 Shield of the Royal Arms	—	—
2009 — BU	—	£7
2009 — Proof	—	—
2009 — Silver Proof	—	£33
2009 — Gold Proof	—	£595

2005

2006

2007

2008

2009

FIFTY PENCE

Introduced as legal tender for 10 shillings to replace the banknote of that value prior to decimalisation, coins of the original size are no longer legal tender. Unless otherwise stated, i.e. for commemoratives, the reverse design is of Britannia. The reverse legend of NEW PENCE became FIFTY PENCE from 1982.

DATE	Mintage	UNC
1969	188,400,000	£5
1970	19,461,500	£5
1971 Proof	—	£7
1972 Proof	—	£7
1973 Accession to EEC	89,775,000	£5
1973 — Proof	—	£10
1973 — Silver Proof Piedfort	—	£2250
1974 Proof	—	£7
1975 Proof	—	£7

DATE	Mintage	UNC
1976	43,746,500	£5
1976 Proof	—	£7
1977	49,536,000	£5
1977 Proof	—	£6
1978	72,005,000	£5
1978 Proof	—	£6
1979	58,680,000	£5
1979 Proof	—	£6
1980	89,086,000	£5
1980 Proof	—	£6
1981	74,002,000	£6
1981 Proof	—	£8
1982	51,312,000	£5
1982 Unc	—	£6
1982 Proof	—	£8
1983	2,824,000	£5
1983 Unc	—	£6
1983 Proof	—	£8
1984 BU	—	£6
1984 Proof	—	£8
1985 New portrait .... estimated approx	3,400,000	£1
1985 BU	—	£5
1985 Proof	—	£6
1986 BU	—	£5
1986 Proof	—	£11
1987 BU	—	£4
1987 Proof	—	£11
1988 BU	—	£4
1988 Proof	—	£11
1989 BU	—	£4
1989 Proof	—	£11
1990 BU	—	£4
1990 Proof	—	£11
1991 BU	—	£5
1991 Proof	—	£10
1992 BU	—	£7
1992 Proof	—	£12
1992 Presidency of EC Council and EC accession 20th anniversary (includes 1993 date)	109,000	£15
1992 — BU	—	£10
1992 — Proof	—	£12
1992 — Silver Proof	—	£30
1992 — — — Piedfort	—	£75
1992 — Gold Proof	—	£500
1993 BU	—	£5
1993 Proof	—	£12
1994 50th Anniversary of the Normandy Landings	6,705,520	£5
1994 — BU (also in presentation folder)	—	£8
1994 — Proof	—	£12
1994 — Silver Proof	—	£35
1994 — — — Piedfort	—	£75
1994 — Gold Proof	—	£500
1995 BU	—	£8
1995 Proof	—	£12
1996 BU	—	£8
1996 Proof	—	£12
1996 Silver Proof	—	£25
1997 BU	—	£7
1997 Proof	—	£9
1997 Silver Proof	—	£30
1997 new reduced size	456,364,100	£4
1997 BU	—	£5
1997 Proof	—	£6
1997 Silver Proof	—	£30
1997 — — Piedfort	—	£45
1998 New portrait	64,306,500	£2
1998 BU	—	£5

DATE	Mintage	UNC
1998 Proof	—	£7
1998 Presidency and 25th anniversary of EU entry	5,043,000	£3
1998 — BU	—	£5
1998 — Proof	—	£7
1998 — Silver Proof	—	£25
1998 — — — Piedfort	—	£75
1998 — Gold Proof	—	£350
1998 50th Anniversary of the National Health Service	5,001,000	£3
1998 — BU	—	£5
1998 — Silver Proof (believed not issued as Cu-Ni proof)	—	£25
1998 — — — Piedfort	—	£85
1998 — Gold Proof	—	£350
1999	24,905,000	£2
1999 BU	—	£5
1999 Proof	—	£9
2000	39,172,000*	£1
2000 BU	—	£5
2000 Proof	—	£7
2000 150th Anniversary of Public Libraries	*Incl in above**	£5
2000 — BU	—	£6
2000 — Proof	—	£9
2000 — Silver Proof	—	£30
2000 — — — Piedfort	—	£45
2000 — Gold proof	—	£300
2001	84,999,500	£1
2001 BU	—	£5
2001 Proof	—	£7
2002	23,907,500	—
2002 BU	—	£5
2002 Proof	—	£7
2002 Gold Proof	—	£250
2003	26,557,030*	—
2003 BU	—	£5
2003 Proof	—	£6
2003 Suffragette	Incl. in above*	—
2003 — BU	—	£6
2003 — Proof	—	£7
2003 — Silver Proof	—	£30
2003 — — — Piedfort	—	£50
2003 — Gold Proof	—	£250
2004	13,904,500*	—
2004 BU	—	£5
2004 Proof	—	£8
2004 Roger Bannister	Incl in above*	—
2004 — BU	—	£5
2004 — Proof	—	£8
2004 — Silver Proof	—	£30
2004 — — — Piedfort	—	£50
2004 — Gold Proof	—	£250
2005	—	—
2005 BU	—	£6
2005 Proof	—	£8
2005 Samuel Johnson	—	—
2005 — BU	—	£5
2005 — Proof	—	£8
2005 — Silver Proof	—	£35
2005 — — — Piedfort	—	£75
2005 — Gold Proof	—	£250
2006	—	—
2006 Proof	—	£8
2006 Silver Proof	—	£30
2006 Victoria Cross, The Award	—	£2
2006 — BU	—	£5
2006 — Proof	—	£8
2006 — Silver Proof	—	£25
2006 — — — — Piedfort	—	£85
2006 — Gold Proof	—	£275

DATE	Mintage	UNC
2006 Victoria Cross, Heroic Acts	—	—
2006 — BU	—	£5
2006 — Proof	—	£8
2006 — Silver Proof	—	£25
2006 — — — — Piedfort	—	£75
2006 — Gold Proof	—	£300
2007	—	—
2007 BU	—	£6
2007 Proof	—	£8
2007 Centenary of Scout Movement	—	£5
2007 — BU	—	£6
2007 — Proof	—	£12
2007 — Silver Proof	—	£35
2007 — — — Piedfort	—	£85
2007 — Gold Proof	—	£375
2008	—	—
2008 — BU	—	£5
2008 — Proof	—	£6
2008 — Silver Proof	—	£15
2008 — Gold Proof	—	£350
2008 Platinum Proof	—	£1500
2008 New Rev.; Obv. rotated by approx 26 degrees	—	£5
2008 BU	—	£6
2008 Proof	—	£8
2008 Silver Proof	—	£15
2008 Silver Proof Piedfort	—	£45
2008 Gold Proof	—	£350
2008 Platinum Proof	—	£1500
2009	—	—
2009 BU	—	—
2009 Proof	—	—
2009 Silver Proof	—	—
2009 250th Anniversary of Kew Gardens	—	—
2009 — BU	—	—
2009 — Proof	—	—
2009 — Silver Proof	—	—
2009 — — — Piedfort	—	—
2009 — Gold Proof	—	—

TWENTY-FIVE PENCE (CROWN)

This series is a continuation of the pre-decimal series, there having been four crowns to the pound. The coins below have a legal tender face value of 25p to this day, and are minted in cupro-nickel except where stated otherwise.

DATE	Mintage	UNC
1972 Royal Silver Wedding	7,452,100	£2
1972 — Proof	150,000	£8
1972 — Silver Proof	100,000	£25
1977 Silver Jubilee	37,061,160	£2
1977 — in Presentation folder	Incl. above	£3
1977 — Proof	193,000	£8
1977 — Silver Proof	377,000	£20
1980 Queen Mother 80th Birthday	9,306,000	£2
1980 — in Presentation folder	Incl. above	£3
1980 — Silver Proof	83,670	£30
1981 Royal Wedding	26,773,600	£2
1981 — in Presentation folder	Incl. above	£3
1981 — Silver Proof	218,140	£30

TWENTY PENCE

The series commenced in 1982, some 11 years after the introduction of decimal coinage. Its presence from introduction date meant that there was no requirement for ten pence circulation—standard coins until the latter's size was reduced in 1992. Unlike the circulation coins on either side of it in face value, it's alloy is 84% copper and 16% nickel.

DATE	UNC
1982	£1
1982 Unc	£3
1982 Proof	£5
1982 Silver Proof Piedfort	£50
1983	£1
1983 Unc	£3
1983 Proof	£4
1984	£1
1984 BU	£3
1984 Proof	£4
1985 New portrait	£1
1985 BU	£3
1985 Proof	£4
1986 BU	£4
1986 Proof	£5
1987	£1
1987 BU	£3
1987 Proof	£5
1988	£1
1988 BU	£3
1988 Proof	£5
1989	£1
1989 BU	£3
1989 Proof	£5
1990	£1
1990 BU	£3
1990 Proof	£5
1991	£1
1991 BU	£3
1991 Proof	£5
1992	£4
1992 Enhanced effigy	£4
1992 — BU	£5
1992 — Proof	£8
1993	£1
1993 BU	£3
1993 Proof	£5
1994	£1
1994 BU	£3
1994 Proof	£5
1995	£1
1995 BU	£3
1995 Proof	£5
1996	£1
1996 BU	£3
1996 Proof	£5
1996 Silver Proof	£20
1997	£1
1997 BU	£3
1997 Proof	£5
1998 New portrait	£1

DATE	UNC
1998 BU	£3
1998 Proof	£5
1999	£1
1999 BU	£3
1999 Proof	£5
2000	£1
2000 BU	£3
2000 Proof	£5
2000 Silver Proof	£30
2001	£1
2001 BU	£3
2001 Proof	£5
2002	£1
2002 BU	£3
2002 Proof	£5
2002 Gold Proof	£175
2003	£1
2003 BU	£4
2003 Proof	£6
2004	£1
2004 BU	£4
2004 Proof	£6
2005	—
2005 BU	£4
2005 Proof	£6
2006	—
2006 BU	£4
2006 Proof	£6
2006 Silver Proof	£15
2007	—
2007 BU	£4
2007 Proof	£6
2008	—
2008 BU	£3
2008 Proof	£6
2008 Silver Proof	£15
2008 Gold Proof	£175
2008 Platinum Proof	£650
2008 New Rev, date on Obv	—
2008 — New Rev paired with old Obv (thus no date)	£50
2008 — BU	—
2008 — Proof	—
2008 — Silver Proof	—
2008 — Silver Proof Piedfort	—
2008 — Gold Proof	—
2008 — Platinum Proof	—
2009	—
2009 BU	—
2009 Proof	—
2009 Silver Proof	—

TEN PENCE

The series commenced before decimalisation with the legend NEW PENCE, this changed to TEN PENCE from 1982. These "florin-sized" coins up to 1992 are no longer legal tender.

DATE	UNC
1968	£3
1969	£4
1970	£3
1971	£3
1971 Proof	£4
1972 Proof	£5
1973	£3
1973 Proof	£4
1974	£3
1974 Proof	£4
1975	£3
1975 Proof	£4
1976	£3
1976 Proof	£4
1977	£4
1977 Proof	£4
1978 Proof	£5
1979	£2
1979 Proof	£4
1980	£2
1980 Proof	£3
1981	£2
1981 Proof	£3
1982 Unc	£4
1982 Proof	£6
1983 Unc	£4
1983 Proof	£2
1984 BU	£4
1984 Proof	£6
1985 New portrait BU	£5
1985 Proof	£7
1986 BU	£4
1986 Proof	£6
1987 BU	£4
1987 Proof	£7
1988 BU	£5
1988 Proof	£7
1989 BU	£6
1989 Proof	£9
1990 BU	£6
1990 Proof	£9
1991 BU	£6
1991 Proof	£9
1992 BU	£5
1992 Proof	£7
1992 Silver Proof	£20
1992 *Size reduced* (24.5mm diam)	£3
1992 BU	£4
1992 Proof	£5
1992 Silver Proof	£20
1992 — — Piedfort	£50
1993 BU	£2
1993 Proof	£7
1994 BU	£2
1994 Proof	£7
1995	£1
1995 BU	£3

DATE	UNC
1995 Proof	£4
1996	£1
1996 BU	£3
1996 Proof	£4
1996 Silver Proof	£25
1997	£1
1997 BU	£3
1997 Proof	£4
1998 New portrait BU	£6
1998 Proof	£9
1999 BU	£3
1999 Proof	£11
2000	£1
2000 BU	£3
2000 Proof	£4
2000 Silver Proof	£25
2001	£1
2001 BU	£3
2001 Proof	£4
2002	£1
2002 BU	£3
2002 Proof	£5
2002 Gold Proof	£175
2003	—
2003 BU	£3
2003 Proof	£5
2004	—
2004 BU	£3
2004 Proof	£5
2005	—
2005 BU	£1
2005 Proof	£4
2006	—
2006 BU	£1
2006 Proof	£5
2006 Silver Proof	£22
2007	—
2007 BU	£4
2007 Proof	£5
2008	—
2008 BU	—
2008 Proof	—
2008 Silver Proof	£25
2008 Gold Proof	£175
2008 Platinum Proof	—
2008 New Rev., no border beads on Obv.	—
2008 — BU	—
2008 — Proof	—
2008 — Silver Proof	—
2008 — Silver Proof Piedfort	—
2008 — Gold Proof	—
2008 — Platinum Proof	—
2009	—
2009 BU	—
2009 Proof	—
2009 Silver Proof	—

FIVE PENCE

This series commenced simultaneously with the Ten Pence (qv). They were the same size and weight as their predecessor, the shilling, and such coins up to 1990 are no longer legal tender.

DATE	UNC
1968	£3
1969	£3
1970	£3
1971	£3
1971 Proof	£3
1972 Proof	£6
1973 Proof	£5
1974 Proof	£6
1975	£3
1975 Proof	£6
1976 Proof	£7
1977	50p
1977 Proof	£6
1978	£3
1978 Proof	£4
1979	£3
1979 Proof	£4
1980	£3
1980 Proof	£4
1981 Proof	£6
1982 Unc	£5
1982 Proof	£6
1983 Unc	£4
1983 Proof	£6
1984 BU	£4
1984 Proof	£6
1985 New Portrait. BU	£2
1985 Proof	£6
1986 BU	£2
1986 Proof	£6
1987	—
1987 BU	£3
1987 Proof	£5
1988	—
1988 BU	£3
1988 Proof	£5
1989	—
1989 BU	£3
1989 Proof	£5
1990 BU	£2
1990 Proof	£5
1990 Silver Proof	£15
1990 *Size reduced to 18mm*	£2
1990 BU	£3
1990 Proof	£4
1990 Silver Proof	£15
1990 — — Piedfort	£45
1991	—
1991 BU	£3
1991 Proof	£5
1992	—
1992 BU	£3
1992 Proof	£5
1993 BU	£3
1993 Proof	£5
1994	—
1994 BU	£3
1994 Proof	£6
1995	—
1995 BU	£3
1995 Proof	£6
1996	—
1996 BU	£3
1996 Proof	£6
1996 Silver proof	£20
1997	—
1997 BU	£1
1997 Proof	£3
1998 New portrait	—
1998 BU	£3
1998 Proof	£6
1999	—
1999 BU	£3
1999 Proof	£6
2000	—
2000 BU	£4
2000 Proof	£6
2000 Silver Proof	£25
2001	—
2001 BU	£3
2001 Proof	£5
2002	—
2002 BU	£3
2002 Proof	£5
2002 Gold Proof	£85
2003	—
2003 BU	£3
2003 Proof	£5
2004	—
2004 BU	£3
2004 Proof	£5
2005	—
2005 BU	£3
2005 Proof	£5
2006	—
2006 BU	£3
2006 Proof	£5
2006 Silver Proof	£15
2007	—
2007 BU	£3
2007 Proof	£5
2008	—
2008 BU	—
2008 Proof	—
2008 Silver Proof	—
2008 Gold Proof	—
2008 Platinum Proof	—
2008 New Rev, no border beads on Obv	—
2008 — BU	—
2008 — Proof	—
2008 — Silver Proof	—
2008 — Silver Proof Piedfort	—
2008 — Gold Proof	—
2008 — Platinum Proof	—
2009	—
2009 BU	—
2009 Proof	—
2009 Silver Proof	—

TWO PENCE

Dated from 1971, and legal tender from Decimal Day that year, early examples are found in the blue Specimen decimal set wallets of 1968. They were minted in bronze up to 1991, and mainly in copper-plated steel from 1992. However details of where this rule does not totally apply (1992, 1996, 1998–2000 and 2002, 2006, 2008 and 2009) are given below. As with other denominations, "NEW" was replaced by the quantity of pence in word from 1982.

DATE	UNC
1971	£2
1971 Proof	£3
1972 Proof	£5
1973 Proof	£5
1974 Proof	£6
1975	£2
1975 Proof	£2
1976	£2
1976 Proof	£2
1977	£2
1977 Proof	£2
1978	£2
1978 Proof	£2
1979	£2
1979 Proof	£2
1980	£1
1980 Proof	£2
1981	£2
1981 Proof	£3
1982 Unc	£2
1982 Proof	£4
1983 Unc	£2
1983 — Error NEW instead of TWO	£450
1983 Proof	£3
1984 BU	£1
1984 Proof	£4
1985 New portrait	£1
1985 BU	£2
1985 Proof	£4
1986	50p
1986 BU	£2
1986 Proof	£4
1987	50p
1987 BU	£2
1987 Proof	£4
1988	50p
1988 BU	£2
1988 Proof	£4
1989	50p
1989 BU	£2
1989 Proof	£4
1990	50p
1990 BU	£2
1990 Proof	£3
1991	50p
1991 BU	£2
1991 Proof	£5
1992 Copper plated steel	£1
1992 Bronze BU	£2
1992 — Proof	£5
1993	50p
1993 BU	£2

DATE	UNC
1993 Proof	£3
1994	50p
1994 BU	£1
1994 Proof	£3
1995	—
1995 BU	£2
1995 Proof	£4
1996	—
1996 BU	£2
1996 Proof	£3
1996 Silver Proof	£20
1997	—
1997 BU	£2
1997 Proof	£4
1998 New portrait	—
1998 BU	£2
1998 Proof	£4
1998 Bronze	£1
1999	£1
1999 Bronze BU	£2
1999 — Proof	£4
2000	—
2000 BU	£2
2000 Proof	£4
2000 Silver Proof	£22
2001	—
2001 BU	£2
2001 Proof	£4
2002	—
2002 BU	£2
2002 Proof	£4
2002 Gold Proof	£100
2003	—
2003 BU	£2
2003 Proof	£4
2004	—
2004 BU	£2
2004 Proof	£4
2005	—
2005 BU	50p
2005 Proof	£2
2006	—
2006 BU	50p
2006 Proof	£2
2006 Silver Proof	£15
2007	—
2007 BU	£2
2007 Proof	£4
2008	—
2008 BU	£2
2008 Proof	£5
2008 Silver Proof	£20

DATE	UNC
2008 Gold Proof	£100
2008 Platinum Proof	—
2008 New Rev., no border beads on Obv.	—
2008 — BU	—
2008 — Proof	—
2008 — Silver Proof	—
2008 — Silver Proof Piedfort	—
2008 — Gold Proof	—
2008 — Platinum Proof	—
2009	—
2009 BU	—
2009 Proof	—
2009 Silver Proof	—

ONE PENNY

The history of this coin is very similar to that of the Two Pence coin (qv) except that all 1998 examples were of copper-plated steel.

DATE	UNC
1971	£1
1971 Proof	£2
1972 Proof	£5
1973	£2
1973 Proof	£3
1974	£2
1974 Proof	£3
1975	£2
1975 Proof	£4
1976	£1
1976 Proof	£2
1977	£2
1977 Proof	£3
1978	£2
1978 Proof	£3
1979	£2
1979 Proof	£3
1980	£2
1980 Proof	£3
1981	£2
1981 Proof	£3
1982 Legend changed to ONE PENNY	50p
1982 Unc	£1
1982 Proof	£2
1983	£1
1983 Unc	£2
1983 Proof	£4
1984	50p
1984 BU	£2
1984 Proof	£3
1985 New portrait	25p
1985 BU	£2
1985 Proof	£3
1986	25p
1986 BU	£2
1986 Proof	£3
1987	25p
1987 BU	£2
1987 Proof	£3
1988	25p
1988 BU	£2
1988 Proof	£3
1989	25p
1989 BU	£2
1989 Proof	£3
1990	£2
1990 BU	£3
1990 Proof	£4
1991	25p
1991 BU	£2
1991 Proof	£4
1992 Copper-plated steel	£1
1992 Bronze BU	£2
1992 — Proof	£4
1993	25p
1993 BU	£2
1993 Proof	£4
1994	£1
1994 BU	£2
1994 Proof	£4
1995	£2
1995 BU	£3
1995 Proof	£4
1996	—
1996 BU	£2
1996 Proof	£4
1996 Silver Proof	£18
1997	—
1997 BU	£2
1997 Proof	£4
1998 New portrait	25p
1998 — BU	£2
1998 Proof	£4
1999	£2
1999 Bronze BU	£2
1999 Bronze Proof	£4
2000	—
2000 BU	£2
2000 Proof	£4
2000 Silver Proof	£22
2001	—
2001 BU	£2
2001 Proof	£4
2002	—
2002 BU	£2
2002 Proof	£4
2002 Gold Proof	£95
2003	—

DATE	UNC
2003 BU	£2
2003 Proof	£3
2004	–
2004 BU	£2
2004 Proof	£4
2005	–
2005 BU	£2
2005 Proof	£3
2006	–
2006 BU	£2
2006 Proof	£4
2006 Silver Proof	£15
2007	–
2007 BU	£2
2007 Proof	£3
2008	–
2008 BU	–
2008 Proof	–
2008 Silver Proof	–
2008 Gold Proof	–
2008 Platinum Proof	–
2008 New Rev, no border beads on Obv	–
2008 – BU	–
2008 – Proof	–
2008 – Silver Proof	–
2008 – Silver Proof Piedfort	–
2008 – Gold Proof	–
2008 – Platinum Proof	–
2009	–
2009 BU	–
2009 Proof	–
2009 Silver BU, in "Lucky Baby Gift Pack"	£15
2009 – Proof	–

HALF PENNY

No longer legal tender, its history tracks that of the Two Pence and One Penny.

DATE	UNC
1971	£2
1971 Proof	£3
1972 Proof	£5
1973	£2
1973 Proof	£3
1974	£2
1974 Proof	£3
1975	£2
1975 Proof	£3
1976	£2
1976 Proof	£3
1977	£1
1977 Proof	£3
1978	£1
1978 Proof	£4
1979	£2
1979 Proof	£4
1980	£2
1980 Proof	£3
1981	£2
1981 Proof	£4
1982 Legend changed to HALF PENNY	50p
1982 Unc	£2
1982 Proof	£3
1983	50p
1983 Unc	£1
1983 Proof	£4
1984	£4
1984 BU	£5
1984 Proof	£6

PROOF AND SPECIMEN SETS

NOTE: The prices quoted in this guide are set at August 2009 with the price of gold at £595 per ounce and silver £8.75 per ounce—market fluctuations will have a marked effect on the values of modern precious metal coins.

The following listings are an attempt to include all officially marketed products from the Royal Mint of two coins or more, but excluding those which included non-UK coins. It is appreciated that not all have been advertised as new to the public, but it is assumed that at some time they have been, or will be, available. In a few cases, therefore, the prices may be conjectural but are, nevertheless, attempts at listing realistic value, in some instances based on an original retail price. In the case of Elizabeth II sets, if no metal is stated in the listing, the coins in the sets are of the same metal as the circulation coin equivalent. In addition to the above we have excluded historical gold coin sets, such as sets of sovereigns from different mints, where the dates of the coins vary from one set to another.

DATE	FDC
GEORGE IV	
1826 £5–farthing (11 coins)	£25,000
WILLIAM IV	
1831 Coronation £2–farthing (14 coins)	£22,000
VICTORIA	
1839 "Una and the Lion" £5–farthing (15 coins)	£40,000
1853 Sovereign–quarter farthing, including "Gothic"crown (16 coins)	£32,500
1887 Golden Jubilee £5–3d (11 coins)	£10,000
1887 Golden Jubilee Crown–3d (7 coins)	£2,000
1893 £5–3d (10 coins)	£12,000
1893 Crown–3d (6 coins)	£3,000
EDWARD VII	
1902 Coronation £5–Maundy penny, matt proofs (13 coins)	£2,500
1902 Coronation Sovereign–Maundy penny, matt proofs (11 coins)	£1,500
GEORGE V	
1911 Coronation £5–Maundy penny (12 coins)	£3,500
1911 Sovereign–Maundy penny (10 coins)	£1,500
1911 Coronation Halfcrown–Maundy penny (8 coins)	£750
1927 New types Crown–3d (6 coins)	£500

DATE	FDC
GEORGE VI	
1937 Coronation £5–half sovereign (4 coins)	£2,750
1937 Coronation Crown–farthing including Maundy money (15 coins)	£350
1950 Mid-century Halfcrown–farthing (9 coins)	£150
1951 Festival of Britain, Crown–farthing (10 coins)	£175
ELIZABETH II	
1953 Proof Coronation Crown–farthing (10 coins)	£75
1953 Currency (plastic) set halfcrown–farthing (9 coins)	£15
1968 Specimen decimal set 10p, 5p and 1971-dated bronze in blue wallet (5 coins)	£2.50
1970 Proof Last £sd coins (issued from 1972) Halfcrown–halfpenny (8 coins)	£20
1971 Proof (issued 1973) 50p–half penny (6 coins)	£18
1972 Proof (issued 1976) 50p–half penny (7 coins including Silver Wedding crown)	£18
1973 Proof (issued 1976) 50p–half penny (6 coins)	£16
1974 Proof (issued 1976) 50p–half penny (6 coins)	£18
1975 Proof (issued 1976) 50p–half penny (6 coins)	£18
1976 Proof 50p–half penny (6 coins)	£18
1977 Proof 50p–half penny (7 coins including Silver Jubilee crown)	£16
1978 Proof 50p–half penny (6 coins)	£16
1979 Proof 50p–half penny (6 coins)	£18
1980 Proof gold sovereign series (4 coins)	£875
1980 — 50p–half penny (6 coins)	£16
1981 Proof £5, sovereign, Royal Wedding Silver crown, 50p–half penny (9 coins)	£800
1981 — 50p–half penny (6 coins)	£18
1982 Proof gold sovereign series (4 coins)	£850
1982 — 50p–half penny (7 coins)	£20
1982 Uncirculated 50p–half penny (7 coins)	£15
1983 Proof gold double-sovereign to half sovereign (3 coins)	£450
1983 — £1–half penny (8 coins) (includes H. J. Heinz sets)	£25
1983 Uncirculated £1–half penny (8 coins) (includes Benson & Hedges and Martini sets)	£30
1983 — 50p–half penny (7 coins) (H. J. Heinz sets)	£16
1984 Proof gold five pounds, sovereign and half-sovereigns (3 coins)	£800
1984 — £1 (Scottish rev.)–half penny (8 coins)	£18
1984 BU £1 (Scottish rev.)–half penny (8 coins)	£16
1985 New portrait proof gold sovereign series (4 coins)	£900
1985 Proof £1–1p in de luxe case (7 coins)	£25
1985 — in standard case	£18
1985 BU £1–1p (7 coins) in folder	£15
1986 Proof gold Commonwealth Games £2, sovereign and half sovereign (3 coins)	£600
1986 — Commonwealth Games £2–1p, de luxe case (8 coins)	£35
1986 — — in standard case (8 coins)	£30
1986 BU £2–1p in folder (8 coins)	£20
1987 Proof gold Britannia set (4 coins)	£950
1987 — — — £25 and £10 (2 coins)	£250
1987 — — double- to half sovereign (3 coins)	£450
1987 — £1–1p in de luxe case (7 coins)	£35
1987 — £1–1p in standard case (7 coins)	£25
1987 BU £1–1p in folder (7 coins)	£20
1988 Proof gold Britannia set (4 coins)	£950
1988 — — — £25 and £10 (2 coins)	£250
1988 — — double- to half sovereign (3 coins)	£450
1988 — £1–1p in de luxe case (7 coins)	£35
1988 — £1–1p in standard case (7 coins)	£30
1988 BU £1–1p in folder (7 coins) (includes Bradford & Bingley sets)	£18
1989 Proof gold Britannia set (4 coins)	£950
1989 — — — £25 and £10 (2 coins)	£200
1989 — — 500th anniversary of the sovereign series set (4 coins)	£1,300
1989 — — — double- to half sovereign (3 coins)	£750
1989 — Silver Bill of Rights £2, Claim of Right £2 (2 coins)	£65
1989 — — Piedfort as above (2 coins)	£100
1989 BU £2 in folder (2 coins)	£25
1989 Proof £2 (both)–1p in de luxe case (9 coins)	£35
1989 — in standard case (9 coins)	£30
1989 BU £1–1p in folder (7 coins)	£25
1990 Proof gold Britannia set (4 coins)	£950
1990 — — sovereign series set (4 coins)	£1,000
1990— — double- to half sovereign (3 coins)	£550

DATE	FDC
1990 — silver 5p, 2 sizes (2 coins)	£28
1990 — £1–1p in de luxe case (8 coins)	£35
1990 — £1–1p standard case (8 coins)	£30
1990 BU £1–1p in folder (8 coins)	£20
1991 Proof gold Britannia set (4 coins)	£900
1991 — — sovereign series set (4 coins)	£1,250
1991 — — double- to half sovereign (3 coins)	£550
1991 — £1–1p in de luxe case (7 coins)	£35
1991 — £1–1p in standard case (7 coins)	£28
1991 BU £1–1p in folder (7 coins)	£18
1992 Proof gold Britannia set (4 coins)	£900
1992 — — sovereign series set (4 coins)	£1,150
1992 — — double- to half sovereign (3 coins)	£500
1992 — £1–1p including two each 50p and 10p in de luxe case (9 coins)	£38
1992 — £1–1p as above in standard case (9 coins)	£32
1992 BU £1–1p as above in folder (9 coins)	£16
1992 Proof silver 10p, two sizes (2 coins)	£38
1993 Proof gold Britannia set 1 (4 coins)	£1,150
1993 — — sovereign series set (4 coins plus silver Pistrucci medal)	£1,250
1993 — — double- to half sovereign (3 coins)	£550
1993 — Coronation anniversary £5–1p in de luxe case (8 coins)	£38
1993 — — in standard case (8 coins)	£35
1993 BU £1–1p including 1992 EU 50p (8 coins)	£15
1994 Proof gold Britannia set (4 coins)	£925
1994 — — sovereign series set (4 coins)	£1,250
1994 — — £2 to half sovereign (3 coins)	£650
1994 — Bank of England Tercentenary £2–1p in de luxe case (8 coins)	£38
1994 — — in standard case (8 coins)	£35
1994 BU £1–1p in folder (7 coins)	£18
1994 Proof gold 1992 and 1994 50p (2 coins)	£200
1994 — "Family silver" set £2–50p (3 coins)	£50
1995 Proof gold Britannia set (4 coins)	£950
1995 — — sovereign series (4 coins)	£1,450
1995 — — £2 to half sovereign (3 coins)	£650
1995 — 50th Anniversary of WWII £2–1p in de luxe case (8 coins)	£45
1995 — — as above in standard case (8 coins)	£38
1995 BU as above in folder (8 coins)	£16
1995 Proof "Family Silver" set £2 (two) and £1 (3 coins)	£55
1996 Proof gold Britannia set (4 coins)	£1,100
1996 — — sovereign series set (4 coins)	£1,250
1996 — — double- to half sovereign (3 coins)	£625
1996 — Royal 70th Birthday £5–1p in de luxe case (9 coins)	£50
1996 — — as above in standard case (9 coins)	£45
1996 BU Football £2–1p in folder (8 coins)	£20
1996 Proof gold Britannia £10 and half-sovereign (2 coins)	£500
1996 — — sovereign and silver £1 (2 coins)	£200
1996 — — "Family silver" set £5–£1 (3 coins)	£60
1996 — silver 25th Anniversary of Decimal currency £1–1p (7 coins)	£150
1996 Circulation and BU 25th Anniversary of Decimalisation 2s 6d–halfpenny (misc.) and £1–1p in folder (14 coins)	£65
1997 Proof gold Britannia set (4 coins)	£1,250
1997 — — sovereign series set (4 coins)	£1,150
1997 — — — £2 to half sovereign (3 coins)	£575
1997 — — Silver Britannia set (4 coins)	£135
1997 — Golden Wedding £5–1p in red leather case	£65
1997 — — as above in standard case (10 coins)	£40
1997 BU £2 to 1p in folder (9 coins)	£25
1997 Proof silver 50p set, two sizes (2 coins)	£38
1997/1998 Proof silver £2 set, both dates (2 coins)	£25
1998 Proof gold Britannia set (4 coins)	£1,250
1998 — — sovereign series set (4 coins)	£1,250
1998 — — — double- to half sovereign (3 coins)	£575
1998 Proof silver Britannia set (4 coins)	£125
1998 — Prince of Wales £5–1p (10 coins) in red leather case	£45
1998 — — as above in standard case (10 coins)	£38
1998 BU £2–1p in folder (9 coins)	£16
1998 Proof silver European/NHS 50p set (2 coins)	£60

DATE	FDC
1998 BU Britannia/EU 50p set (2 coins)	£8
1999 Proof gold Britannia set (4 coins)	£1,250
1999 — — Sovereign series set (4 coins)	£1,250
1999 — — — £2 to half sovereign (3 coins)	£650
1999 — Princess Diana £5–1p in red leather case (9 coins)	£60
1999 — — as above in standard case (9 coins)	£45
1999 BU £2–1p (8 coins) in folder	£18
1999 Proof "Family Silver" set. Both £5, £2 and £1 (4 coins)	£55
1999 Britannia Millennium set. Bullion £2 and BU £5 (2 coins)	£30
1999/2000 Reverse frosted proof set, two x £1 (2 coins)	£75
2000 Proof gold Britannia set (4 coins)	£1,250
2000 — — Sovereign series set (4 coins)	£1,250
2000 — — — double- to half sovereign (3 coins)	£575
2000 — Millennium £5–1p in red leather case (10 coins)	£60
2000 — — as above in de luxe case (10 coins)	£50
2000 — — as above in standard case (10 coins)	£45
2000 — Silver set Millennium £5 to 1p plus Maundy (13 coins)	£150
2000 BU £2–1p set in folder (9 coins)	£17
2000 Millennium "Time Capsule" BU £5 to 1p (9 coins)	£28
2001 Proof gold Britannia set (4 coins)	£950
2001 — — Sovereign series set (4 coins)	£1,250
2001 — — — £2–half sovereign (3 coins)	£600
2001 — Silver Britannia set (4 coins)	£120
2001 — Victoria £5–1p in Executive case (10 coins)	£85
2001 — — as above in red leather case (10 coins)	£55
2001 — — as above in "Gift" case (10 coins)	£48
2001 — — as above in standard case (10 coins)	£40
2001 BU £2–1p in folder (9 coins)	£18
2002 Proof gold Britannia set (4 coins)	£1,150
2002 — — Sovereign series set, all Shield rev. (4 coins)	£1,250
2002 — — — double- to half sovereign (3 coins)	£550
2002 — — Golden Jubilee set £5–1p plus Maundy (13 coins)	£3000
2002 — Golden Jubilee £5–1p in Executive case (9 coins)	£75
2002 — — as above in red leather de luxe case (9 coins)	£48
2002 — — as above in "Gift" case (9 coins)	£42
2002 — — as above in standard case (9 coins)	£35
2002 BU £2–1p (8 coins) in folder	£16
2002 Proof Gold Commonwealth Games £2 set (4 coins)	£1,450
2002 — Silver Piedfort Commonwealth Games £2 set (4 coins)	£250
2002 — — Commonwealth Games £2 set (4 coins)	£125
2002 — Commonwealth Games £2 set (4 coins)	£30
2002 BU Commonwealth Games £2 set (4 coins) in folder	£17
2003 Proof gold Britannia set (4 coins)	£1,150
2003 — — — £50–£10 (3 coins)	£500
2003 — — — type set, one of each £100 reverse (4 coins)	£1,550
2003 — — Sovereign series set (4 coins)	£1,250
2003 — — — series £2–half sovereign (3 coins)	£500
2003 — Silver Britannia set (4 coins)	£135
2003 — — — type set (one of each £2 reverse) (4 coins)	£80
2003 — £5 to 1p, two of each £2 and 50p in Executive case (11 coins)	£80
2003 — — as above in red leather case (11 coins)	£55
2003 — — as above in standard case (11 coins)	£48
2003 BU £2 (two)–1p in folder (10 coins)	£22
2003 Proof silver Piedfort set. DNA £2, £1 and Suffragette 50p (3 coins)	£185
2003 Proof "Family Silver" set £5, Britannia and DNA £2, £1 and Suffragette 50p (5 coins)	£165
2003 Circ & BU "God Save the Queen" Coronation anniversary set 5s/0d to farthing (1953) and £5 to 1p (2003) in folder (19 coins)	£85
2003 Circulation or bullion "Royal Sovereign" collection, example of each Elizabeth II date (21 coins)	£2,850
2004 Proof gold Britannia set (4 coins)	£1,150
2004 — — — £50 to £10 (3 coins)	£450
2004 — — Sovereign series set (4 coins)	£1,150
2004 — — — Series £2-half sovereign (3 coins)	£475
2004 (Issue date) Royal Portrait gold sovereign set, all proof except the first: Gillick, Machin, Maklouf and Rank-Broadley sovereigns, and the 2nd, 3rd and 4th of above half-sovereigns, various dates (7 coins)	£950
2004 Proof silver Britannia set (4 coins)	£135

DATE		FDC
2004	— "Family Silver" set £5, Britannia and Trevithick £2, £1 and Bannister 50p (5 coins)	£165
2004	— Silver Piedfort set, Trevithick £2, £1 and Bannister 50p (3 coins)	£185
2004	— £2 to 1p, two each of £2 and 50p in Executive case (10 coins)	£75
2004	— — as above in red leather case (10 coins)	£45
2004	— — as above in standard case (10 coins)	£35
2004	BU £2 to 1p in folder (10 coins)	£17
2004	— "New Coinage" set, Trevithick £2, £1 and Bannister 50p (3 coins)	£12
2004	BU "Season's Greetings" £2 to 1p and Royal Mint Christmas medal in folder (8 coins)	£17
2005	Proof Gold Britannia set (4 coins)	£1,000
2005	— — — £50 to £10 (3 coins)	£500
2005	— — Sovereign series set (4 coins)	£1,250
2005	— — — series, double to half sovereign (3 coins)	£550
2005	— Silver Britannia (4 coins)	£135
2005	— Gold Trafalgar and Nelson £5 crowns (2 coins)	£1,350
2005	— Silver, as above (2 coins)	£85
2005	— — Piedfort, as above (2 coins)	£135
2005	— Silver Piedfort set, Gunpowder Plot and World War II £2, £1 and Johnson 50p (4 coins)	£225
2005	— £5 to 1p, two of each of £5, £2 and 50p in Executive case (12 coins)	£80
2005	— — as above in red leather case (12 coins)	£58
2005	— — as above in standard case (12 coins)	£45
2005	BU Trafalgar and Nelson £5 crowns in pack (2 coins)	£25
2005	— £2 (two) to 1p in folder (10 coins)	£16
2005	— "New Coinage" set, Gunpowder Plot £2, £1 and Johnson 50p (3 coins)	£10
2005	— "Merry Xmas" £2 to 1p and Royal Mint Christmas medal in folder (8 coins)	£20
2006	Proof Gold Britannia set (4 coins)	£1,000
2006	— — Sovereign Series set (4 coins)	£1,250
2006	— — — series, double to half sovereign (3 coins)	£600
2006	— Silver Britannia (4 coins)	£135
2006	— Silver Brunel £2 coin set (2 coins)	£75
2006	— — Piedfort Brunel £2 coin set (2 coins)	£125
2006	— Gold Brunel £2 coin set (2 coins)	£800
2006	— Silver VC 50p coin set (2 coins)	£58
2006	— Silver Piedfort VC 50p coin set (2 coins)	£115
2006	— Gold VC 50p coin set (2 coins)	£675
2006	— Silver proof set, £5 to 1p plus Maundy coins (13 coins)	£325
2006	— — — Piedfort collection £5, with trumpets enhanced with 23 carat gold, both Brunel £2, £1, both VC 50p (6 coins) ... estimated	£350
2006	— — Britannia £2 "Golden Silhouette" collection, five different reverses, all dated 2006 (5 coins)	£300
2006	— £5 to 1p, three of each £2 and 50p in Executive case (13 coins)	£80
2006	— as above in red leather case (13 coins)	£55
2006	— as above in standard case (13 coins)	£45
2006	BU £2 (two), £1, 50p (two) and to 1p in folder (10 coins)	£18
2006	Proof Brunel £2 in folder (2 coins)	£12
2006	— VC 50p in folder (2 coins)	£12
2006	— Gold Half-Sovereign set dated 2005 Noad and 2006 Pistrucci St George and the Dragon (2 coins)	£220
2007	— Gold Britannia set (4 coins)	£1,350
2007	— — Sovereign Series set (4 coins)	£1,550
2007	— — — series, double to half sovereign (3 coins)	£650
2007	— — Sovereign and half-sovereign (2 coins)	£300
2007	— "Family Silver" set, Britannia, £5 crown, Union and Slavery £2, Gateshead £1 and Scouting 50p (6 coins)	£225
2007	Proof Silver Piedfort Collection, as "Family Silver" above but excluding a Britannia (5 coins)	£2,850
2007	— Silver £1 Bridge series coins, dated 2004 to 2007 (4 coins)	£135
2007	— Silver Proof Piedfort £1 Bridge Series, dated 2004 to 2007 (4 coins)	£275
2007	— Gold £1 Bridge series coins, dated as above (4 coins)	£1,650
2007	— £5 to 1p, three £2 and two 50p in Executive case (12 coins)	£85
2007	— as above, Deluxe in red leather case (12 coins)	£65
2007	— as above, in standard case (12 coins)	£50
2007	BU £2 (two) to 1p (9 coins)	£18
2007	Proof Silver Britannia (four coins)	£135
2007	Proof Platinum Britannia (4 coins)	£3,500
2007	Satin Proof Silver Britannia, 20th Anniversary Collection, six different reverses, all dated 2007 (6 coins)	£225
2007	50th Anniversary Sovereign set, 1957 circulation standard and 2007 Proof (2 coins)	£425
2008	Proof Gold Britannia set (4 coins)	£1,500
2008	— Platinum Britannia set (4 coins)	£3,475
2008	— Silver Britannia set (4 coins)	—

DATE	FDC
2008 Gold Sovereign series set (4 coins)	£1,600
2008 — — — double to half-sovereign (3 coins)	£725
2008 — — Sovereign and half-sovereign (2 coins)	£325
2008 — "Family silver" set, 2x £5, Britannia £2, Olympiad £2 and Royal Arms £1 (5 coins)	£185
2008 — Silver Piedfort Collection, 2x £5, Olympiad £2 and Shield of Royal Arms £1 (4 coins)	£275
2008 — 2 x £5, 2 x £2, £1 to 1p in Executive case (11 coins)	£85
2008 — as above, Deluxe in black leather case (11 coins)	£55
2008 - as above, in standard back case (11 coins)	£45
2008 BU 2 x £2, Royal Arms £1 tp 1p (9 coins)	£18
2008 — "Emblems of Britain" ("old" Revs) Royal Arms £1 to 1p (7 coins)	£12
2008 — "Royal Shield of Arms" ("new" Revs) Shield of Royal Arms £1 to 1p (7 coins)	£12
2008 — Above two sets housed in one sleeve	£22
2008 Proof Base Metal "Royal Shield of Arms" set, £1 to 1p (7 coins)	£38
2008 — Silver Emblems of Britain" set, £1 to 1p (7 coins)	£160
2008 — — "Royal Shield of Arms" set, £1 to 1p (7 coins)	£160
2008 — — Above two sets in one black case	£325
2008 — Gold "Emblems of Britain" set, £1 to 1p (7 coins)	£2,600
2008 — — "Royal Shield of Arms" set, £1 to 1p (7 coins)	£2,600
2008 — — Above two sets in one oak-veneer case	£5,000
2008 — Platinum "Emblems of Britain" set, £1 to 1p (7 coins)	£6,500
2008 — — "Royal Shield of Arms" set, £1 to 1p (7 coins)	£6,500
2008 — — Above two sets in one walnut veneer case	£12,750
2008 — Silver Piedfort "Royal Shield of Arms" set, £1 to 1p (7 coins)	£325
2008 — Gold set of 14 £1 coins, one of each Rev used since 1983, all dated 2008 (25th anniversary) (14 coins)	£7,500
2008 — Silver with gold Rev highlighting as above (14 coins)	£425
2008 — 2 x £2, Royal Arms £1 to 1p (9 coins) Christmas Coin Sets, two different outer sleeves, Father Christmas or Three Wise men	£20
2009 Proof Gold Britannia set (4 coins)	£2,250
2009 — Platinum Britannia set (4 coins)	£3,475
2009 — Silver Britannia set (4 coins)	£125
2009 — Gold Sovereign series set (5 coins)	£2,500
2009 — — — double to half-sovereign (3 coins)	£1,000
2009 — — sovereign and half-sovereign (2 coins)	£425
2009 — "Family Silver" set, Henry VIII £5, Britannia £2, Darwin and Burns £2, £1 and Kew 50p (6 coins)	£225
2009 — Silver Piedfort collection, Henry VIII £5, Darwin and Burns £2 and Kew Gardens 50p (4 coins)	£275
2009 — Silver Set, £5 to 1p (12 coins)	£275
2009 — Base metal Executive set, £5 to 1p (12 coins)	£80
2009 — — — Deluxe set, £5 to 1p (12 coins)	£55
2009 — — — Standard set, £5 to 1p (12 coins)	£45
2009 BU Base metal set, £2 to 1p (11 coins)	£22
2009 — — —, £1 to 1p "Royal Shield of Arms" set (7 coins)	£12

In addition to the above the Royal Mint produce the BU sets detailed above in Wedding and in Baby gift packs each year. Also the following patterns have been made available:

1999 (dated 1994) Bi-metal £2, plus three unprocessed or part-processed elements	—
2003 Proof gold £1 featuring future reverse Bridge designs, hall-marked on edge (4 coins)	£1,750

SCOTLAND

The coins illustrated are pennies representative of the reign, unless otherwise stated.

DAVID I (1124–53)

Berwick, Carlisle, Edinburgh and Roxburgh Mints

	F	VF
Penny	£675	£2000

David I

HENRY (1136–52)

Bamborough, Carlisle and Corbridge Mints for the Earl of Huntingdon and Northumberland

	F	VF
Penny	£1600	£5550

Henry

MALCOLM IV (1153–65)

Berwick and Roxburgh Mints

	F	VF
Penny (5 different types)	£4250	£12000

WILLIAM THE LION (1165–1214)

Berwick, Edinburgh, Dun (Dunbar?), Perth and Roxburgh Mints

	F	VF
Penny	£125	£300

William the Lion

ALEXANDER II (1214–49)

Berwick and Roxburgh Mints

	F	VF
Penny	£900	£2250

Alexander II

ALEXANDER III (1249–86)

FIRST COINAGE (1250–80)

Pennies struck at the Mints at

	F	VF
Aberdeen	£120	£450
Ayr	£120	£450
Berwick	£100	£250
"Dun" (Dumfries?)	£165	£525
Edinburgh	£70	£225
Forfar	£165	£550
Forres	£180	£550
Glasgow	£190	£580
Inverness	£190	£575
Kinghorn	£210	£600
Lanark	£190	£575
Montrose	£325	£790
Perth	£120	£250
Renfrew	£230	£825
Roxburgh	£120	£275
St Andrews	£160	£400
Sterling	£220	£675

Alexander III

SECOND COINAGE (1280–86)

	F	VF
Penny	£65	£150
Halfpenny	£120	£350
Farthing	£220	£675

JOHN BALIOL (1292–1306)

FIRST COINAGE *(Rough Surface issue)*

	F	VF
Penny	£150	£475
Halfpenny	Extremely rare	

SECOND COINAGE *(Smooth Surface issue)*

	F	VF
Penny	£185	£450
Halfpenny	£280	£900
Farthing	£695	£2250

John Baliol

ROBERT BRUCE (1306–29)

Berwick Mint

	F	VF
Penny	£370	£1250
Halfpenny	£570	£1600
Farthing	Extremely Rare	

Robert Bruce

DAVID II (1329–71)

Aberdeen and Edinburgh Mints

	F	VF
Noble	Extremely Rare	
Groat	£100	£325
Halfgroat	£120	£350
Penny	£70	£170
Halfpenny	£245	£650
Farthing	£660	£2500

David II

ROBERT II (1371–90)

Dundee, Edinburgh and Perth Mints

	F	VF
Groat	£145	£275
Halfgroat	£145	£350
Penny	£115	£325
Halfpenny	£175	£570

Robert II

ROBERT III (1390–1406)

Aberdeen, Dumbarton, Edinburgh, Perth Mints

	F	VF
Lion or crown	£615	£1500
Demy lion or halfcrown	£615	£1500
Groat	£100	£270
Halfgroat	£150	£500
Penny	£250	£625
Halfpenny	£370	£1250

JAMES I (1406–37)

Aberdeen, Edinburgh, Inverness, Linlithgow, Perth, Stirling Mints

	F	VF
Demy	£495	£1250
Half demy	£610	£1350
Groat	£225	£550
Penny	£200	£455
Halfpenny	£425	£1225

Robert III Lion

JAMES II (1437–60)

Aberdeen, Edinburgh, Linlithgow, Perth, Roxburgh, Stirling Mints

	F	VF
Demy	£625	£1500
Lion	£795	£2500
Half lion	Extremely rare	
Groat	£230	£750
Halfgroat	£610	£1200
Penny (billon)	£425	£950

JAMES III (1460–88)

Aberdeen, Berwick and Edinburgh Mints

	F	VF
Rider	£1000	£2500
Half rider	£1250	£3300
Quarter rider	£1500	£3300
Unicorn	£930	£2475
Groat	£250	£625
Halfgroat	£655	£1250
Penny (silver)	£285	£7400
Plack (billon)	£120	£500
Half plack	Extremely rare	
Penny (billon)	£120	£500
Farthing (copper)	£315	£525

James III Groat, Berwick Mint

JAMES IV (1488–1513)

Edinburgh Mint

	F	VF
Unicorn	£860	£2000
Half unicorn	£725	£1500
Lion or crown	£995	£2500
Half lion	£1900	£4750
Groat	£550	£1150
Halfgroat	£550	£1150
Penny (silver)	£550	£1675
Plack	£75	£225
Half plack	£140	£375
Penny (billon)	£75	£225

James IV

JAMES V (1513–42)

Edinburgh Mint

	F	VF
Unicorn	£1375	£3500
Half Unicorn	£1800	£5200
Crown	£750	£1720
Ducat or Bonnet piece	£2500	£6000
Two-thirds ducat	£2350	£4250
One -third ducat	£3200	£5800
Groat	£185	£550
One-third groat	£185	£550
Plack	£65	£175
Bawbee	£55	£165
Half bawbee	£125	£275
Quarter bawbee	Extremely rare	

James V Edinburgh Groat

MARY (1542–67)

Edinburgh and Stirling Mints

FIRST PERIOD (1542–58)

	F	VF
Crown	£1300	£3250
Twenty shillings	£2390	£4500
Lions (Forty-four shillings)	£1155	£3300
Half lions (Twenty-two shillings)	£900	£2500
Ryals (Three pounds)	£2500	£6600
Half ryal	£3500	£8000
Portrait testoon	£1225	£5000
Non-portrait testoon	£225	£665
Half testoon	£220	£645
Bawbee	£70	£175
Half bawbee	£110	£280
Penny (facing bust)	£225	£700
Penny (no bust)	Extremely rare	
Lion	£75	£225
Plack	£75	£225

SECOND PERIOD (Francis and Mary, 1558–60)

	F	VF
Ducat (Sixty shillings)	Extremely rare	
Non-portrait testoon	£225	£675
Half testoon	£245	£750
12 penny groat	£145	£375
Lion	£75	£175

Mary First Period Testoon

THIRD PERIOD (Widowhood, 1560–65)

	F	VF
Portrait testoon	£1100	£3300
Half testoon	£1250	£4000

FOURTH PERIOD (Henry and Mary, 1565–67)

	F	VF
Portrait ryal	Extremely rare	
Non-portrait ryal	£275	£675
Two-third ryal	£475	£900

	F	VF
One-third ryal	£500	£1375
Testoon	£300	£1175

FIFTH PERIOD (Second widowhood, 1567)

	F	VF
Non-portrait ryal	£350	£950
Two thirds ryal	£300	£850
One-third ryal	£375	£1000

JAMES VI
(Before accession to the English throne) (1567–1603)

FIRST COINAGE (1567–71)

	F	VF
Ryal	£245	£750
Two-thirds ryal	£240	£700
One-third ryal	£245	£725

SECOND COINAGE (1571–80)

	F	VF
Twenty pounds	Extremely rare	
Noble (or half merk)	£150	£575
Half noble (or quarter merk)	£150	£450
Two merks or Thistle dollar	£1725	£2750
Merk	£1700	–

James VI Fourth coinage thirty shillings

THIRD COINAGE (1580–81)

	F	VF
Ducat	£2650	£6600
Sixteen shillings	£1500	£3000
Eight shillings	£1100	£3000
Four shillings	£1100	£3000
Two shillings	Extremely rare	

FOURTH COINAGE (1582–88)

	F	VF
Lion noble	£3250	£8750
Two-third lion noble	£3250	£8750
One-third lion noble	£3750	£10000
Forty shillings	£3150	£9750
Thirty shillings	£440	£1350
Twenty shillings	£440	£1000
Ten shillings	£290	£725

FIFTH COINAGE (1588)

	F	VF
Thistle noble	£1950	£4275

SIXTH COINAGE (1591–93)

	F	VF
"Hat" piece	£3250	£8000
"Balance" half merk	£250	£575
"Balance" quarter merk	£475	£1100

SEVENTH COINAGE (1594–1601)

	F	VF
Rider	£660	£1375
Half rider	£535	£1350
Ten shillings	£130	£450
Five shillings	£165	£500
Thirty pence	£125	£425
Twelve pence	£130	£425

EIGHTH COINAGE (1601–04)

	F	VF
Sword and sceptre piece	£360	£725
Half sword and sceptre piece	£300	£650
Thistle-merk	£100	£650
Half thistle-merk	£65	£250
Quarter thistle-merk	£65	£250
Eighth thistle-merk	£65	£250

Billon and copper issues

	F	VF
Eightpenny groat	£45	£100
Fourpenny groat	£195	–
Twopenny plack	£95	£280
Hardhead	£145	£375
Twopence	£95	£330
Penny plack	£110	£350
Penny	£175	£600

JAMES VI
(After accession to the English throne) (1603–25)

	F	VF
Unit	£525	£1100
Double crown	£675	£2000
British crown	£665	£1750
Halfcrown	£400	£975
Thistle crown	£450	£875
Sixty shillings	£385	£950
Thirty shillings	£145	£380
Twelve shillings	£135	£360
Six shillings	£360	£975
Two shillings	£75	£350
One shilling	£145	£450
Copper twopence	£50	£145
Copper penny	£50	£145

James VI after accession thirty shillings

CHARLES I (1625–49)

FIRST COINAGE (1625–36)

	F	VF
Unit	£800	£1295
Double crown	£1450	£3300
British crown	£2220	£6600
Sixty shillings	£435	£1250
Thirty shillings	£110	£335
Twelve shillings	£110	£335
Six shillings	£265	£585
Two shillings	£125	£485
One shilling	£125	£475

SECOND COINAGE (1636)

	F	VF
Half merk	£75	£285
Forty penny piece	£75	£250
Twenty penny piece	£80	£425

THIRD COINAGE (1637–42)

	F	VF
Unit	£725	£2250
Half unit	£785	£2500
British crown	£675	£2150
British half crown	£480	£1375
Sixty shillings	£395	£1250
Thirty shillings	£110	£375
Twelve shillings	£85	£275
Six shillings	£80	£250
Half merk	£75	£250
Forty pence	£50	£150
Twenty pence	£45	£125
Three shillings	£65	£225
Two shillings	£65	£225
Twopence (copper)	£45	£115
Penny	Extremely rare	
Twopence (CR crowned)	£30	£75
Twopence (Stirling turner)	£30	£60

Charles I Third coinage thirty shillings

CHARLES II (1660–85)

FIRST COINAGE

	F	VF
Four merks		
1664 Thistle above bust	£675	£1500
1664 Thistle below bust	£790	£1500
1665	Extremely rare	
1670	£530	£1000
1673	£530	£1250
1674 F below bust	£595	£1350
1675	£595	£1350
Two merks		
1664 Thistle above bust	£265	£875
1664 Thistle below bust	£300	£1000
1670	£245	£850
1673	£245	£850
1673 F below bust	£390	£1250
1674	£310	£1250
1674 F below bust	£325	£1475
1675	£235	£675
Merk		
1664	£125	£280
1665	£125	£325
1666	£200	£590
1668	£125	£325
1669	£145	£375
1670	£105	£400
1671	£95	£270
1672	£95	£275
1673	£95	£275
1674	£95	£325
1674 F Below bust	£125	£325
1675 F below bust	£125	£485
1675	£125	£485
Half merk		
1664	£150	£425
1665	£125	£375
1666	£150	£500
1667	£125	£425
1668	£125	£425
1669	£150	£450
1670	£125	£500
1671	£95	£325
1672	£95	£325
1673	£110	£300
1675 F below bust	£150	£425
1675	£125	£350

Charles II two merks

SECOND COINAGE

	F	VF
Dollar		
1676	£360	£950
1679	£360	£1000
1680	£485	£1475
1681	£360	£975
1682	£355	£950
Half Dollar		
1675	£305	£775
1676	£360	£970
1681	£230	£625
Quarter Dollar		
1675	£120	£325
1676	£120	£325
1677	£200	£550

	F	VF
1678	£55	£225
1679	£125	£500
1680	£155	£575
1681	£130	£485
1682	£170	£485
Eighth Dollar		
1676	£100	£250
1677	£100	£250
1678/7		Rare
1679	£325	£925
1680	£125	£325
1682	£260	£725
Sixteenth Dollar		
1677	£85	£225
1678/7	£95	£250
1679/7		Rare
1680	£265	£725
1681	£125	£325
Twopence CR crowned	£50	£185
Bawbees	£85	£250
Turners	£50	£185

James VII ten shillings

JAMES VII (1685–89)

	F	VF
Sixty shillings		
1688 proof only	–	£2200
Forty shillings		
1687	£160	£600
1688	£245	£685
Ten shillings		
1687	£125	£425
1688	£160	£575

WILLIAM & MARY (1689–94)

	F	VF
Sixty shillings		
1691	£265	£1000
1692	£330	£1000
Forty shillings		
1689	£265	£550
1690	£130	£465
1691	£175	£550
1692	£155	£475
1693	£160	£585
1694	£165	£585
Twenty shillings		
1693	£275	£925
1694	£460	£1500
Ten shillings		
1689	Extremely rare	
1690	£265	£555
1691	£190	£350
1692	£125	£350
1694	£225	£575
Five shillings		
1691	£160	£500
1694	£95	£325
Bawbee		
1691–94	£85	£175
Bodle		
1691–94	£55	£150

William & Mary ten shillings

WILLIAM II (1694–1702)

	F	VF
Pistole	£3225	£6850
Half pistole	£3500	£8000
Forty shillings		
1695	£175	£575
1696	£180	£475
1697	£270	£575
1698	£200	£475
1699	£270	£525
1700	Extremely rare	
Twenty shillings		
1695	£145	£475
1696	£145	£475
1697	£245	£800
1698	£180	£800
1699	£180	£550
Ten shillings		
1695	£125	£475
1696	£125	£375
1697	£125	£375
1698	£150	£450
1699	£250	£600
Five shillings		
1695	£115	£455
1696	£75	£225
1697	£95	£375
1699	£85	£375
1700	£85	£375
1701	£125	£475
1702	£125	£475
Bawbee		
1695–97	£55	£175
Bodle		
1695–97	£55	£250

William II ten shillings

ANNE (1702–14)

PRE-UNION 1702–7

	F	VF
Ten shillings		
1705	£195	£450
1706	£195	£575
Five shillings		
1705	£85	£275
1706	£65	£100

Anne five shillings

POST-UNION 1707–14

See listing in English section.

JAMES VIII (The Old Pretender) (1688–1766)

A number of Guineas and Crowns in various metals were struck in 1828 using original dies prepared by Norbert Roettiers, all bearing the date 1716. These coins are extremely rare and are keenly sought after.

ISLE OF MAN

DATE	F	VF	EF	UNC

PENNY

DATE	F	VF	EF	UNC
1709 Cast	£40	£95	£250	—
1709 Silver cast Proof	—	—	—	£1900
1709 Brass	£40	£105	£250	—
1733 “Quocunque”	£35	£50	£220	£360
1733 “Ouocunoue”	£35	£60	£250	£650
1733 Bath metal “Quocunque”	£25	£45	£210	—
1733 Silver Proof	—	—	—	£750
1733 Bronze Proof	—	—	—	£450
1733 Proof	—	—	—	£650
1733 Cap frosted	£25	£45	£250	£360
1733 Brass, cap frosted	£35	£55	£265	£500
1733 Silver Proof cap frosted	—	—	—	£560
1733 Bronze annulets instead of pellets	£45	£90	£350	£250
1758	£25	£40	£200	£390
1758 Proof	—	—	—	£610
1758 Silver Proof	—	—	—	£975
1786 Engrailed edge	£30	£45	£220	£450
1786 Engrailed edge Proof	—	—	—	£475
1786 Plain edge Proof	—	—	—	£970
1786 Pellet below bust	£30	£55	£275	£530
1798	£30	£55	£200	£410
1798 Proof	—	—	—	£370
1798 Bronze Proof	—	—	—	£370
1798 Copper-gilt Proof	—	—	—	£1750
1798 Silver Proof	—	—	—	£2450
1813	£35	£55	£185	£365
1813 Proof	—	—	—	£390
1813 Bronze Proof	—	—	—	£365
1813 Copper-gilt Proof	—	—	—	£2450
1839	£30	£45	£155	£300
1839 Proof	—	—	—	£450

HALF PENCE

DATE	F	VF	EF	UNC
1709 Cast	£45	£100	£250	—
1709 Brass	£50	£180	£490	—
1723 Silver	£635	£1200	£3100	—
1723 Copper	£275	£565	£1750	£2450
1733 Copper	£30	£50	£225	£390
1733 Bronze	£30	£50	£225	£390
1733 Silver Proof plain cap	—	—	—	£575
1733 Silver Proof frosted cap	—	—	—	—
1733 Bronze Proof	—	—	—	£450
1733 Bath metal plain cap	£35	£45	£210	—
1733 Bath metal frosted cap	£35	£45	£210	—
1758	£35	£45	£210	£370
1758 Proof	—	—	—	£750
1786 Engrailed edge	£25	£40	£120	£320
1786 Proof engrailed edge	—	—	—	£400
1786 Plain edge	£35	£60	£250	£330
1786 Proof plain edge	—	—	—	£650
1786 Bronze Proof	—	—	—	£425
1798	£30	£40	£110	£320
1798 Proof	—	—	—	£380
1798 Bronze Proof	—	—	—	£375

DATE	F	VF	EF	UNC
1798 Copper-gilt Proof	—	—	—	£1100
1798 Silver Proof	—	—	—	£1450
1813	£25	£40	£110	£250
1813 Proof	—	—	—	£350
1813 Bronze Proof	—	—	—	£310
1813 Copper-gilt Proof	—	—	—	£1200
1839	£25	£40	£80	£210
1839 Bronze Proof	—	—	—	£375

FARTHING

DATE	F	VF	EF	UNC
1839 Copper	£25	£40	£90	£220
1839 Bronze Proof	—	—	—	£370
1839 Copper-gilt Proof	—	—	—	£2250

The last issue of coins made in the Isle of Man had been in 1839 but in 1970 Spink & Son Ltd was commissioned to produce a modern coinage for the Isle of Man Government which was struck at the Royal Mint. From 1973 onwards the Pobjoy Mint took over the contract and has been a very prolific producer of definitive and commemorative issues. It is not proposed to give a complete listing of all these coins but the Crown and 25p, which from the collector's point of view are the most interesting in the series, have been selected. Additionally a special 50p coin is issued to celebrate Christmas each year.

The listings that follow are of the ordinary uncirculated cupro-nickel crown-size coins. The Island has also issued most of the coins listed in other metals, including silver, gold and platinum in non proof and proof form and in 1984 some were also issued in silver clad cupro-nickel in proof form.

DATE	UNC
1970 Manx Cat	£15
1972 Royal Silver Wedding	£15
1974 Centenary of Churchill's birth	£15
1975 Manx Cat	£15
1976 Bi-Centenary of American Independence	£15
1976 Centenary of the Horse Drawn Tram	£10
1977 Silver Jubilee	£10
1977 Silver Jubilee Appeal	£10
1978 25th Anniversary of the Coronation	£10
1979 300th Anniversary of Manx Coinage	£10
1979 Millennium of Tynwald (5 coins)	£20
1980 Winter Olympics	£15
1980 Derby Bicentennial	£15
1980 22nd Olympics (3 coins)	£20
1980 80th Birthday of Queen Mother	£10
1981 Duke of Edinburgh Award Scheme (4 coins)	£15
1981 Year of Disabled (4 coins)	£15
1981 Prince of Wales' Wedding (2 coins)	£15
1982 12th World Cup—Spain (4 coins)	£20
1982 Maritime Heritage (4 coins)	£20
1983 Manned Flight (4 coins)	£20
1984 23rd Olympics (4 coins)	£20
1984 Quincentenary of College of Arms (4 coins)	£20
1984 Commonwealth Parliamentary Conference (4 coins)	£20
1985 Queen Mother (6 coins)	£20
1986 13th World Cup—Mexico (6 coins)	£15
1986 Prince Andrew Wedding (2 coins)	£15
1987 200th Anniversary of the United States Constitution	£15

DATE	UNC
1987 America's Cup Races (5 coins)	£20
1988 Bicentenary of Steam Navigation (6 coins)	£20
1988 Australia Bicentennial (6 coins)	£20
1988 Manx Cat	£15
1989 Royal Visit	£10
1989 Bicentenary of the Mutiny on the Bounty (4 coins)	£20
1989 Persian Cat	£15
1989 Bicentenary of Washington's Inauguration (4 coins)	£15
1990 150th Anniversary of the Penny Black	£15
1990 World Cup—Italy (4 coins)	£20
1990 25th Anniversary of Churchill's Death (2 coins)	£15
1990 Alley Cat	£15
1990 Queen Mother's 90th Birthday	£10
1991 Norwegian Forest Cat	£10
1991 Centenary of the American Numismatic Association	£10
1991 1992 America's Cup	£15
1991 10th Anniversary of Prince of Wales' Wedding (2 coins)	£15
1992 Discovery of America (4 coins)	£20
1992 Siamese Cat	£15
1992 1992 America's Cup	£10
1993 Maine Coon Cat	£10
1993 Preserve Planet Earth—Dinosaurs (2 coins)	£15
1994 Preserve Planet Earth—Mammoth	£15
1994 Year of the Dog	£15
1994 World Football Cup (6 coins)	£30
1994 Japanese Bobtail Cat	£10
1994 Normandy Landings (8 coins)	£40
1994 Preserve Planet Earth—Endangered Animals (3 coins)	£20
1995 Man in Flight—Series i (8 coins)	£60
1995 Man in Flight—Series ii (8 coins)	£60
1995 Queen Mother's 95th Birthday	£15
1995 Year of the Pig	£15
1995 Turkish Cat	£15
1995 Preserve Planet Earth—Egret and Otter	£15
1995 America's Cup	£15
1995 Aircraft of World War II (19 coins)	£130
1995 Famous World Inventions—Series i (12 coins)	£120
1996 Year of the Rat	£15
1996 70th Birthday of HM the Queen	£20
1996 The Flower Fairies—Series i (4 coins)	£40
1996 Famous World Inventions—Series ii (6 coins)	£40
1996 Olympic Games (6 coins)	£35
1996 Preserve Planet Earth—Killer Whale and Razorbill	£15
1996 Burmese Cat	£15
1996 Robert Burns (4 coins)	£30
1996 King Arthur & the Knights of the Round Table (5 coins)	£35
1996 European Football Championships (8 coins)	£50
1996 Football Championships Winner	£15
1996 Explorers (2 coins)	£20
1997 Year of the Ox	£20
1997 The Flower Fairies—Series ii (4 coins)	£25
1997 Royal Golden Wedding (2 coins)	£20
1997 Explorers—Eriksson and Nansen (2 coins)	£15
1997 Long-haired Smoke Cat	£15
1997 10th Anniversary of the "Cats on Coins" series (silver only)	£45
1997 90th Anniversary of the TT Races (4 coins)	£35
1998 The Millennium (16 coins issued over 3 years)	—
1998 Year of the Tiger	£20
1998 FIFA World Cup (4 coins)	£35
1998 Birman Cat	£20
1998 The Flower Fairies—Series iii (4 coins)	£30
1998 18th Winter Olympics, Nagano (4 coins)	£30
1998 Explorers—Vasco da Gama and Marco Polo (2 coins)	£25
1998 125th Anniversary of Steam Railway (8 coins)	£65
1998 International Year of the Oceans (4 coins)	£33
1999 50th Birthday of HRH the Prince of Wales	£15
1999 Year of the Rabbit	£15

DATE	UNC
1999 27th Olympics in Sydney (5 coins)	£40
1999 Rugby World Cup (6 coins)	£40
1999 Wedding of HRH Prince Edward and Sophie Rhys-Jones	£15
1999 Queen Mother's 100th Birthday (4 coins)	£35
1999 The Millennium (4 coins)	£35
1999 Titanium Millennium crown	£15
2000 Year of the Dragon	£15
2000 Scottish Fold cat	£15
2000 Millennium—own a piece of time	£15
2000 Explorers, Francisco Piarro and Wilem Brents (2 coins)	£15
2000 Life and times of the Queen Mother (4 coins)	£30
2000 Queen Mother's 100th Birthday	£15
2000 60th Anniversary of the Battle of Britain	£15
2000 BT Global Challenge	£15
2000 18th Birthday of HRH Prince William	£15
2001 Year of the Snake	£15
2001 The Somali cat	£15
2001 Life and times of the Queen Mother (2 coins)	£15
2001 Explorers, Martin Frobisher and Roald Amundsen (2 coins)	£15
2001 75th Birthday of HM the Queen	£15
2001 Joey Dunlop	£15
2001 Harry Potter (6 coins)	£80
2002 Year of the Horse	£15
2002 The XIX Winter Olympiad, Salt Lake City (2 coins)	£20
2002 World Cup 2002 in Japan/Korea (4 coins)	£35
2002 The Bengal Cat	£15
2002 The Queen's Golden Jubilee—i (1 coin)	£15
2002 Introduction of the Euro	£15
2002 The Queen's Golden Jubilee—ii (4 coins)	£60
2002 A Tribute to Diana Princess of Wales—5 years on	£30
2003 Year of the Goat	£15
2003 The Balinese Cat	£15
2003 Anniversary of the "Star of India"	£15
2003 Lord of the Rings (5 coins)	£60
2004 Olympics (4 coins)	£50
2004 100 Years of Powered Flight (2 coins)	£30
2005 Lord of the Rings: The Return of the King	£30
2005 Manx Hero Lt. John Quilliam and the Battle of Trafalgar (2 coins)	£30
2005 The Himalayan Cat with kittens	£20
2005 Bicentenary of the Battle of Trafalgar (6 coins)	£55
2005 60th Anniversary of D-Day (6 coins)	£65
2005 60th Anniversary of Victory in Europe	£30
2005 200th Anniversary of the Battle of Trafalgar	£30
2005 400th Anniversary of the Gun Powder Plot (2 coins)	£30
2005 Bicentenary of the Battle of Trafalgar and Death of Nelson	£30
2005 Italy and the Isle of Man TT races (2 coins)	£30
2005 Harry Potter and the Goblet of Fire (4 coins)	£35
2006 100 Years of Norwegian Independence	£25
2006 80th Birthday of Her Majesty the Queen (4 coins)	£35
2006 The Battles that Changed the World—Part II (6 coins)	£55
2006 150th Anniversary of the Victoria Cross (2 coins)	£30
2006 30th Anniversary of the first Translantic Flight	£25
2007 The Ragdoll Cat	£15
2007 Fairy Tales—Sleeping Beauty, The Three Little Pigs (2 coins)	£25
2007 The Graceful Swan	£15
2007 The Royal Diamond Wedding Anniversary	£15
2007 The Centenary of the TT races	£15
2007 The Centenary of the Scouting	£15
2008 50th Anniversary of Paddington Bear	—
2008 Prince Charles 60th Birthday	—
2008 Centenary of the Olympics	—
2008 Burmilla Cat	—
2008 Year of Planet Earth	—
2008 The Adorable Snowman	—
2008 UEFA European Football Championships	—
2008 The Return of Tutankhamun	—

DATE	UNC
2008 The Olympic Collection—The Olympics coming to London	—
2009 Winter Olympics (2 coins)	—
2009 The Chinchilla Cat	—
2009 40th Anniversary of the 1st Concorde Test Flight	—
2009 Fifa World Cup South Africa 2010	—
2010 2012 Olympics	—

Winner of 13 COIN OF THE YEAR AWARDS
Pobjoy Mint
Over 300 years of Tradition
Official Minters to Foreign Governments - Custom Minters to the World
Olympic Coin Collection
Tutankhamun Pyramid Sand Coin
Paddington Bear™
Olympic Colour Titanium Coin
Silver and Crystal Turtle
POBJOY, MORE THAN A NAME, A GUARANTEE!
Pobjoy Mint Ltd, Millennia House, Kingswood Park,
Bonsor Drive, Kingswood, Surrey, KT20 6AY, U.K.
TEL: (+44) 1737 818181 FAX: (+44) 1737 818199
Internet: www.pobjoy.com Email: (General info & Sales) sales@pobjoy.com

GUERNSEY

DATE	F	VF	EF	UNC
TEN SHILLINGS				
1966	—	£5	£9	£10
1966 Proof	—	—	—	£18
THREEPENCE				
1956	70p	£4	£8	£8
1956 Proof	—	—	—	£15
1959	70p	£4	£8	£10
1966 Proof	—	—	—	£13
EIGHT DOUBLES				
1834	£10	£10	£45	£140
1858 5 berries	£6	£9	£45	£130
1858 4 berries	£6	£9	£45	£140
1864 1 stalk	£6	£4	£35	£65
1864 3 stalks	£6	£4	£25	£60
1868	£7	£8	£25	£60
1874	£4	£6	£13	£45
1885H	£4	£6	£13	£40
1889H	£3	£4	£11	£35
1893H small date	£3	£4	£11	£35
1893H large date	£3	£4	£11	£35
1902H	£3	£4	£11	£35
1903H	£3	£4	£11	£35
1910	£3	£4	£11	£35
1911H	£3	£4	£11	£40
1914H	60p	£3	£9	£25
1918H	60p	£3	£8	£20
1920H	60p	£3	£8	£20
1934H	70p	£3	£8	£27
1934H Proof	—	—	—	£120
1938H	70p	£3	£8	£23
1945H	60p	£2	£7	£15
1947H	50p	£2	£7	£15
1949H	50p	£2	£6	£15
1956	40p	60p	£5	£14
1956	40p	60p	£5	£14
1959	40p	60p	£5	£14
1966 Proof	—	—	—	£26
FOUR DOUBLES				
1830	£4	£9	£50	£100
1830 Mule with obv. St Helena 1/2 d	—	£780	—	—
1858	£6	£12	£57	£100
1864 Single stalk	£2	£6	£18	£57
1864 3 stalks	£2	£6	£20	£65
1868	£3	£7	£22	£70
1874	£2	£6	£22	£70
1885H	£2	£6	£20	£42
1889H	£2	£3	£13	£35
1893H	£2	£3	£13	£35
1902H	£2	£3	£9	£30
1903H	£2	£3	£13	£30
1906H	£2	£3	£9	£26
1908H	£2	£3	£9	£26
1910H	£2	£3	£9	£26
1911H	£2	£3	£8	£25
1914H	£2	£3	£13	£40
1918H	£2	£3	£12	£35
1920H	£2	£3	£9	£35
1945H	£2	£3	£9	£33
1949H	£2	£3	£12	£33
1956	60p	£2	£7	£14
1966 Proof	—	—	—	£14

DATE	F	VF	EF	UNC
TWO DOUBLES				
1858	£6	£9	£50	£180
1868 Single stick	£6	£11	£55	£180
1868 3 stalks	£7	£13	£80	£185
1874	£4	£9	£50	£130
1885H	£3	£6	£17	£35
1889H	£3	£4	£17	£35
1899H	£3	£5	£21	£42
1902H	£3	£4	£19	£35
1902H	£3	£4	£19	£35
1906H	£3	£4	£19	£35
1908H	£3	£5	£19	£35
1911H	£3	£5	£22	£42
1914H	£3	£5	£22	£42
1917H	£7	£18	£80	£190
1918H	£3	£4	£13	£30
1920H	£3	£4	£13	£30
1929H	£2	£3	£11	£18
ONE DOUBLE				
1830	£3	£4	£22	£45
1868	£4	£10	£33	£90
1868/30	£5	£7	£27	£85
1885H	£2	£3	£8	£20
1889H	60p	£2	£6	£20
1893H	60p	£2	£6	£20
1899H	60p	£2	£6	£20
1902	60p	£2	£6	£20
1903H	60p	£2	£6	£20
1911H	60p	£2	£8	£20
1911 (new shield)	60p	£2	£6	£20
1914H	60p	£2	£8	£20
1929H	60p	£2	£6	£20
1933H	60p	£2	£6	£20
1938H	60p	£2	£6	£20

DECIMAL COINAGE

Ordinary circulating coinage from 1986 onwards is usually available in uncirculated condition at a small premium above face value thus it is not listed here. The coins listed are cupro-nickel unless otherwise stated.

	UNC
ONE HUNDRED POUNDS—Gold	
1994 50th Anniversary of Normandy Landings. Proof	£850
1995 Anniversary of the Liberation. Proof	£850
FIFTY POUNDS—Gold	
1994 50th Anniversary of Normandy Landings. Proof	£400
1995 Anniversary of the Liberation. Proof	£400
TWENTY-FIVE POUNDS—Gold	
1994 50th Anniversary of Normandy Landings	£250
1994 — Proof	£250
1995 Anniversary of the Liberation. Proof	£250
1996 European Football Championships. Proof	£250
1997 Royal Golden Wedding. Proof	£300
1998 Royal Air Force. Proof	£250
2000 Queen Mother 100th Birthday. Proof	£270
2001 Queen Victoria centennial	£270
2001 HM the Queen's 75th Birthday	£265
2002 Princess Diana memorial	£265
2002 Duke of Wellington	£270
TEN POUNDS	
1994 50th Anniversary of Normandy Landings. Gold proof	£175
1995 Anniversary of the Liberation. Gold proof	£175
2000 Century of Monarchy. Silver proof	£140
2001 19th Century Monarchy. Silver proof	£140
2002 18th Century Monarchy. Silver proof	£140

NOTE: Most of the five pound coins from the Channel Islands are struck in precious metals as well as base metals. From 2005 therefore it has been decided to simply list the theme of the issues. However, we are extensively revising this section for next year's Yearbook, to include all issues.

DATE	UNC
FIVE POUNDS	
1995 Queen Mother's 95th birthday	£25
1995 — Silver proof	£55
1995 — Small size gold	£130
1996 HM the Queen's 70th birthday	£18
1996 — Silver proof	£45
1996 European Football Championships	£30
1996 — Silver proof	£60
1997 Royal Golden Wedding	£21
1997 — Silver proof	£60
1997 — Small size gold. BU	£80
1997 Castles of the British Isles—Castle Cornet, Guernsey	£18
1997 — Silver proof	£65
1997 Castles of the British Isles—Caernarfon Castle. Silver proof	£65
1997 Castles of the British Isles—Leeds Castle. Silver proof	£65
1998 Royal Air Force.	£14
1998 Royal Air Force. Silver proof	£65
1999 Millennium. Brass	£22
1999 — Silver proof	£45
1999 Wedding of HRH Prince Edward and Sophie Rhys-Jones	£21
1999 — Silver proof	£70
1999 Queen Mother	£22
1999 — Silver proof	£70
1999 Winston Churchill	£12
1999 — Gold	£860
2000 Queen Mother's 100th Birthday	£10
2000 — Silver proof	£65
2000 — Small size gold. Proof	£75
2000 Centuries of the British Monarchy	£27
2000 — Silver proof	£65
2000 — Small size gold. Proof	£75
2001 The Reign of Queen Victoria	£18
2001 — Proof	£55
2001 — Silver proof	£55
2001 HM the Queen's 75th Birthday	£14
2001 — Silver proof	£55
2001 — Small size gold. Proof	£75
2001 19th Century Monarchy	£15
2001 — Silver proof	£55
2001 — Small size gold. Proof	£75
2002 Golden Jubilee (two types)	£10
2002 — Silver proof	£60
2002 Princess Diana Memorial	£11
2002 — Proof	£55
2002 — Gold proof	£750
2002 Century of Monarchy	£10
2002 — Silver proof	£55
2002 — Small size gold. Proof	£75
2002 Queen Mother Memoriam	£15
2002 — Proof	£20
2002 — Silver proof	£55
2002 — Small size gold. Proof	£75
2003 Duke of Wellington	£14
2003 — Silver proof	£45
2003 — Gold proof	£100
2005 200th Anniversary of the Battle of Trafalgar	—
2005 60th Anniversary of the Liberation of the Channel Islands	—
2006 Great Britons—Sir Winston Churchill Silver. Issued as part of set.	—
2006 80th Birthday of Her Majesty the Queen	—
2007 History of the Royal Navy—Henry VIII, The Golden Hind (2 coins)	—
2007 Royal Diamond Wedding	—
TWO POUNDS	
1985 40th anniversary of Liberation	£10
1985 — Proof	£27
1985 — Silver proof	£55
1986 Commonwealth Games, in plastic case	£12

DATE	UNC
1986 — in special folder	£12
1986 — .500 Silver	£45
1986 — .925 Silver proof	£55
1987 900th anniv. of death of William the Conqueror, in folder	£14
1987 — Silver proof	£50
1987 — Gold proof	£1200
1988 William II, in presentation folder	£14
1988 — Silver proof	£55
1989 Henry I, in presentation folder	£14
1989 — Silver proof	£55
1989 Royal Visit	£14
1989 — Silver proof	£55
1990 Queen Mother's 90th birthday	£14
1990 — Silver proof	£55
1991 Henry II, in presentation folder	£14
1991 — Silver proof	£55
1993 40th Anniversary of the Coronation	£14
1993 — Silver proof	£60
1994 Anniversary of the Normandy Landings	£14
1994 — Silver proof	£55
1995 50th Anniversary of Liberation	£14
1995 — Silver proof	£55
1995 — Silver Piedfort proof	£100
1997 Conserving Nature i	£10
1997 — Silver proof	£55
1998 Conserving Nature ii	£10

ONE POUND

DATE	UNC
1981	£10
1981 Gold proof	£145
1981 Gold piedfort	£345
1983 New specification, new reverse	£9
1985 New design (in folder)	£9
1995 Queen Mother's 95th Birthday. Silver proof	£50
1996 Queen's 70th Birthday. Silver proof	£55
1997 Royal Golden Wedding. Silver BU	£18
1997 — Silver proof	£55
1997 Castles of the British Isles—Tower of London. Silver proof only	£27
1998 Royal Air Force. Silver proof	£42
1999 Wedding of Prince Edward. Silver proof	£55
1999 Queen Mother. Silver proof	£55
1999 Winston Churchill. Silver proof	£55
2000 Millennium. Silver proof (gold plated)	£65
2000 Queen Mother's 100th Birthday. Silver proof	£42
2001 HM the Queen's 75th Birthday. Silver proof	£42

FIFTY PENCE

DATE	UNC
1969	£4
1970	£6
1971 Proof	£9
1981	£4
1982	£4
1985 New design	£4
2000 60th Anniversary of the Battle of Britain.	£4
2000 — Silver proof	£55
2000 — Silver piedfort	£55
2000 — Gold proof	£365

TWENTY-FIVE PENCE

DATE	UNC
1972 Royal Silver Wedding	£12
1972 — Silver proof	£42
1977 Royal Silver Jubilee	£9
1977 — Silver proof	£42
1978 Royal Visit	£9
1978 — Silver proof	£42
1980 Queen Mother's 80th birthday	£9
1980 — Silver proof	£42
1981 Royal Wedding	£9
1981 — Silver proof	£42

JERSEY

DATE	F	VF	EF	UNC
FIVE SHILLINGS				
1966	–	£3	£7	£13
1966 Proof	–	£3	£9	£22
ONE QUARTER OF A SHILLING				
1957	–	£2	£5	£10
1960 Proof	–	–	£5	£14
1964	–	–	£4	£10
1966	–	–	£4	£10

DATE	F	VF	EF	UNC
ONE TWELFTH OF A SHILLING				
1877H	£2	£3	£18	£55
1877H Proof in nickel	–	–	–	£1265
1877 Proof only	–	–	–	£475
1877 Proof in nickel	–	–	–	£1265
1881	£3	£3	£14	£60
1888	£2	£3	£14	£48
1894	£2	£3	£17	£48
1909	£2	£3	£14	£35
1911	£2	£3	£7	£30
1913	£2	£3	£7	£30
1923 Spade shield	£2	£3	£7	£30
1923 Square shield	£2	£3	£7	£30
1926	£2	£3	£8	£42
1931	£2	£3	£5	£12
1933	£2	£3	£7	£12
1935	£2	£3	£7	£12
1937	£2	£3	£7	£12
1946	£2	£3	£7	£12
1947	–	£3	£7	£12
"1945" GVI	–	–	85p	£9
"1945" QE2	–	–	85p	£7
1957	–	–	85p	£7
1960 1660–1960 300th anniversary	–	–	70p	£7
1960 Mule	–	–	–	£130
1966 "1066–1966"	–	–	85p	£7

DATE	F	VF	EF	UNC
ONE THIRTEENTH OF A SHILLING				
1841	£4	£8	£40	£180
1844	£4	£9	£40	£180
1851	£5	£13	£57	£185
1858	£4	£9	£45	£180
1861	£5	£13	£60	£165
1865 Proof only	–	–	–	£660
1866 with LCW	£2	£5	£95	£110
1866 without LCW Proof only	–	–	–	£350
1870	£4	£8	£40	£100
1871	£4	£8	£42	£100

DATE	F	VF	EF	UNC
ONE TWENTY-FOURTH OF A SHILLING				
1877H	£3	£4	£11	£55
1877 Proof only	–	–	–	£270
1888	£3	£4	£11	£42
1894	£3	£4	£11	£42
1909	£3	£4	£11	£42
1911	£2	£3	£8	£42
1913	£2	£3	£8	£42

DATE	F	VF	EF	UNC
1923 Spade shield	£2	£3	£9	£33
1923 Square shield	£2	£3	£8	£35
1926	£2	£3	£8	£22
1931	£2	£3	£8	£22
1933	£2	£3	£8	£22
1935	£2	£3	£8	£22
1937	60p	£2	£6	£16
1946	60p	£2	£6	£19
1947	60p	£2	£6	£16

ONE TWENTY-SIXTH OF A SHILLING

DATE	F	VF	EF	UNC
1841	£4	£7	£30	£90
1844	£4	£7	£25	£90
1851	£3	£6	£25	£90
1858	£4	£11	£48	£160
1861	£3	£6	£25	£65
1866	£3	£6	£27	£77
1870	£3	£6	£20	£55
1871	£3	£6	£20	£55

ONE FORTY-EIGHTH OF A SHILLING

DATE	F	VF	EF	UNC
1877H	£6	£12	£57	£110
1877 Proof only	—	—	—	£360

ONE FIFTY-SECOND OF A SHILLING

DATE	F	VF	EF	UNC
1841	£9	£25	£60	£180
1861 Proof only	—	—	—	£630

(Reduced)

DECIMAL COINAGE

Ordinary circulating coinage from 1986 onwards is usually available in uncirculated condition at a small premium above face value thus it is not listed here.

ONE HUNDRED POUNDS—Gold

1995 50th Anniversary of Liberation. Gold proof	£690

FIFTY POUNDS—Gold

1972 25th Royal Wedding anniversary. Gold proof	£550
1995 50th Anniversary of Liberation. Gold proof	£580

TWENTY-FIVE POUNDS—Gold

1972 25th Royal Wedding anniversary. Gold	£280
1972 — Gold proof	£270
1990 50th Anniversary of Battle of Britain. Gold proof	£270
1995 50th Anniversary of Liberation. Gold proof	£270
2002 Princess Diana memorial. Gold proof	£330

(Enlarged)

TWENTY-FIVE POUNDS—Gold

1972 25th Royal Wedding anniversary. Gold proof	£330

TEN POUNDS—Gold

1972 25th Royal Wedding anniversary. Gold proof	£75
1990 50th Anniversary of the Battle of Britain. Gold proof	£220
1995 50th Anniversary of Liberation. Gold proof	£190

FIVE POUNDS

1972 25th Royal Wedding anniversary. Gold	£65
1990 50th Anniversary of the Battle of Britain. Silver Proof (5 ounces)	£150
1997 Royal Golden Wedding	£30
1997 — Silver proof	£70
2000 Millennium. Silver proof	£55
2002 Princess Diana memorial	£18
2002 — Silver proof	£42
2002 — Gold proof	£770
2002 Royal Golden Jubilee	—
2005 200th Anniversary of the Battle of Trafalgar	—
2006 60th Anniversary of the Liberation of the Channel Islands	—

DATE	UNC
2006 80th Birthday of Her Majesty the Queen (3-coin set)	—
2007 History of the Royal Navy—Sir Francis Drake (2 coins)	—
2007 Royal Diamond Wedding	—
TWO POUNDS FIFTY PENCE	
1972 Royal Silver Wedding	£22
1972 — Silver proof	£33
TWO POUNDS	
(note all modern Proof coins have frosted relief)	
1972 Royal Silver Wedding	£22
1972 — Silver proof	£35
1981 Royal Wedding, nickel silver (crown size)	£15
1981— in presentation pack	£21
1981 — Silver proof	£33
1981 — Gold proof	£410
1985 40th Anniversary of Liberation (crown size)	£15
1985 — in presentation pack	£15
1985 — Silver proof	£40
1985 — Gold proof	£1265
1986 Commonwealth Games	£18
1986 — in presentation case	£18
1986 — .500 silver	£40
1986 — .925 silver proof	£45
1987 World Wildlife Fund 25th Anniversary	£20
1987 — Silver proof	£45
1989 Royal Visit	£20
1989 — Silver proof	£45
1990 Queen Mother's 90th Birthday	£20
1990 — Silver proof	£14
1990 — Gold proof	£575
1990 50th Anniversary of the Battle of Britain, silver proof	£55
1993 40th Anniversary of the Coronation	£18
1993 — Silver proof	£60
1995 50th Anniversary of Liberation	£20
1995 — Silver Proof	£60
1996 HM the Queen's 70th Birthday	£19
1996 — Silver proof	£52
1997 Bi-metal	£33
1997 — Silver proof	£50
1997 — new portrait	£20
ONE POUND	
1972 Royal Silver Wedding	£15
1972 — Silver proof	£20
1981	£15
1981 Silver proof	£45
1981 Gold proof	£300
1983 New designs and specifications on presentation card (St Helier)	£21
1983 — Silver proof	£45
1983 — Gold proof	£385
1984 Presentation wallet (St Saviour)	£21
1984 — Silver proof	£45
1984 — Gold proof	£440
1984 Presentation wallet (St Brelade)	£20
1984 — Silver proof	£45
1984 — Gold proof	£480
1985 Presentation wallet (St Clement)	£25
1985 — Silver proof	£45
1985 — Gold proof	£460
1985 Presentation wallet (St Lawrence)	£25
1985 — Silver proof	£40
1985 — Gold proof	£440

DATE	UNC
1986 Presentation wallet (St Peter)	£16
1986 — Silver proof	£35
1986 — Gold proof	£440
1986 Presentation wallet (Grouville)	£18
1986 — Silver proof	£40
1986 — Gold proof	£440
1987 Presentation wallet (St Martin)	£18
1987 — Silver proof	£40
1987 — Gold proof	£440
1987 Presentation wallet (St Ouen)	£12
1987 — Silver proof	£40
1987 — Gold proof	£440
1988 Presentation wallet (Trinity)	£13
1988 — Silver proof	£40
1988 — Gold proof	£440
1988 Presentation wallet (St John)	£14
1988 — Silver proof	£40
1988 — Gold proof	£440
1989 Presentation wallet (St Mary)	£14
1989 — Silver proof	£40
1989 — Gold proof	£440

1991 Ship Building in Jersey Series

1991 "Tickler" Silver proof	£55
1991 — Gold proof	£440
1991 "Percy Douglas" Silver proof	£50
1991 — Gold proof	£440
1992 "The Hebe" Silver proof	£40
1992 — Gold proof	£440
1992 "Coat of Arms" Silver proof	£40
1992 — Gold proof	£440
1993 "The Gemini" Silver proof	£40
1993 — Gold proof	£440
1993 "The Century" Silver proof	£40
1993 — Gold proof	£440
1994 "Resolute" Silver proof	£50
1994 — Gold proof	£440

FIFTY PENCE

1969	£10
1972 Royal Silver Wedding	£11
1972 — Silver proof	£11
1983 New design	£10
1985 40th Anniversary of Liberation	£11
2003 Coronation Jubilee	£11

TWENTY-FIVE PENCE

1977 Royal Jubilee	£9
1977 — Silver proof	£19

TWENTY PENCE

1982 Date on rocks on rev. (cased)	8
1982 — Silver proof piedfort	£55
1983 New obv. with date, rev. no date on rocks	£5

SOVEREIGN—Gold sovereign size

1999 The Millennium	£130
1999 — Gold proof	£220

ALDERNEY

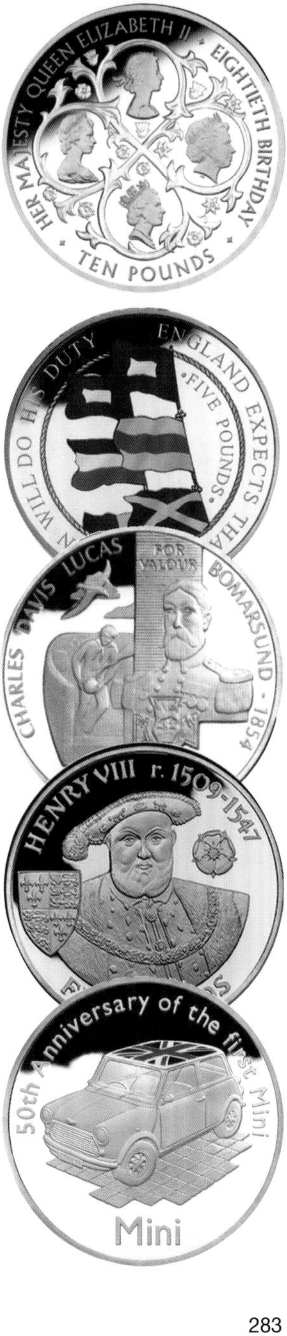

DATE	UNC

ONE HUNDRED POUNDS

1994 50th Anniversary of D-Day Landings. Gold proof	£660

FIFTY POUNDS

1994 50th Anniversary of D–Day Landing. Gold proof	£365
2005 200th Anniversary of the Battle of Trafalgar	£360

TWENTY FIVE POUNDS

1993 40th Anniversary of Coronation. Gold proof	£250
1994 50th Anniversary of D-Day Landings. Gold proof	£250
1997 Royal Golden Wedding. Gold proof	£250
1997 — Silver proof	£50
2000 60th Anniversary of the Battle of Britain. Gold proof	£240
2002 Princess Diana memorial	£285
2002 Duke of Wellington	£285
2006 World Cup 2006 (4 Coins). Gold	£850

TEN POUNDS

1994 50th Anniversary of D–Day Landing. Gold proof	£90
2004 Concorde	£270
2005 60th Anniversary of the Liberation of the Channel Islands (65mm)	£140
2005 60th Anniversary of the Liberation of the Channel Islands	£45
2007 80th Birthday of Her Majesty the Queen	—
2008 Concorde. Silver proof	—
2008 90th Anniversary of the end of WWI. Silver Proof	—
2009 50th Anniversary of the Mini—Silver	—

FIVE POUNDS

1995 Queen Mother	£22
1995 — Silver proof	£50
1995 — Silver piedfort	£90
1995 — Gold proof	£810
1996 HM the Queen's 70th Birthday	£18
1996 — Silver proof	£60
1996 — Silver piedfort	£90
1996 — Gold proof	£825
1999 Eclipse of the Sun	£25
1999 — Silver proof with colour centre	£47
1999 Winston Churchill. Gold proof	£825
2000 60th Anniversary of the Battle of Britain	£22
2000 — Silver proof	£55
2002 Golden Jubilee. Silver proof	£50
2002 50 Years of Reign. Silver proof	£50
2002 Diana memorial	£15
2002 — Silver proof	£45
2002 — Gold proof	£770
2002 Duke of Wellington	£20
2002 — Silver proof	£50
2002 — Gold proof	£765
2004 Concorde	£13
2005 2004 European Football Championships	£16
2005 200th Anniversary of the Battle of Trafalgar	£16
2006 Diamond Set—80th Birthday of Her Majesty the Queen (3-coin set)	—
2006 Gold plated portraits of Her Majesty the Queen	—
2006 80th Birthday of Her Majesty the Queen (3-coin set)	—
2007 History of the Royal Navy—*Mary Rose* (2 coins)	—
2007 150th Anniversary of the Victoria Cross	—
2007 Monarchs of England (12 coins)	—
2008 90th Anniversary of the end of WWI	—
2008 Classic British Motorcars	—
2008 Concorde. Gold proof	—
2009 50th Anniversary of the Mini	—

DATE	UNC
TWO POUNDS	
1989 Royal Visit	£18
1989 — Silver proof	£50
1989 — Silver piedfort	£90
1989 — Gold proof	£1100
1990 Queen Mother's 90th Birthday	£18
1990 — Silver proof	£50
1990 — Silver piedfort	£90
1990 — Gold proof	£1100
1992 40th Anniversary of Accession	£20
1992 — Silver proof	£50
1992 — Silver piedfort	£90
1992 — Gold proof	£1100
1993 40th Anniversary of Coronation	£20
1993 — Silver proof	£50
1993 — Silver piedfort	£90
1994 50th Anniversary of D-Day Landings	£20
1994 — Silver proof	£55
1994 — Silver piedfort	£95
1995 50th Anniversary of Return of Islanders	£20
1995 — Silver proof	£50
1995 — Silver piedfort	£80
1995 — Gold proof	£960
1997 WWF Puffin	£20
1997 — Silver proof	£55
1997 Royal Golden Wedding	£20
1997 — Silver proof	£65
1999 Eclipse of the Sun. Silver	£20
1999 — Silver proof	£50
1999 — Gold proof	£1150
2000 Millennium. Silver proof	£50
ONE POUND	
1993 40th Anniversary of Coronation Silver proof	£50
1995 50th Anniversary of VE Day Silver proof	£45
1995 — Gold proof	£425
2008 Concorde. Gold proof	—
2009 50th Anniversary of the Mini—Gold	—

Along with the rest of the Channel Islands, Alderney's coinage is often issued as part of a set incorporating coins from other countries. Illustrated is the special set issued to mark the 90th Anniversary of the end of World War I which also included coins from the Cayman and Solomon Islands as well as Alderney.

IRELAND

As in the English hammered section (q.v.) the prices given here are for the most common coins in the series. For a more specialised listing the reader is referred to *Coincraft's Standard Catalogue of Scotland, Ireland, Channel Islands & Isle of Man*, or other specialised publications. Collectors should be aware that with most of the coins of the Irish series there are many varieties struck at different mints. The coins listed are all silver unless mentioned otherwise. Another important factor to consider when collecting early Irish coins is that few examples exist in high grades.

HIBERNO-NORSE ISSUES (995–1155)

	F	VF
Penny, imitating English silver pennies, many various types	£200	£450

A typical Hiberno-Norse period example.

JOHN, Lord of Ireland (1185–99)

Halfpenny, profile	Extremely rare	
Halfpenny, facing	£90	£220
Farthing	£350	£900

John Lord of Ireland halfpenny.

JOHN de COURCY, Lord of Ulster (1177–1205)

Halfpenny	Extremely rare	
Farthing	£650	£2500

JOHN as King of England and Lord of Ireland (c. 1199–1216)

Penny	£65	£220
Halfpenny	£150	£350
Farthing	£650	£1800

HENRY III (1216–72)

Penny	£65	£250

Henry III penny.

EDWARD I (1272–1307)

Penny	£65	£250
Halfpenny	£65	£250
Farthing	£140	£350

No Irish coins were struck for Edward II (1307–27).

EDWARD III (1327–77)

Halfpenny	Extremely rare	

No Irish coins were struck for Richard II (1377–99), Henry IV (1399–1413) or Henry V (1413–22).

Edward III halfpenny.

HENRY VI (1422–61)

Penny	Extremely rare	

EDWARD IV (1461–83)

	F	VF
"Anonymous crown" groat	£600	£11500
— penny	£1000	—
"Titled crown" groat	£1500	—
— halfgroat		Extremely rare
— penny		Extremely rare
Cross on rose/Sun groat	£1650	—
Bust/Rose on sun double groat	£2150	£5750
— groat	£2150	—
— halfgroat		Extremely rare
— penny		Extremely rare
Bust/Cross & pellets groat—First issue	£100	£350
— halfgroat	£550	£1200
— penny	£75	£200
— halfpenny		Extremely rare
— Second (light) issue	£100	£350
— halfgroat	£550	£1100
— penny	£90	£200
— halfpenny		Extremely rare
Bust/Rose on cross groat	£450	£1050
— penny	£65	£150

Edward IV groat. "Anonymous crown" issue.

Billon/Copper issues

	F	VF
Small crown/Cross farthing (1460–61)	£1500	—
— half farthing ("Patrick")	£1050	—
Large crown/Cross farthing (1462)		Extremely rare
Patricius/Salvator farthing (1463–65)	£350	£1800
— half farthing		Extremely rare
Shield/Rose on sun farthing	£175	£750

Edward IV penny. "Anonymous crown" issue.

RICHARD III (1483–85)

	F	VF
Bust/Rose on cross groat	£1000	£3500
— halfgroat		Unique
— penny		Unique
Bust/Cross and pellets penny	£100	£2500
Shield/Three-crowns groat	£600	£2300

Richard III bust/rose on cross groat.

HENRY VII (1485–1509)

	F	VF
Early issues (1483–90)		
Shield/Three crowns groat	£150	£400
— halfgroat	£260	£550
— penny	£600	£1800
— halfpenny		Extremely rare
Later issues (1488–90)		
Shield/Three crowns groat	£100	£300
— halfgroat	£200	£550
— penny	£500	£1000
Facing bust groat (1496–1505)	£120	£300
— halfgroat	£1000	—
— penny	£850	—

LAMBERT SIMNEL (as EDWARD VI, Pretender, 1487)

	F	VF
Shield/Three crowns groat	£1000	£3500

Henry VII "three crowns" half groat.

HENRY VIII (1509–47)

	F	VF
"Harp" groat	£90	£250
— halfgroat	£450	£1800

The "Harp" coins have crowned initials either side of the reverse harp, e.g. HR (Henricus Rex), HA (Henry and Anne Boleyn), HI (Henry and Jane Seymour), HK (Henry and Katherine Howard).

Posthumous (Portrait) issues	F	VF
Sixpence	£140	£350
Threepence	£150	£475
Threehalfpence	£500	£1500
Threefarthings	£650	£1800

Henry VIII "harp" halfgroat.

EDWARD VI (1547–53)

	F	VF
Shilling (base silver) 1552 (MDLII)	£900	£3000
Brass contemporary copy	£90	£350

MARY (1553–54)

	F	VF
Shilling 1553 (MDLIII)	£850	£3000
Shilling 1554 (MDLIIII)		Extremely rare
Groat		Extremely rare
Halfgroat		Extremely rare
Penny		Extremely rare

Mary Tudor shilling.

PHILIP & MARY (1554–58)

	F	VF
Shilling	£350	£1200
Groat	£100	£300
Penny		Extremely rare

ELIZABETH I (1558–1603)

	F	VF
Base silver portrait coinage		
Shilling	£350	£1200
Groat	£180	£600
Fine silver, portrait coinage (1561)		
Shilling	£270	£825
Groat	£325	£1000
Third (base silver) shield coinage		
Shilling	£200	£600
Sixpence	£150	£450
Copper		
Threepence	£200	£625
Penny	£60	£160
Halfpenny	£100	£275

Reverse of a "fine" Elizabeth I shilling.

JAMES I (1603–25)

	F	VF
Shilling	£100	£350
Sixpence	£75	£200

Coins struck under Royal Licence from 1613

	F	VF
"Harrington" farthing (small size)	£55	£180
"Harrington" farthing (large size)	£50	£150
"Lennox" farthing	£50	£150

James I sixpence.

CHARLES I (1625–49)

During the reign of Charles I and the Great Rebellion many coins were struck under unusual circumstances, making the series a difficult but fascinating area for study. Many of the "coins" were simply made from odd-shaped pieces of plate struck with the weight or value.

Charles I "Maltravers" farthing.

	F	VF
Coins struck under Royal Licence from 1625		
"Richmond" farthing	£45	£120
"Maltravers" farthing	£55	£175
"Rose" farthing	£45	£150

Siege money of the Irish Rebellion, 1642–49

"Inchiquin" Money (1642)

	F	VF
Crown	£2100	£5500
Halfcrown	£1800	£4650
Shilling		Extremely rare
Ninepence		Extremely rare
Sixpence		Extremely rare
Groat		Extremely rare

"Dublin" Money (1643)

	F	VF
Crown	£850	£3000
Halfcrown	£600	£2400

Coinage of the Great Rebellion—a "Dublin Money" crown.

"Ormonde" Money (1643–44)

	F	VF
Crown	£500	£1200
Halfcrown	£325	£900
Shilling	£130	£425
Sixpence	£130	£425
Groat	£120	£300
Threepence	£110	£260
Twopence	£450	£1100

"Ormonde" money threepence.

"Ormonde" gold coinage (1646)

	F	VF
Double pistole. 2 known (both in museums)		Extremely rare
Pistole. 10 known (only 1 in private ownership		Extremely rare

"Ormonde" Money (1649)

	F	VF
Crown		Extremely rare
Halfcrown	£1100	£3500

Dublin Money 1649

	F	VF
Crown	£2750	£7000
Halfcrown	£2100	£4000

Issues of the Confederated Catholics

Kilkenny issues (1642–43)

	F	VF
Halfpenny	£265	£800
Farthing	£390	£1000

Rebel Money (1643–44)

	F	VF
Crown	£2000	£4500
Halfcrown	£2650	£4800

Kilkenny halfpenny.

	F	VF
"Blacksmith's" Money (16??)		
Imitation of English Tower halfcrown.....	£650	£2850

Local Town issues of "Cities of Refuge"

	F	VF
Bandon		
Farthing (copper)..................................		Extremely rare
Cork		
Shilling..		Extremely rare
Sixpence..	£750	£1850
Halfpenny (copper)................................		Extremely rare
Farthing (copper)..................................	£550	–
Kinsale		
Farthing (copper)..................................	£400	–
Youghal		
Farthing (copper)..................................	£480	£1500

"Cork" countermarked on a copper coin.

CHARLES II (1660–85)

	Fair	F	VF	EF
"Armstrong" coinage				
Farthing (1660–61)................................	£65	£225	–	–
"St Patrick's" coinage				
Halfpenny	£225	£465	–	–
Farthing	£65	£165	£500	£1200
Legg's Regal coinage				
Halfpennies				
1680 large lettering...............................	£35	£90	£250	–
1681 large lettering...............................	–	£195	£625	–
1681 small lettering			Extremely rare	
1682 small lettering	–	£195	£625	–
1683 small lettering	£30	£40	£350	
1684 small lettering	£40	£110	£600	–

"St Patrick" farthing of Charles II.

JAMES II (1685–88)

REGAL COINAGE

Halfpennies				
1685..	£22	£75	£300	£650
1686..	£22	£60	£200	£550
1687..		Extremely rare		
1688..	£22	£75	£300	£1000

	Fair	F	VF	EF

EMERGENCY COINAGE

GUN MONEY

Most of these coins were struck in gun metal but a few rare specimens are also known struck in gold and in silver

"Gun Money" crown.

	Fair	F	VF	EF
Crowns				
1690 (many varieties).......................from	£45	£60	£500	–
Large halfcrowns				
Dated July 1689–May 1690				
Prices from	£35	£60	£185	–
Small halfcrowns				
Dated April–October1690				
Prices from	£35	£60	£185	–
Large shillings				
Dated from July 1689–April 1690				
Prices from	£35	£55	£120	£400
Small shillings				
Dated from April–September 1690				
Prices from	£22	£35	£120	£385
Sixpences				
Dated from June 1689–October 1690				
Prices from	£35	£60	£200	–

"Gun Money" shilling (large size).

	Fair	F	VF	EF
***PEWTER MONEY* (1689–90)**				
Crown..	£600	£1000	£2750	–
Groat..			Extremely rare	
Penny large bust....................................	£230	£650	–	–
— small bust	£165	£485	£1200	–
Halfpenny large bust	£130	£325	£700	–
— small bust	£110	£225	£650	–
***LIMERICK MONEY* (1690–91)**				
Halfpenny, reversed N in HIBERNIA......	£35	£75	£220	–
Farthing, reversed N in HIBERNIA.........	£35	£75	£220	–
— normal N	£45	£100	£275	–

WILLIAM & MARY (1688–94)

Reverse of a "Pewter Money" penny.

	Fair	F	VF	EF
Halfpennies				
1692..	£12	£40	£100	£550
1693..	£12	£40	£85	£550
1694..	£17	£45	£110	£625

WILLIAM III (1694–1702)

	Fair	F	VF	EF
1696 Halfpenny draped bust..................	£35	£65	£200	–
1696 — crude undraped bust	£45	£265	£795	–

No Irish coins were struck during the reign of Queen Anne (1706–11).

GEORGE I (1714–27)

Farthing of George I.

Farthings

DATE	F	VF	EF	UNC
1722 D.G. REX Harp to left (Pattern)	£650	£1350	£2400	–
1723 D.G. REX Harp to right	£120	£225	£480	–
1723 DEI GRATIA REX Harp to right	£35	£65	£200	£525
1723 — Silver Proof	–	–	–	£1800
1724 DEI GRATIA REX Harp to right	£60	£130	£350	£775

Halfpennies

DATE	F	VF	EF	UNC
1722 Holding Harp left	£55	£130	£385	£800
1722 Holding Harp right	£45	£110	£350	£700
1723/2 Harp right	£50	£120	£350	£700
1723 Harp right	£25	£65	£200	£425
1723 Silver Proof	–	–	–	£3000
1723 Obv. Rs altered from Bs	£35	£100	£265	–
1723 No stop after date	£25	£80	£265	£400
1724 Rev. legend divided	£40	£100	£300	–
1724 Rev. legend continuous	£40	£110	£350	–

GEORGE II (1727–60)

Halfpenny of George II

Farthings

DATE	F	VF	EF	UNC
1737	£35	£60	£175	£385
1737 Proof	–	–	–	£400
1737 Silver Proof	–	–	–	£785
1738	£35	£65	£165	£400
1744	£35	£65	£165	£400
1760	£30	£45	£100	£300

Halfpennies

DATE	F	VF	EF	UNC
1736	£25	£60	£200	£400
1736 Proof	–	–	–	£575
1736 Silver Proof	–	–	–	£1000
1737	£25	£45	£175	–
1738	£30	£60	£200	–
1741	£30	£60	£200	–
1742	£30	£60	£200	–
1743	£30	£60	£180	–
1744/3	£30	£60	£175	–
1744	£30	£60	£300	–
1746	£30	£60	£200	–
1747	£30	£60	£200	–
1748	£30	£60	£200	–
1749	£30	£60	£200	–
1750	£30	£60	£200	–
1751	£30	£60	£200	–
1752	£30	£60	£200	–
1753	£30	£60	£200	–
1755	£30	£100	£300	–
*1760	£25	£55	£175	–

GEORGE III (1760–1820)

All copper unless otherwise stated

Pennies

DATE	F	VF	EF	UNC
1805	£17	£40	£180	£385
1805 Proof	–	–	–	£525
1805 in Bronze Proof	–	–	–	£525
1805 in Copper Gilt Proof	–	–	–	£525
1805 in Silver Proof (restrike)	–	–	–	£2850
1822	£17	£40	£180	£385

DATE	F	VF	EF	UNC
1822 Proof	—	—	—	£525
1823	£12	£25	£150	£350
1823 Proof	—	—	—	£525

Halfpennies

DATE	F	VF	EF	UNC
1766	£30	£55	£165	—
1769	£30	£55	£165	—
1769 Longer bust	£40	£75	£200	£550
1774 Pattern only Proof	—	—	—	£1650
1775	£30	£55	£200	£400
1775 Proof	—	—	—	£600
1776	£55	£140	£400	—
1781	£45	£60	£165	£385
1782	£45	£60	£165	£385
1805	£18	£45	£120	£385
1805 Copper Proof	—	—	—	£385
1805 in Bronze	—	—	—	£265
1805 in Gilt Copper	—	—	—	£400
1805 in Silver (restrike)	—	—	—	£1650
1822	£18	£40	£120	£350
1822 Proof	—	—	—	£575
1823	£18	£40	£120	£350
1823 Proof	—	—	—	£600

1806 farthing

NB Prooflike Uncirculated Pennies and Halfpennies of 1822/23 are often misdescribed as Proofs. The true Proofs are rare. Some are on heavier, thicker flans.

Farthings

DATE	F	VF	EF	UNC
1806	£18	£35	£75	£150
1806 Copper Proof	—	—	—	£300
1806 Bronzed Copper Proof	—	—	—	£200
1806 Copper Gilt Proof	—	—	—	£300
1806 Silver Proof (restrike)	—	—	—	£850
1822 George IV (Pattern) Proof	—	—	—	£1500

TOKEN ISSUES BY THE BANK OF IRELAND

Five Pence in Silver

DATE	F	VF	EF	UNC
1805	£30	£45	£75	£300
1806	£30	£65	£150	£325
1806/5	£55	£140	£450	£1100

Ten Pence in Silver

DATE	F	VF	EF	UNC
1805	£17	£35	£95	£200
1806	£17	£60	£150	£240
1813	£17	£35	£90	£225
1813 Proof	—	—	—	£400

Thirty Pence in Silver

DATE	F	VF	EF	UNC
1808	£35	£95	£220	£525

Six Shillings

DATE	F	VF	EF	UNC
1804 in Silver	£95	£200	£400	£1500
1804 Proof	—	—	—	£1500
1804 in Copper (restrike)	—	—	—	£685
1804 Copper Gilt	—	—	—	£1500
1804 in Gilt Silver	—	—	—	£2650

In this series fully struck specimens, with sharp hair curls, etc., are worth appreciably more than the prices quoted.

IRISH FREE STATE/EIRE

DATE	F	VF	EF	UNC
TEN SHILLINGS				
1966 Easter Rising	—	£12	£17	£25
1966 Cased Proof	—	—	—	£30
1966 special double case	—	—	—	£60
HALF CROWNS				
1928	£7	£12	£40	£70
1928 Proof	—	—	—	£75
1930	£12	£35	£130	£475
1931	£12	£35	£165	£500
1933	£12	£25	£165	£400
1934	£12	£12	£55	£240
1937	£60	£150	£600	£1500
1938				Unique
1939	£7	£17	£30	£85
1939 Proof	—	—	—	£625
1940	£8	£13	£35	£80
1941	£7	£17	£35	£80
1942	£7	£130	£35	£75
1943	£85	£200	£925	£3000
1951	£2	£3	£17	£40
1951 Proof	—	—	—	£475
1954	£2	£3	£9	£60
1954 Proof	—	—	—	£475
1955	£2	£3	£9	£35
1955	—	—	—	£570
1959	£2	£3	£12	£35
1961	£2	£3	£25	£45
1961 Obv as 1928, rev. as 1951	£30	£60	£300	—
1962	£2	£3	£6	£25
1963	£2	£3	£6	£17
1964	£2	£3	£6	£17
1966	£2	£3	£6	£17
1967	£2	£3	£6	£17
FLORINS				
1928	£3	£6	£25	£45
1928 Proof	—	—	—	£65
1930	£4	£12	£140	£400
1930 Proof				Unique
1931	£5	£19	£170	£400
1933	£4	£17	£140	£400
1934	£6	£110	£240	£650
1934 Proof	—	—	—	£2750
1935	£3	£12	£65	£180
1937	£6	£25	£140	£385
1939	£2	£6	£35	£60
1939 Proof	—	—	—	£625
1940	£3	£6	£30	£60
1941	£3	£6	£35	£65
1941 Proof	—	—	—	£780
1942	£6	£12	£30	£60
1943	£2675	£5250	£9500	£22000
1951	60p	£2	£12	£30
1951 Proof	—	—	—	£450
1954	60p	£2	£9	£30
1954 Proof	—	—	—	£350

DATE	F	VF	EF	UNC
1955	—	£2	£6	£30
1955 Proof	—	—	—	£525
1959	40p	£2	£6	£25
1961	60p	£3	£13	£40
1962	40p	£2	£6	£17
1963	30p	£2	£6	£13
1964	30p	£2	£6	£13
1965	30p	£2	£6	£13
1966	30p	£2	£6	£13
1968	30p	£2	£6	£13

SHILLINGS

DATE	F	VF	EF	UNC
1928	£2	£6	£17	£35
1928 Proof	—	—	—	£60
1930	£6	£25	£95	£400
1930 Proof	—	—	—	£825
1931	£3	£17	£95	£400
1933	£3	£17	£95	£400
1935	£3	£13	£50	£140
1937	£6	£60	£220	£1000
1939	£2	£6	£25	£50
1939 Proof	—	—	—	£685
1940	£2	£6	£17	£45
1941	£2	£5	£17	£45
1942	£2	£5	£12	£33
1951	60p	£2	£6	£17
1951 Proof	—	—	—	£400
1954	60p	£2	£6	£17
1954 Proof	—	—	—	£480
1955	60p	£2	£6	£17
1959	60p	£2	£6	£25
1962	30p	£2	£3	£13
1963	30p	£2	£3	£6
1964	30p	£2	£3	£6
1966	30p	£2	£3	£6
1968	30p	£2	£3	£6

SIXPENCES

DATE	F	VF	EF	UNC
1928	60p	£2	£11	£35
1928 Proof	—	—	—	£40
1934	60p	£3	£17	£80
1935	85p	£3	£25	£110
1939	60p	£2	£6	£40
1939 Proof	—	—	—	£600
1940	60p	£2	£6	£40
1942	60p	£2	£9	£50
1945	£3	£11	£35	£90
1946	£3	£6	£65	£385
1947	£2	£2	£22	£65
1948	60p	£3	£13	£50
1949	60p	£2	£8	£35
1950	£2	£3	£25	£85
1952	60p	£2	£4	£17
1953	60p	£2	£4	£17
1953 Proof	—	—	—	£110
1955	60p	£2	£4	£17
1956	60p	£2	£3	£14
1956 Proof	—	—	—	£150
1958	£2	£3	£11	£60
1958 Proof	—	—	—	£350
1959	30p	60p	£3	£13
1960	30p	60p	£2	£13

DATE	F	VF	EF	UNC
1961	—	£2	£3	£17
1962	£2	£6	£30	£65
1963	60p	£3	£6	£13
1964	60p	£2	£4	£7
1966	60p	£2	£4	£7
1967	60p	£2	£2	£6
1968	60p	£2	£2	£6
1969	£2	£3	£6	£13

THREEPENCES

DATE	F	VF	EF	UNC
1928	£2	£3	£9	£25
1928 Proof	—	—	—	£35
1933	£3	£13	£70	£350
1934	70p	£3	£10	£70
1935	£2	£4	£30	£200
1939	£3	£7	£60	£350
1939 Proof	—	—	—	£1050
1940	£2	£3	£13	£55
1942	—	£2	£6	£40
1943	£2	£3	£13	£70
1946	—	£1	£6	£35
1946 Proof	—	—	—	£265
1948	£2	£3	£25	£70
1949	—	£2	£6	£30
1949 Proof	—	—	—	£230
1950	—	£2	£6	£17
1950 Proof	—	—	—	£220
1953	—	£2	£4	£13
1956	—	£2	£3	£6
1961	—	60p	£2	£4
1962	—	60p	£2	£6
1963	—	60p	£2	£6
1964	—	60p	£2	£4
1965	—	60p	£2	£3
1966	—	60p	£2	£3
1967	—	60p	£2	£3
1968	—	—	£2	£3

PENNIES

DATE	F	VF	EF	UNC
1928	£2	£3	£11	£35
1928 Proof	—	—	—	£50
1931	£2	£4	£35	£110
1931 Proof	—	—	—	£925
1933	£2	£5	£50	£200
1935	60p	£2	£25	£65
1937	90p	£2	£35	£110
1937 Proof	—	—	—	£925
1938				2 known
1940	£6	£30	£140	—
1941	60p	£2	£9	£25
1942	—	60p	£4	£14
1943	—	£2	£6	£25
1946	—	£2	£4	£14
1948	—	£2	£4	£14
1949	—	£2	£4	£14
1949 Proof	—	—	—	£385
1950	—	£2	£6	£25
1952	—	£2	£4	£8
1962	—	£2	£4	£10
1962 Proof	—	—	—	£150
1963	—	—	£2	£7
1963 Proof	—	—	—	£95

DATE	F	VF	EF	UNC
1964	—	—	£2	£7
1965	—	—	60p	£4
1966	—	—	60p	£4
1967	—	—	60p	£4
1968	—	—	60p	£4
1968 Proof	—	—	—	£240

HALFPENNIES

1928	£2	£3	£12	£30
1928 Proof	—	—	—	£40
1933	£6	£17	£65	£500
1935	£3	£6	£30	£160
1937	£2	£4	£12	£50
1939	£3	£6	£35	£170
1939 Proof	—	—	—	£800
1940	£2	£4	£50	£180
1941	60p	£2	£6	£25
1942	60p	£2	£6	£25
1943	60p	£2	£7	£30
1946	£2	£3	£17	£70
1949	60p	£2	£6	£25
1953	—	£2	£3	£9
1953 Proof	—	—	—	£475
1964	—	—	60p	£3
1965	—	—	90p	£4
1966	—	—	60p	£3
1967	—	—	60p	£3

FARTHINGS

1928	£3	£4	£9	£13
1928 Proof	—	—	—	£40
1930	£3	£4	£9	£25
1931	£4	£6	£14	£30
1931 Proof	—	—	—	£800
1932	£4	£6	£17	£40
1933	£3	£4	£12	£25
1935	£4	£6	£17	£30
1936	£4	£6	£17	£30
1937	£3	£4	£12	£25
1939	£3	£4	£6	£12
1939 Proof	—	—	—	£565
1940	£4	£5	£8	£17
1941	£3	£4	£6	£10
1943	£3	£4	£6	£10
1944	£3	£4	£6	£10
1946	£3	£4	£6	£10
1949	£4	£6	£8	£16
1949 Proof	—	—	—	£425
1953	£3	£4	£5	£6
1953 Proof	—	—	—	£300
1959	£3	£4	£5	£6
1966	£3	£4	£5	£6

For the 1928–50 copper issues it is worth noting that UNC means UNC with some lustre. BU examples with full lustre are extremely elusive and are worth much more than the quoted prices.

IRISH DECIMAL COINAGE

DATE	MINTAGE	BU
HALF PENCE		
1971	100,500,000	£4
1975	10,500,000	£5
1976	5,500,000	£5
1978	20,300,000	£4
1980	20,600,000	£3
1982	9,700,000	£3
1985	2,800,000	Rare
1986. Only issued in the 1986 set	19,750,000	£300
ONE PENNY		
1971	100,500,000	£2
1974	10,000,000	£9
1975	10,000,000	£13
1976	38,200,000	£5
1978	25,700,000	£7
1979	21,800,000	£9
1980	86,700,000	£3
1982	54,200,000	£5
1985	19,200,000	£7
1986	36,600,000	£5
1988	56,800,000	£5
1990	65,100,000	£4
1992	25,600,000	£5
1993	10,000,000	£5
1994	45,800,000	£3
1995	70,800,000	£2
1996	190,100,000	75p
1998	40,700,000	75p
2000	Unknown	75p

DATE	MINTAGE	BU
TWO PENCE		
1971	75,500,000	£2
1975	20,000,000	£7
1976	5400,000	£9
1978	12,000,000	£8
1979	32,400,000	£7
1980	59,800,000	£6
1982	30,400,000	£5
1985	14,500,000	£6
1986	23,900,000	£6
1988	35,900,000	£5
1990	34,300,000	£5
1992	10,200,000	£7
1995	55,500,000	£3
1996	69,300,000	£2
1998	33,700,000	£2
2000	Unknown	75p

DATE	MINTAGE	BU
FIVE PENCE		
1969 Toned	5,000,000	£5
1970	10,000,000	£4
1971	8,000,000	£6
1974	7,000,000	£7
1975	10,000,000	£7
1976	20,600,000	£5
1978	28,500,000	£4
1980	22,200,000	£5

DATE	MINTAGE	BU
1982	24,400,000	£4
1985	4,200,000	£7
1986	15,300,000	£5
1990	7,500,000	£5
Size reduced to 18.4mm		
1992	74,500,000	£3
1993	89,100,000	£3
1994	31,100,000	£3
1995	12,000,000	£3
1996	14,700,000	£2
1998	158,500,000	75p
2000	Unknown	75p

TEN PENCE

1969	27,000,000	£6
1971	4,000,000	£8
1973	2,500,000	£16
1974	7,500,000	£11
1975	15,000,000	£11
1976	9,400,000	£11
1978	30,900,000	£10
1980	44,600,000	£7
1982	7,400,000	£7
1985	4,100,000	£8
1986. Only issued in the 1986 set	11,280	£250
Size reduced to 22mm		
1993	80,100,000	£3
1994	58,500,000	£3
1995	16,100,000	£3
1996	18,400,000	£2
1997	10,000,000	£3
1998	10,000,000	£3
1999	24,500,000	£2
2000	Unknown	£1

TWENTY PENCE

1985. Only 600 minted and 556 melted down, only 3 known		Extremely rare
1986	50,400,000	£6
1988	20,700,000	£6
1992	14,800,000	£5
1994	11,100,000	£5
1995	18,200,000	£5
1996	29,300,000	£4
1998	25,000,000	£3
1999	11,000,000	£3
2000	Unknown	£2

FIFTY PENCE

1970	9,000,000	£7
1971	650,000	£6
1974	1,000,000	£55
1975	2,000,000	£55
1976	3,000,000	£45
1977	4,800,000	£55
1978	4,500,000	£45
1979	4,000,000	£45
1981	6,000,000	£25
1982	2,000,000	£25
1983	7,000,000	£25
1986. Only issued in the 1986 set	10,000	£275
1988	7,000,000	£5

1988 Dublin Millennium	5,000,000	£5
1988 — Proof	50,000	£25
1996	6,000,000	£7
1997	6,000,000	£7
1998	13,800,000	£5
1999	7,000,000	£4
2000	Unknown	£4

ONE POUND

1990	42,300,000	£4
1990 Proof	50,000	£25
1994	14,900,000	£5
1995	9,200,000	£5
1995 UN silver proof in case of issue	2,850	£165
1996	9,200,000	£5
1998	22,960,000	£4
1999	10,000,000	£5
2000	4,000,000	£4
2000 Millennium	5,000,000	£4
2000 – Silver Proof Piedfort	90,000	£35

OFFICIAL COIN SETS ISSUED BY THE CENTRAL BANK

1971 Specimen set in green wallet. 6 coins	£16
1975 6 coin set	£55
1978 6 coin set	£55
1978 6 coin set. Black cover, scarce	£75
1982 6 coin set. Black cover	£75
1986 Specimen set in card folder 1/2p to 50p, 7 coins. Very scarce. Most sets have glue problems	£600
1996 7 coin set	£55
1998 7 coin set	£50
2000 Millennium set. Last decimal set	£120
2000 — With 1999 instead of the 2000 £1 coin	£225

Crowds at the Dublin Coin Fair.

OFFICIAL AND SEMI-OFFICIAL COMMEMORATIVE MEDALS

It is probably a strong love of history, rather than the strict disciplines of coin collecting that make collectors turn to commemorative medals. The link between the two is intertwined, and it is to be hoped that collectors will be encouraged to venture into the wider world of medallions, encouraged by this brief guide, supplied by courtesy of Daniel Fearon, acknowledged expert and author of the *Catalogue of British Commemorative Medals*.

DATE	VF	EF
JAMES I		
1603 Coronation (possibly by C. Anthony), 29mm, Silver	£375	£850
QUEEN ANNE		
1603 Coronation, 29mm, AR	£375	£850
CHARLES I		
1626 Coronation (by N. Briot), 30mm, Silver	£300	£650
1633 Scottish Coronation (by N. Briot), 28mm, Silver	£175	£350
1649 Memorial (by J. Roettier). Struck after the Restoration, 50mm, Bronze	£100	£250
CHARLES II		
1651 Scottish Coronation, in exile (from design by Sir J. Balfour), 32mm, Silver	£375	£1000
CROMWELL		
1651 Lord Protector (by T. Simon), 38mm, Silver	£350	£800
— Cast examples	£85	£200
CHARLES II		
1661 Coronation (by T. Simon), 29mm		
— Gold	£1000	£2000
— Silver	£150	£300
1685 Death (by N. Roettier), 39mm, Bronze	£150	£250

James I Coronation, 1603

Charles II Coronation, 1661

DATE	VF	EF
JAMES II		
1685 Coronation (by J. Roettier), 34mm		
— Gold	£1500	£2500
— Silver	£200	£400
MARY		
1685 Coronation (by J. Roettier), 34mm		
— Gold	£950	£2000
— Silver	£150	£350
WILLIAM & MARY		
1689 Coronation (by J. Roettier), 32mm		
— Gold	£950	£2000
— Silver	£150	£250
1689 Coronation,"Perseus" (by G. Bower), 38mm, Gold	£850	£1750
MARY		
1694 Death (by N. Roettier), 39mm, Bronze	£85	£200
WILLIAM III		
1697 "The State of Britain" (by J. Croker), 69mm, Silver	£350	£850
ANNE		
1702 Accession, "Entirely English" (by J. Croker), 34mm		
— Gold	£750	£1750
— Silver	£85	£175
1702 Coronation (by J. Croker), 36mm		
— Gold	£750	£1750
— Silver	£100	£200
1707 Union with Scotland (by J. Croker, rev. by S. Bull), 34mm		
— Gold	£750	£1250
— Silver	£85	£175
1713 Peace of Utrecht (by J. Croker—issued in gold to Members of Parliament), 34mm		
— Gold	£650	£1500
— Silver	£75	£150
GEORGE I		
1714 Coronation(by J. Croker), 34mm		
— Gold	£850	£2250
— Silver	£100	£225
1727 Death (by J. Dassier), 31mm, Silver	£75	£150
GEORGE II		
1727Coronation (by J. Croker), 34mm		
— Gold	£750	£2000
— Silver	£85	£175
QUEEN CAROLINE		
1727 Coronation (by J. Croker), 34mm		
— Gold	£750	£2000
— Silver	£85	£175
1732 The Royal Family (by J. Croker), 70mm		
— Silver	£175	£400
— Bronze	£85	£175

Queen Anne Peace of Utrecht, 1713

George III, Coronation, 1761

DATE	VF	EF
GEORGE III		
1761 Coronation (by L. Natter), 34mm		
— Gold	£950	£2250
— Silver	£150	£300
— Bronze	£65	£175
QUEEN CHARLOTTE		
1761 Coronation (by L. Natter), 34mm		
— Gold	£950	£2250
— Silver	£150	£300
— Bronze	£65	£125
1810 Golden Jubilee, "Frogmore", 48mm, Silver	£100	£250
— Bronze	£55	£125
GEORGE IV		
1821 Coronation (by B. Pistrucci), 35mm		
— Gold	£650	£1250
— Silver	£75	£175
— Bronze	£45	£75
WILLIAM IV		
1831 Coronation (by W. Wyon; rev.shows Queen Adelaide), 33mm		
— Gold	£495	£1250
— Silver	£75	£150
— Bronze	£45	£85
QUEEN VICTORIA		
1838 Coronation (by B. Pistrucci), 37mm		
— Gold	£425	£1250
— Silver	£75	£175
— Bronze	£45	£100

George IV Coronation, 1821

Queen Victoria Coronation, 1838

Queen Victoria Diamond Jubilee 1897

DATE	VF	EF
1887 Golden Jubilee (by J. E. Boehm, rev. by Lord Leighton)		
— Gold, 58mm	£1000	£1750
— Silver, 78mm	£100	£225
— Bronze, 78mm	£55	£150
1897 Diamond Jubilee (by T. Brock),		
— Gold, 56mm	£850	£1250
— Silver, 56mm	£65	£100
— Bronze, 56mm	£25	£45
— Gold, 25mm	£150	£200
— Silver, 25mm	£35	£55

EDWARD VII

1902 Coronation (August 9) (by G. W. de Saulles)		
— Gold, 56mm	£850	£1250
— Silver, 56mm	£45	£85
— Bronze, 56mm	£25	£45
— Gold, 31mm	£155	£225
— Silver, 31mm	£25	£45

**Some rare examples of the official medal show the date as June 26, the original date set for the Coronation which was postponed because the King developed appendicitis.*

GEORGE V

1911 Coronation (by B. Mackennal)		
— Gold, 51mm	£850	£1250
— Silver, 51mm	£34	£85
— Bronze, 51mm	£25	£45
— Gold, 31mm	£175	£225
— Silver, 31mm	£20	£35
1935 Silver Jubilee (by P. Metcalfe)		
— Gold, 58mm	£850	£1250
— Silver, 58mm	£30	£65
— Gold, 32mm	£150	£200
— Silver, 32mm	£25	£40

George V Silver Jubilee, 1935

PRINCE EDWARD

1911 Investiture as Prince of Wales (by W. Goscombe John)		
— Gold, 31mm	£375	£650
— Silver, 31mm	£35	£55

Edward, Prince of Wales, 1911

EDWARD VIII

1936 Abdication (by L. E. Pinches), 35mm		
— Gold	£425	£950
— Silver	£35	£65
— Bronze	£15	£35

GEORGE VI

1937 Coronation (by P. Metcalfe)		
— Gold, 58mm	£950	£1500
— Silver, 58mm	£45	£85
— Gold, 32mm	£175	£225
— Silver, 32mm	£15	£25
— Bronze, 32mm	£5	£12

DATE	VF	EF
ELIZABETH II		
1953 Coronation (by Spink & Son)		
— Gold, 57mm	£850	£1500
— Silver, 57mm	£25	£75
— Bronze, 57mm	£15	£25
— Gold, 32mm	£185	£500
— Silver, 32mm	£15	£35
— Bronze, 32mm	£10	£15
1977 Silver Jubilee (by A. Machin)		
— Silver, 57mm	—	£55
— Silver, 44mm	—	£35

**The gold medals are priced for 18ct—they can also be found as 22ct and 9ct, and prices should be adjusted accordingly.*

PRINCE CHARLES		
1969 Investiture as Prince of Wales (by M. Rizello)		
— Silver, 57mm	—	£50
— Bronze gilt, 57mm	—	£35
— Silver, 45mm	—	£35
— Gold, 32mm	—	£275
— Silver, 32mm	—	£35
— Bronze, 32mm	—	£15

QUEEN ELIZABETH THE QUEEN MOTHER		
1980 80th Birthday (by L. Durbin)		
— Silver, 57mm	—	£50
— Silver, 38mm	—	£35
— Bronze, 38mm	—	£20

N.B.—Official Medals usually command a premium when still in their original cases of issue.

Edward VIII Abdication, 1936

Directory section

ON the following pages will be found the most useful names and addresses needed by the coin collector.

At the time of going to press with this edition of the YEARBOOK the information is correct, as far as we have been able to ascertain. However, people move and establishments change, so it is always advisable to make contact with the person or organisation listed before travelling any distance, to ensure that the journey is not wasted.

Should any of the information in this section not be correct we would very much appreciate being advised in good time for the preparation of the next edition of the COIN YEARBOOK.

BNTA MEMBERSHIPS IN COUNTY ORDER

(Those members with a retail premises are indicated with an*)

LONDON AREA
*A.H. Baldwin & Sons Ltd.
ATS Bullion Ltd
Beaver Coin Room
Keith Chapman
* Classical Numismatic Group Inc / Seaby Coins
*Philip Cohen Numismatics
Andre de Clermont
Michael Dickinson
*Dix Noonan Webb
Christopher Eimer
Glendining's
Harrow Coin & Stamp Centre
*Knightsbridge Coins
Lubbock & Son Ltd.
C. J. Martin (Coins) Ltd.
Nigel Mills
Morton & Eden Ltd.
Moruzzi Ltd
*Colin Narbeth & Son Ltd.
Numismatica Ars Classica
*Pavlos S Pavlou
Predecimal.com incorporating Rotographic Publications
Simmons Gallery
*Spink & Son Ltd.
Surena Ancient Art & Numismatic

BEDFORSHIRE
*Cambridge Coins and Jewellery
Simon Monks

BERKSHIRE
Frank Milward

BRISTOL
Saltford Coins

BUCKINGHAMSHIRE
Charles Riley

CAMBRIDGESHIRE
*Den of Antiquity International Ltd

CORNWALL
Richard W Jeffery

DEVON
Glenn S Ogden

DORSET
*Dorset Coin Co. Ltd.

ESSEX
Time Line Originals

ESSEX/HERTS/LONDON BORDERS
David Seaman

HAMPSHIRE
*SPM Jewellers
Studio Coins
*Victory Coins
West Essex Coin Investments

HERTFORDSHIRE
K B Coins

KENT
Allgold of Sevenoaks
London Coins
*Peter Morris

LANCASHIRE
A F BROCK & Co Ltd
*Colin de Rouffignac
James Murphy
*Peter Ireland Ltd.

MONMOUTHSHIRE
Anthony M. Halse

NORFOLK
*Roderick Richardson
Chris Rudd
BucksCoins

NORTHAMPTONSHIRE
*Giuseppe Miceli Coin & Medal Centre

NORTHUMBERLAND
*Corbitt Stamps Ltd.

NOTTINGHAMSHIRE
History in Coins

SUFFOLK
*Lockdale Coins Ltd
Mike R. Vosper Coins

SURREY
Daniel Fearon
KMCC Ltd
Graeme & Linda Monk
Mark Rasmussen Numismatist
Nigel Tooley Ltd

SUSSEX
*Brighton Coin Co.
Tim Wilkes

WEST MIDLANDS
*Birmingham Coins
David Craddock
*Format of Birmingham Ltd.
Mint Coins Ltd
Paul Davis Birmingham Ltd

WARWICKSHIRE
*Peter Viola
*Warwick & Warwick Ltd

WORCESTERSHIRE
J. Whitmore

YORKSHIRE
Airedale Coins
Paul Clayton
Paul Davies Ltd.
Weighton Coin Wonders*

WALES
Lloyd Bennett
*Cardiff Coins & Medals
*North Wales Coins Ltd.
Colin Rumney

IRELAND
Ormonde Coins

Museums and libraries

Listed below are the Museums and Libraries in the UK which have coins or items of numismatic interest on display or available to the general public.

A

• Anthropological Museum, University of Aberdeen, Broad Street, **Aberdeen,** AB9 1AS (01224 272014).

• Curtis Museum (1855), High Street, **Alton,** Hants (01420 2802). *General collection of British coins.*

• Ashburton Museum, 1 West Street, **Ashburton,** Devon. *Ancient British and Roman antiquities including local coin finds.*

• Ashwell Village Museum (1930), Swan Street, **Ashwell,** Baldock, Herts. *Roman coins from local finds, local trade tokens, Anglo-Gallic coins and jetons.*

• Buckinghamshire County Museum (1862), Church Street, **Aylesbury,** Bucks (01296 88849). *Roman and medieval English coins found locally, 17th/18th century Buckinghamshire tokens, commemorative medals.*

B

• Public Library and Museum (1948), Marlborough Road, **Banbury,** Oxon (01295 259855). *Wrexlin Hoard of Roman coins.*

• Museum of North Devon (1931), The Square, **Barnstaple,** EX32 8LN (01271 46747). *General coin and medal collection, including local finds. Medals of the Royal Devonshire Yeomanry.*

• Roman Baths Museum, Pump Room, **Bath,** Avon (01225 461111 ext 2785). *Comprehensive collection of Roman coins from local finds.*

• Bagshaw Museum and Art Gallery (1911), Wilton Park, **Batley,** West Yorkshire (01924 472514). *Roman, Scottish, Irish, English hammered, British and foreign coins, local traders' tokens, political medalets, campaign medals and decorations.*

• Bedford Museum (1961), Castle Lane, **Bedford** (01234 353323). *Collections of the Bedford Library and Scientific Institute, the Beds Archaeological Society and Bedford Modern School (Pritchard Memorial) Museum.*

• Ulster Museum (1928), Botanic Gardens, **Belfast** BT9 5AB (01232 381251). *Irish, English and British coins and commemorative medals.*

• Berwick Borough Museum (1867), The Clock Block, Berwick Barracks, Ravensdowne, **Berwick**. TD15 1DQ (01289 330044). *Roman, Scottish and medievial coins.*

• Public Library, Art Gallery and Museum (1910), Champney Road, **Beverley,** Humberside (01482 882255). *Beverley trade tokens, Roman, English, British and foreign coins.*

• Bignor Roman Villa (1811), **Bignor,** nr Pulborough, West Sussex (017987 202). *Roman coins found locally.*

• City Museum and Art Gallery (1861), Chamberlain Square, **Birmingham** B3 3DH (0121 235 2834). *Coins, medals and tokens, with special emphasis on the products of the Soho, Heaton, Birmingham and Watt mints.*

• Blackburn Museum, Museum Street, **Blackburn,** Lancs (01254 667130). *Incorporates the Hart (5,000 Greek, Roman and early English) and Hornby (500 English coins) collections, as well as the museum's own collection of British and Commonwealth coins.*

• Museum Collection, Town Hall, **Bognor Regis,** West Sussex. *Roman, English and British coins and trade tokens.*

• Museum and Art Gallery,(1893), Civic Centre, **Bolton,** Lancashire (01204 22311 ext 2191). *General collection of about 3000 British and foreign coins, and over 500 British medals. Numismatic library.*

• Art Gallery and Museum, Central Library, Oriel Road, **Bootle,** Lancs. *Greek, Roman, English, British and some foreign coins, local trade tokens.*

• Roman Town and Museum (1949) Main Street, **Boroughbridge,** N. Yorks. YO2 3PH (01423 322768). *Roman coins.*

• The Museum (1929), The Guildhall, **Boston,** Lincs (01205 365954). *Small collection of English coins.*

• Natural Science Society Museum (1903), 39 Christchurch Road, **Bournemouth,** Dorset (01202 553525). *Greek, Roman and English hammered coins (including the Hengistbury Hoard), local trade tokens.*

• Bolling Hall Museum (1915), Bolling Hall Road, **Bradford,** West Yorkshire BD4 7LP (01274 723057). *Some 2,000 coins and tokens, mostly 18th–20th centuries.*

• Cartwright Hall Museum and Art Gallery (1904), Lister Park, **Bradford,** West Yorkshire BD9 4NS (01274 493313). *Roman coins found locally.*

• Museum and Art Gallery (1932), South Street, **Bridport,** Dorset (01308 22116). *Roman coins, mainly from excavations at Claudian Fort.*

• The City Museum (1820), Queen's Road, **Bristol** BS8 1RL (0117 9 27256). *Ancient British, Roman (mainly from local hoards), English hammered coins, especially from the Bristol mint, and several hundred local trade tokens.*

• District Library and Museum (1891), Terrace Road, **Buxton,** Derbyshire SK17 6DU (01298 24658). *English and British coins, tokens and commemorative medals. Numismatic library.*

C

• Segontium Museum (1928), Beddgelert Road, **Caernarfon,** Gwynedd (01286 675625) *Roman coins and artifacts excavated from the fort.*

• Fitzwilliam Museum (1816), Department of Coins and Medals, Trumpington Street, **Cambridge** (01223 332900). *Ancient, English, medieval European, oriental coins, medals, plaques, seals and cameos.*

• National Museum & Galleries of Wales, Cathays Park, **Cardiff** (029 20397951). *Greek, Celtic, Roman and British coins and tokens with the emphasis on Welsh interest. Also military, civilian and commemorative medals.*

• Guildhall Museum (1979), Greenmarket, **Carlisle,** Cumbria (01228 819925). *General collection of coins and medals.*

• Tullie House (1877), Castle Street, **Carlisle,** Cumbria (01228 34781). *Roman, medieval and later coins from local finds, including medieval counterfeiter's coin-moulds.*

• Gough's Caves Museum (1934), The Cliffs, **Cheddar,** Somerset (01934 343). *Roman coins.*

• Chelmsford and Essex Museum (1835), Oaklands Park, Moulsham Street, **Chelmsford,** Essex CM2 9AQ (01245 615100). *Ancient British, Roman, medieval and later coins mainly from local finds, local medals.*

• Town Gate Museum (1949), **Chepstow,** Gwent. *Local coins and trade tokens.*

• Grosvenor Museum (1886), Grosvenor Street, **Chester** (01244 21616). *Roman coins from the fortress site, Anglo-Saxon, English medieval and post-medieval coins of the Chester and Rhuddlan mints, trade tokens of Chester and Cheshire, English and British milled coins.*

• Public Library (1879), Corporation Street, **Chesterfield,** Derbyshire (01246 2047). *Roman coins from local finds, Derbyshire trade tokens, medals, seals and railway passes. Numismatic library. Numismatic library and publications.*

• Red House Museum (1919), Quay Road, **Christchurch,** Dorset (01202 482860). *Coins of archaeological significance from Hampshire and Dorset, notably the South Hants Hoard, ancient British, Armorican, Gallo-Belgic, Celtic and Roman coins, local trade tokens and medals.*

• Corinium Museum (1856), Park Street, **Cirencester,** Glos (01285 655611). *Roman coins from archaeological excavations.*

• Colchester and Essex Museum (1860), The Castle, **Colchester,** Essex (01206 712931/2). *Ancient British and Roman coins from local finds, medieval coins (especially the Colchester Hoard), later English coins and Essex trade tokens, commemorative medals.*

D

• Public Library, Museum and Art Gallery (1921), Crown Street, **Darlington,** Co Durham (01325 463795). *General collection of coins, medals and tokens.*

• Borough Museum (1908), Central Park, **Dartford,** Kent (01322 343555). *Roman, medieval and later English hammered coins, trade tokens and commemorative medals.*

• Dartmouth Museum (1953), The Butterknowle, **Dartmouth,** Devon (01803 832923). *Coins and medals of a historical and maritime nature.*

• Museum and Art Gallery (1878), The Strand, **Derby** (01332 255586). *Roman coins, English silver and copper regal coins, Derbyshire tradesmen's tokens, British campaign medals and decorations of the Derbyshire Yeomanry and the 9/12 Royal Lancers.*

• Museum and Art Gallery (1909), Chequer Road, **Doncaster,** South Yorkshire (01302 734293). *General collection of English and foreign silver and bronze coins. Representative collection of Roman imperial silver and bronze coins, including a number from local hoards. English trade tokens, principally of local issues, medals.*

• Dorset County Museum(1846), **Dorchester,** Dorset (01305 262735). *British, Roman, medieval and later coins of local interest.*

• Central Museum (1884), Central Library, St James's Road, **Dudley,** West Midlands (01384 453576). *Small general collection of coins, medals and tokens.*

• Burgh Museum (1835), The Observatory, Corberry Hill, **Dumfries** (01387 53374). *Greek, Roman, Anglo-Saxon, medieval English and Scottish coins, especially from local hoards. Numismatic library.*

• Dundee Art Galleries and Museums (1873). Albert Square, **Dundee** DD1 1DA (01382 23141). *Coins and medals of local interest.*

• The Cathedral Treasury (995 AD), The College, **Durham** (0191-384 4854). *Greek and Roman coins bequeathed by Canon Sir George Wheeler (1724), general collection of medals from the Renaissance to modern times, medieval English coins, especially those struck at the Durham ecclesiastical mint.*

• Durham Heritage Centre, St Mary le Bow, North Bailey, **Durham** (0191-384 2214). *Roman, medieval and later coins, mainly from local finds.*

E

• Royal Museum of Scotland (1781), Queen Street, **Edinburgh** EH1 (0131 225 7534). *Roman, Anglo-Saxon, Englsh and Scottish coins, trade tokens, commemorative medals and communion tokens. Numismatic library. Publications.*

• Royal Albert Memorial Museum (1868), Queen St, **Exeter** EX4 3RX (01392 265858). *Roman and medieval. Coins of the Exeter Mint.*

G

• Hunterian Museum (1807), Glasgow University, University Avenue, **Glasgow** G12 8QQ (0141 339 8855). *Greek, Roman, Byzantine, Scottish, English and Irish coins, Papal and other European medals, Indian and Oriental coins, trade and communion tokens.*

• Art Gallery and Museum (1888), Kelvingrove, **Glasgow** G3 (0141 357 3929). *General collection of coins, trade tokens, communion tokens, commemorative and military medals.*

• Museum of Transport (1974), Kelvin Hall, Bunhouse Road, **Glasgow** G3 (0141 357 3929). *Transport tokens and passes, commemorative medals, badges and insignia of railway companies and shipping lines.*

• City Museum and Art Gallery (1859), Brunswick Road, **Gloucester** (01452 524131). *Ancient British, Roman, Anglo-Saxon (from local finds), early medieval (from local mints), Gloucestershire trade tokens.*

• Guernsey Museum and Art Gallery, St Peter Port, **Guernsey** (01481 726518). *Armorican, Roman, medieval and later coins, including the coins, medals, tokens and paper money of Guernsey.*

• Guildford Museum (1898), Castle Arch, **Guildford,** Surrey GU1 3SX (01483 444750). *Roman and medieval coins and later medals.*

H

• Gray Museum and Art Gallery, Clarence Road, **Hartlepool,** Cleveland (01429 268916). *General collection, including coins from local finds.*

• Public Museum and Art Gallery (1890), John's Place, Cambridge Road, **Hastings,** East Sussex (01424 721952). *General collection of English and British coins, collection of Anglo-Saxon coins from Sussex mints.*

• City Museum (1874), Broad Street, **Hereford** (01432 268121 ext 207). *Coins from the Hereford mint and local finds, Herefordshire trade tokens, general collection of later coins and medals.*

• Hertford Museum (1902), 18 Bull Plain, **Hertford** (01992 582686). *British, Roman, medieval and later English coins and medals.*

• Honiton and Allhallows Public Museum (1946), High Street, **Honiton,** Devon (01404 44966). *Small general collection, including coins from local finds.*

• Museum and Art Gallery (1891), 19 New Church Road, **Hove,** East Sussex (01273 779410). *English coins, Sussex trade tokens and hop tallies, campaign medals, orders and decorations, commemorative medals.*

• Tolson Memorial Museum (1920), Ravensknowle Park, **Huddersfield,** West Yorkshire (01484 541455). *Representative collection of British coins and tokens, Roman and medieval coins, mainly from local finds.*

• Hull and East Riding Museum (1928), 36 High Street, **Hull** (01482 593902). *Celtic, Roman and medieval coins and artifacts from local finds. Some later coins including tradesmen's tokens.*

I

• The Manx Museum, Douglas, **Isle of Man** (01624 675522). *Roman, Celtic, Hiberno-Norse, Viking, medieval English and Scottish coins, mainly from local finds, Manx traders' tokens from the 17th to 19th centuries, Manx coins from 1709 to the present day.*

J

• Jersey Museum, Weighbridge, St Helier, **Jersey** (01534 30511). *Armorican, Gallo-Belgic, Roman, medieval English and French coins, coins, paper money and tokens of Jersey.*

K

• Dick Institute Museum and Art Gallery (1893), Elmbank Avenue, **Kilmarnock,** Ayrshire (01563 26401). *General collection of coins and medals, and the Hunter-Selkirk collection of communion tokens.*

L

• City Museum (1923), Old Town Hall, Market Square, **Lancaster** (01524 64637). *Roman, Anglo-Saxon, medieval English coins, provincial trade tokens, medals of the King's Own Royal Lancashire Regiment.*

• City Museum (1820), Municipal Buildings, The Headrow, **Leeds,** West Yorkshire (01532 478279). *Greek, Roman, Anglo-Saxon, English medieval, Scottish, Irish, British, Commonwealth and foreign coins. Several Roman and Saxon hoards. The Backhouse collection of Yorkshire banknotes, the Thornton collection of Yorkshire tokens, British and foreign commemorative medals.*

• Leicester Museum and Art Gallery (1849), New Walk, **Leicester** (01533 554100). *Roman, medieval and later coins, mainly from local finds, tokens, commemorative medals, campaign medals and decorations.*

• Pennington Hall Museum and Art Gallery, **Leigh,** Lancashire. *General collection of Roman, English and British coins and medals.*

• Museum and Art Gallery (1914), Broadway, **Letchworth,** Herts (01462 65647). *Ancient British coins minted at Camulodunum, Roman, medieval and English coins, Hertfordshire trade tokens, commemorative and campaign medals.*

• City Library, Art Gallery and Museum (1859), Bird Street, **Lichfield,** Staffs (01543 2177). *Roman, medieval and later English coins, Staffordshire trade tokens and commemorative medals.*

• Liverpool Museum(1851), William Brown Street, **Liverpool** L3 8EN (0151 207 0001). *General collection of Roman, medievaland later British coins, tokens.*

• Bank of England Museum, Threadneedle Street, **London** EC2 (020-7601 5545). *Exhibits relating to gold bullion, coins, tokens and medals, the design and manufacture of banknotes, and a comprehensive collection of bank notes dating from the 17th century to the present day.*

• British Museum(1752), HSBC Coin Gallery, Great Russell Street, **London** WC1 (020-7636 1555). *Almost a million coins, medals, tokens and badges of all period from Lydia, 7th century BC to the present time. Extensive library of books and periodicals.*

• British Numismatic Society (1903), Warburg Institute, Woburn Square, **London** WC1. *Library containing over 5,000 volumes, including sale catalogues, periodicals and pamphlets. Open to members only.*

• Cuming Museum (1906), Walworth Road, **London** SE17 (020-7703 3324/5529). *Some 8,000 items, including Greek, Roman, medieval English and modern British coins, English tokens and commemorative medals.*

• Gunnersbury Park Museum (1927), Acton, **London** W3. *Ancient British, Greek, Roman, medieval English, British and some foreign coins, tradesmen's tokens and commemorative medals, including local finds. Small numismatic library.*

• Horniman Museum and Library (1890), London Road, Forest Hill, **London** SE23 (020-7699 2339). *General collection, primitive currency, some tokens.*

• Imperial War Museum, Lambeth Road, **London** SE1 6HZ (020-7416 5000). *Emergency coinage of two world wars, occupation and invasion money, extensive collection of German Notgeld, commemorative, propaganda and military medals, badges and insignia.*

• Sir John Soane's Museum (1833), 13 Lincoln's Inn Fields, **London** WC2 (020-7405 2107). *Napoleonic medals and medallic series of the late 18th and early 19th centuries.*

• National Maritime Museum, Romney Road, Greenwich, **London** SE10 (020-8858 4422). *Commemorative medals with a nautical or maritime theme, naval medals and decorations.*

• Victoria and Albert Museum (1852), South Kensington, **London** SW7 (020-7938 8441). *Byzantine gold and medieval Hispano-Mauresque coins (Department of Metalwork), large collection of Renaissance and later medals (Department of Architecture and Sculpture). Library of numismatic books.*

• Ludlow Museum (1833). The Assembly Rooms. Castle Square, **Ludlow** (01584 873857). *Roman and medieval coins from local finds.*

• Luton Museum and Art Gallery (1927), Wardown Park, **Luton**, Beds (01582 36941). *Coins, tokens and medals.*

M

• Museum and Art Gallery (1858), **Maidstone**, Kent (01622 754497). *Ancient British, Roman, Anglo-Saxon and medieval coins found in Kent, modern British coins, Kent trade tokens, banknotes, hop tallies and tokens, primitive currency, collections of Kent Numismatic Society.*

• The Manchester Museum (1868), The University, **Manchester** M13 (0161-275 2634). *Very fine collections of Greek and Roman coins, comprehensive collections of English, European and Oriental coins, over 30,000 in all.*

• Margate Museum (1923), The Old Town Hall, Market Place, **Margate**, Kent (01843 225511 ext 2520). *Small collection of coins, including Roman from local finds.*

• Montrose Museum and Art Gallery (1836). Panmure Place, **Montrose**, Angus DD10 8HE (01674 73232). *Scottish and British coins.*

N

• Newark-on-Trent Museum (1912), Appleton Gate, **Newark**, Notts (01636 702358). *Siege pieces, trade tokens and coins from local finds and hoards.*

• Newbury District Museum, The Wharf, **Newbury**, Berkshire (01635 30511). *Ancient British, Roman and medieval coins and artifacts, later coins and tokens.*

• The Greek Museum, Percy Building, **Newcastle-upon-Tyne** (0191 2226000 ext 7966). *Ancient coins.*

O

• Heberden Coin Room, Ashmolean Museum (1683), **Oxford** (01865 278000). *Extensive collections of all periods, notably Greek, Roman, English and Oriental coins, Renaissance portrait and later medals, tokens and paper money. Large library. Numerous publications.*

P

• Peterborough Museum (1881), Priestgate, **Peterborough**, Cambs (01733 340 3329). *Roman (mainly from local hoards and finds), Anglo-Saxon, medieval English, British and modern European coins, English and British commemorative medals and tokens.*

• City Museum and Art Gallery (1897), Drake Circus, **Plymouth**, Devon (01752 264878). *General collections of British and Commonwealth coins and tokens, Devon trade tokens and Plymouth tradesmen's checks, Ancient British and Roman coins from local sites.*

• Waterfront Museum, 4 High Street, **Poole**, Dorset (01202 683138). *General collection of British and foreign coins, medals and tokens (view by appointment).*

• City Museum (1972), Museum Road, Old **Portsmouth** PO1 (023 80827261). *Roman, medieval and later coins mainly from local finds and archaeological excavation, British coins, trade tokens of Hampshire, commemorative medals.*

• Harris Museum and Art Gallery (1893), Market Square, **Preston**, Lancashire (01772 58248). *English and British coins, tokens and medals.*

R

• The Museum of Reading (1883), Blagrave Street, **Reading**, Berks (0118 939 9800). *British, Roman and medieval English coins, many from local finds, tradesmen's tokens and commemorative medals.*

• Rochdale Museum (1905), Sparrow Hill, **Rochdale**, Lancs (01706 41085). *Roman and medieval coins from local finds, Rochdale trade tokens, miscellaneous British and foreign coins and medals.*

• Municipal Museum and Art Gallery (1893), Clifton Park, **Rotherham** (01709 382121). *Roman coins from Templeborough Forts, medieval English coins from local hoards and a general collection of British coins.*

S

• Saffron Walden Museum (1832) (1939), Museum Street, **Saffron** Walden, Essex (01799 522494). *Ancient British, Roman, medieval and later coins, mainly from local finds and archaeological excavation, trade tokens and commemorative medals.*

• Verulamium Museum, St Michael's, **St Albans**, Herts (01727 819339). *Coins and artifacts excavated from the Roman town.*

• Salisbury and South Wiltshire Museum (1861), The Cathedral Close, **Salisbury,** Wilts (01722 332151). *Collection of coins minted or found locally, including finds of Iron Age, Roman, Saxon and medieval coins, as well as 18th and 19th century tradesmen's tokens.*

• Richborough Castle Museum (1930), **Sandwich,** Kent (0304 612013). *Roman coins of 1st–5th centuries from excavations of the Richborough site.*

• Scarborough Museum (1829), The Rotunda, Vernon Road, **Scarborough**, North Yorkshire (01723 374839). *Over 4,000 Roman coins, 1,500 English and 600 coins from local finds, siege pieces and trade tokens.*

• Shaftesbury and Dorset Local History Museum (1946), 1 Gold Hill, **Shaftesbury**, Dorset (01747 52157). *Hoard of Saxon coins.*

• City Museum (1875), Weston Park, **Sheffield** (0114 2 768588). *Over 5,000 coins of all periods, but mainly English and modern British. European coins, imperial Roman (including three hoards of about 500 coins each), Yorkshire trade tokens, British historical medals, campaign medals. Library.*

• Rowley's House Museum, Barker Street, **Shrewsbury**, Salop (01743 361196). *Coins minted at Shrewsbury 925-1180, Civil War coinage of 1642, Shropshire tradesmen's tokens, English coins and medals.*

• Museum of Archaeology (1951), God's House Tower, Town Quay, **Southampton**, Hants (023 8022 0007). *Main emphasis lies in Ancient British, Roman and medieval English coins from local archaeological excavations. General collection of later coins and medals.*

• Atkinson Art Gallery (1878), Lord Street, **Southport,** Lancs (01704 533133). *Roman coins.*

• Botanic Gardens Museum, Churchtown, **Southport,** Lancs (01704 87547). *English and British coins and medals, military medals and decorations.*

• Southwold Museum (1933), St Bartholomew's Green, **Southwold**, Suffolk (01502 722375). *General collection of coins, specialised Suffolk trade tokens.*

• Stamford Museum (1961), Broad Street, **Stamford**, Lincs (01780 66317). *General collection of coins, medals and tokens, including a selection from the Stamford mint.*

• Municipal Museum (1860), Vernon Park, Turncroft Lane, **Stockport**, Cheshire (0161 474 4460) *Miscellaneous general collection of coins, tokens and medals.*

• Stroud Museum (1899), Lansdown, **Stroud**, Glos (01453 376394). *Ancient British, Roman, Saxon, Norman, later medieval English, British coins and Gloucestershire trade tokens.*

• Museum and Art Gallery (1846), Borough Road, **Sunderland,** Tyne & Wear (0191 514 1235). *Roman imperial, medieval and later English, including examples of the pennies minted at Durham, modern British and foreign coins, 17th-19th century tradesmen's tokens, local medallions and campaign medals.*

• Swansea Museum (1835), Victoria Road, **Swansea**, W. Glamorgan, SA1 1SN (0792 653765). *Coins and medals of local interest.*

T

• Tamworth Castle and Museum (1899), The Holloway, **Tamworth**, Staffs (01827 63563). *Anglo-Saxon coins, medieval English including coins of the Tamworth mint, later English and British coins, tokens, commemorative medallions and medals.*

• Somerset County Museum, Taunton Castle, **Taunton**, Somerset (01823 255510/320200). *Celtic, Roman, Anglo-Saxon, early Medieval, tokens, medallions and banknotes. Strong emphasis on locally-found items.*

• Thurrock Local History Museum (1956), Civic Square, **Tilbury**, Essex (01375 390000 ext 2414). *Roman coins.*

• Royal Cornwall Museum (1818), River Street, **Truro,** Cornwall (01872 72205). *Coins, tokens and medals pertaining principally to the county of Cornwall.*

W

• Wakefield Museum (1919), Wood Street, **Wakefield,** West Yorkshire (01924 295351). *Roman and medieval English silver and copper coins.*

• Epping Forest District Museum, 39/41 Sun Street, **Waltham Abbey**, Essex EN 9. *Ancient British, Roman and medieval coins, Essex tradesmen's tokensof local interest.*

• Warrington Museum and Art Gallery (1848). Bold Street, **Warrington**, Cheshire, WA1 1JG (01925 30550). *Coins, medals and tokens.*

• Worcester City Museum (1833), Foregate Street, **Worcester** (01905 25371). *Roman, medieval and later coins and tokens. Coins of the Worcester mint.*

• Wells Museum (18903), 8 Cathedral Green, **Wells,** Somerset (01749 3477). *Ancient and modern British and world coins, local trade tokens and medals.*

• Municipal Museum and Art Gallery (1878), Station Road, **Wigan**, Lancashire. *British, Commonwealth and foreign coins from about 1660 to the present. Roman coins from local sites, commemorative medals.*

• City Museum (1851), The Square, **Winchester**, Hants (01962 848269). *Roman and medieval coins chiefly from local hoards and finds. Hampshire tradesmen's tokens and commemorative medals. Small reference library.*

• Wisbech and Fenland Museum (1835), Museum Square, **Wisbech,** Cambridgeshire (01945 583817), *British Roman, medieval and later coins, medals and tokens.*

Y

• The Museum of South Somerset (1928), Hendford, **Yeovil,** Somerset (01935 24774). *Roman coins from local sites, medieval English, modern British coins and medals and a fine collection of tokens (particularly 17th century Somerset).*

• Castle Museum (1938), **York** (01904 653611). *English and British coins, campaign medals, orders and decorations, comemorative medals.*

• Jorvik Viking Centre (1984), Coppergate, **York** (01904 643211). *Coins and artefacts pertaining to the Viking occupation of York.*

• The Yorkshire Museum (1823), **York** (01904 629745). *Roman imperial, medieval English and later coins, about 12,000 in all.*

Club directory

Details given here are the names of Numismatic Clubs and Societies, their date of foundation, and their usual venues, days and times of meetings. Meetings are monthly unless otherwise stated. Finally, the telephone number of the club secretary is given; the names and addresses of club secretaries are withheld for security reasons, but full details may be obtained by writing to the Secretary of the British Association of Numismatic Societies, Phyllis Stoddart, Honorary Curatorial Assistant, Deptartment of Numismatics, Manchester Museum, Oxford Road, Manchester M13 9PL or visiting the website at www.coinclubs.freeserve.co.uk.

Banbury & District NS (1967). St John's Social Club, St John's Church, Oxford Road, Banbury 2nd Mon (exc Jul & Aug), 19.45. (01295 275128).

Bath & Bristol Numismatic Society (1950). Fry's Club, Keynsham, Bristol. 2nd Thu, 19.30. (0117 968 7259).

Bedfordshire Numismatic Society (1966). Dave Allen, Secretary (01234 870645).

Bexley Coin Club (1968). St Martin's Church Hall, Erith Road, Barnehurst, Bexleyheath, Kent. 1st Mon (exc Jan & Aug), 19.30. (020 8303 0510).

Birmingham Numismatic Society (1964). Friend's Meeting House, Bull Street. (0121 308 1616).

Matthew Boulton Society (1994). PO Box 395, Bir-mingham B31 2TB (0121 781 6558 fax 0121 781 6574).

Bradford & District Numismatic Society (1967). East Bowling Unity Club, Leicester Street, Bradford, West Yorkshire. 3rd Mon, 19.00. (01532 677151).

British Cheque Collectors' Society (1980). John Purser, 71 Mile Lane, Cheylesmore, Coventry, West Midlands CV3 5GB.

British Numismatic Society (1903). Warburg Institute, Woburn Square, London WC1H 0AB. Monthly (exc Aug & Dec), 18.00. (020 7323 8585)

Cambridgeshire Numismatic Society (1946). Friends' Meeting House, 12 Jesus Lane (entrance in Park Street), Cambridge, CB5 8BA. 3rd Mon, Sept–June, 19.30. (01480 210992).

Chester & North Wales Coin & Banknote Society (1996). Liver Hotel, 110 Brook Street, Chester. 4th Tue, 20.00. (0151 478 4293)

Cheltenham Numismatic Society, The Reddings & District Community Association, North Road, The Reddings, Cheltenham. 3rd Mon, 19.45 (01242 673263)

Coin Correspondence Club (1988). Postal only. A.H. Chubb, 49 White Hart Lane, Barnes, London SW13 0PP. (0181-878 0472).

Cornwall Collectors' Club (1990). The Swan Inn, 40 Bosvigo Road, Truro. 1st Wed, 20.00. (01872 73376).

Crawley Coin Club (1969). Furnace Green Community Centre, Ashburnham Road, Furnace Green, Crawley, West Sussex. 1st Tue, 20.00. (01293 548671).

Crewe & District Coin & Medal Club (1968). Memorial Hall, Church Lane, Wistaston, Crewe, 2nd Tue (exc Jan & July), 19.30. (01270 569836).

Darlington & District Numismatic Society (1968). Darlington Arts Centre, Vane Terrace, Darlington, Co Durhm. 3rd Wed, 19.30. (01609 772976).

Derbyshire Numismatic Society (1964). The Friends' Meeting House, St Helens Street, Derby. 3rd Mon (exc August), 19.45. (01283 211623).

Devon & Exeter Numismatic Society (1965). Courtenay Room, The St. James Centre, Stadium Way, Exeter, Devon. 3rd Tue, 19.30. (01395 568830).

Edinburgh Numismatic Society (1996). Department of History and Applied Arts, Royal Museum of Scotland, Chambers Street, Edinburgh EH1 1JF. 3rd Mon, 19.30. (0131 225 7534).

Enfield & District Numismatic Society (1969). Millfield House Arts Centre, Silver Street, Edmonton, London N18 1PJ. 3rd Mon, 20.00. (0181-340 0767).

Essex Numismatic Society (1966). Chelmsford Museum, Moulsham Street, Chelmsford, Essex. 4th Fri (exc Dec), 20.00. (01277 656627).

Glasgow & West of Scotland Numismatic Society (1947). Woodside Halls, 26 Glenfarg Street, Glasgow, G3. 2nd Thu, Oct-May, 19.30. (0141 9424776).

Harrow Coin Club (1968). Telephone for details of venue. 2nd and 4th Mon, 19.30. (020 8952 8765).

Havering Numismatic Society (1967). Fairkytes Arts Centre, Billet Lane, Hornchurch, Essex. 1st Tue, 19.30. (07910 124549).

Horncastle & District Coin Club (1963). Bull Hotel, Bull Ring, Horncastle, Lincs. 2nd Thu (exc Aug), 19.30. (01754 2706).

Huddersfield Numismatic Society (1947). Huddersfield Library, Princess Alexandra Walk, Huddersfield, West Yorkshire. 1st Mon (exc Jul & Aug), 19.30. (01484 866814).

Hull & District Numismatic Society (1967). The Young People's Institute, George Street, Hull. Monthly (exc Aug & Dec), 19.30. (01482 441933).

International Bank Note Society (1961). Victory Services Club, 63–79 Seymour Street, London W1. Website: www.ibns.org.uk. Last Thu (exc Dec), 18.00. (www.ibnslondon.org.uk).

International Bank Note Society (East Midlands Branch), Wollaton Park Community Association, Wollaton Park, Nottingham. (0115 928 9720).

International Bank Note Society, **Scottish Chapter** (1995). West End Hotel, Palmerston Place, Edinburgh. Last Sat (exc Dec), 14.30.

Ireland, Numismatic Society of (Northern Branch). Denman International, Clandeboye Road, Bangor or Shaws Bridge Sports Association,123 Milltown Road, Belfast. 1st Fri (exc Jan) 19.30. (028 9146 6743)

Ireland, Numismatic Society of. (Southern Branch). Ely House, 8 Ely Place, Dublin. Third Fri, 20.00. (0035 3 283 2027).

Ipswich Numismatic Society (1966). Ipswich Citizens Advice Bureau, 19 Tower Street, Ipswich, Suffolk. Monthly meetings, 19.30. (01473 728653).

Kent Towns Numismatic Society (1913). (Mr. R. Josland, 01634 721187).

Kingston Numismatic Society (1966). King Athel-stan's School, Villiers Road, Kingston-upon-Thames, Surrey. 3rd Thu (exc Dec & Jan), 19.30. (020-8397 6944).

Lancashire & Cheshire Numismatic Society (1933). Reception Room, 2nd Floor, Manchester Central Library, St Peter's Square, Manchester. Monthly, Sep-June, Sat (14.00). Manchester Museum (May & Dec only). (0161 275 2661).

Lincolnshire Numismatic Society (1932). Grimsby Bridge Club, Bargate, Grimsby, South Humberside. 4th Wed (exc Aug), 19.30.

London Numismatic Club (1947). Warburg Institute, Woburn Square, London WC1H 0AB. First Tuesday of month (except January and August), 1830. (01223 332918).

Loughborough Coin & Search Society (1964). Wallace Humphry Room, Shelthorpe Community Centre, Loughborough, Leics. 1st Thu, 19.30. (01509 261352).

Mid Lanark Coin Circle (1969). Hospitality Room, The Civic Centre, Motherwell, Lanarkshire. 4th Thu, Sep–Apr (exc Dec), 19.30. (0141-552 2083).

Morecambe & Lancaster Numismatic Society. Monthly, 19.30. (01524 411036).

Newbury Coin & Medal Club (1971). Monthly, 20.00. (01635 41233).

Northampton Numismatic Society (1969). Old Scouts RFC, Rushmere Road, Northampton. 1st Thurs, 20.00.

Norwich Coin & Medal Society, The White Horse, Trowse, Norwich. (01603 408393).

Norwich Numismatic Society (1967). Assembly House, Theatre Street, Norwich, Norfolk. 3rd Mon, 19.30. (01603 408393).

Nottinghamshire Numismatic Society (1948). The Cecil Roberts Room, County Library, Angel Row, Nottingham NG1 6HP. 2nd Tue (Sep-Apr), 18.45. (0115 9257674).

Nuneaton & District Coin Club (1968). United Reformed Church Room, Coton Road, opposite Council House, Nuneaton, Warwickshire. 2nd Tue, 19.30. (01203 371556).

Orders & Medals Research Society (1942). National Army Museum, Royal Hospital Road, Chelsea, London SW3. Monthly, 14.30 (020-8680 2701).

Ormskirk & West Lancashire Numismatic Society (1970).The Eagle & Child, Maltkiln Lane, Bispham Green L40 1SN. 1st Thu, 20.15. (01704 531266).

Peterborough & District Numismatic Society (1967). Belsize Community Centre, Celta Road Peter-borough, Cambs. 4th Tue (exc July & Aug), 19.30. (01733 562768 or 567763).

Plymouth Numismatics Society (1970). Mutley Conservative Club, Mutley Plain, Plymouth, Devon. 2nd Wed (exc Dec), 19.30. (01752 490 394).

Preston & District Numismatic Society (1965). Eldon Hotel, Eldon Street, Preston, Lancs. 1st and 3rd Tue, 20.00. (012572 66869).

Reading Coin Club (1964). Abbey Baptist Church, Abbey Square, Reading. 1st Mon, 20.00. (0118 933 2842).

Romsey Numismatic Society (1969). Romsey WM Conservative Club, Market Place, Romsey, Hants SO5 8NA. 4th Fri (exc Dec), 19.30. (01703 253921).

Rotherham & District Coin Club (1982). Rotherham Art Centre, Rotherham, South Yorkshire. 1st Wed, 19.00. (01709 528179).

Royal Mint Coin Club, PO Box 500, Cardiff CF1 1HA (01443 222111).

Royal Numismatic Society (1836). Warburg Institute, Woburn Square, London, WC1H 0AB.(some meetings held at British Museum). Third Thursday of monthly (Oct-June), 18.00. Joe Cribb, Coins and Medals, British Museum, London WC1B 3DG (020-7323 8175).

Rye Coin Club (1955). Rye Further Education Centre, Lion Street, Rye, East Sussex. 2nd Thu (Oct-Dec, Feb-May), 19.30. (01424 422974).

St Albans & Hertfordshire Numismatic Society (1948). St Michael's Parish Centre, Museum Entrance, Verulamium Park, St Albans, Herts AL3 4SL. 2nd Tue (exc Aug), 19.30. (01727 824434).

South East Hants Numismatic Society. The Langstone Conservative Club, Havant. Second Fri. Contact: Tony Matthews, (01292 389419)

South Manchester Numismatic Society (1967). Nursery Inn, Green Lane, Heaton Mersey, Stockport. 1st & 3rd Mondays of each month (excl. Public hols), 20.15. (0161-476 3184).

South Wales & Monmouthshire Numismatic Society (1958). 1st Mon (except Bank Holidays when 2nd Mon, 19.30. (For location tel: 029 20561564).

Thurrock Numismatic Society (1970). Stanley Lazell Hall, Dell Road, Grays, Essex. 3rd Wed, 19.00.

Tyneside Numismatic Society (1954). RAFA Club, Eric Nelson House, 16 Berwick Road, Gateshead, Tyne & Wear. 2nd Wed, 19.30. (01661 825824).

Wessex NS (1948). Edward Wright Room, Beaufort Community Centre, Southbourne, Bournemouth, Dorset. 2nd Thurs (exc Aug), 20.00. (020 7731 1702).

Wiltshire Numismatic Society (1965). The Village Hall, Poulshot, Nr. Devizes, Wiltshire. 3rd Mon, Mar-Dec, 20.00. (01380 828453).

Worthing & District Numismatic Society (1967). Berkeley Hotel, Marine Parade, Worthing, West Sussex BN11 3QQ. 3rd Thu, 20.00. (01634 260114).

Yorkshire Numismatic Society (1909). Swarthmore Institute, Woodhouse Square, Leeds. 1st Sat (exc Jan, Aug & Dec) (0113 3910848).

Important Notice to Club Secretaries:

If your details as listed are incorrect please let us know in time for the next edition of the COIN YEARBOOK. Amendments can be sent via post or email janis@tokenpublishing.com

IMPORTANT ORGANISATIONS

ADA
The Antiquities Dealers Association
Secretary: Susan Hadida, Duke's Court, 32 Duke Street, London SW1Y 6DU

IBNS
International Bank Note Society
Membership Secretary:
Clive Rice, 25 Copse Side, Binscombe, Godalming, Surrey, GU7 3RU

ANA
The American Numismatic Association
818 North Cascade Avenue, Colorado Springs, CO 80903-3279, USA

RNS
Royal Numismatic Society
Dept of Coins & Medals, British Museum, London WC1B 3DG.

BNTA
The British Numismatic Trade Association
Secretary: Mrs R. Cooke, General Secretary, BNTA, PO Box 2, Rye, East Sussex TN31 7WE

BAMS
British Art Medal Society
Philip Attwood, Dept of Coins & Medals, British Museum, London WC1B 3DG.

IAPN
International Association of Professional Numismatists
Secretary: Jean-Luc Van der Schueren, 14 Rue de la Bourse, B–1000, Brussels.

BNS
British Numismatic Society
Dr K. Clancy, The Royal Mint, Llantrisant, Pontyclun, Mid Glamorgan CF72 8YT

Directory of Auctioneers

Listed here are the major auction houses which handle coins, medals, banknotes and other items of numismatic interest. Many of them hold regular public auctions, whilst others handle numismatic material infrequently. A number of coin companies also hold regular Postal Auctions—these are marked with a (P)

Baldwin's Auctions Ltd
11 Adelphi Terrace, London WC2N 6BJ
(020 7930 6879 fax 020 7930 9450,
auctions@baldwin.sh, www.baldwin.sh)

Banking Memorabilia
PO Box 14, Carlisle CA3 8DZ (016974 76465).

Birmingham Auctions
PO Box 178, Worcester WR5 3RY
(01885 488871, barryfaulkner@btopenworld.com,
www.birmauctions.co.uk).

Blyth & Co
7/9 Market Square, Ely, Cambs, CB7 4NP
(01353 668320, auctions@fenlord.com)

Bonhams (incorporating Glendinings)
Montpelier Street, Knightsbridge, London
SW7 1HH (020 7393 3914, www.bonhams.com).

A. F. Brock & Company
269 London Road, Hazel Grove, Stockport,
Cheshire SK7 4PL (0161 456 5050
fax 0161 456 5112, www.afbrock.co.uk,
info@afbrock.co.uk).

Christie, Manson & Wood Ltd
8 King Street, St James's, London SW1Y 6QT
(020 7839 9060).

Classical Numismatic Group Inc (Seaby Coins)
14 Old Bond Street, London W1X 4JL
(020 7495 1888 fax 020 7499 5916,
cng@historicalcoins.com,
www.historicalcoins.com). (P)

Coins4u.net
38 Livingstone Place, Galashiels, Scotland
TD1 1ED. On-line coin auction.

Corbitts
5 Moseley Sreet, Newcastle upon Tyne NE1 1YE
(0191-232 7268, fax 0191-261 4130).

Croydon Coin Auctions
PO Box 201, Croydon, CR9 7AQ (020 8656 4583,
www.croydoncoinauctions.co.uk)

Dix Noonan Webb
16 Bolton Street, Piccadilly, London.
(020 7016 1700, www.dnw.co.uk,
auctions@dnw.co.uk).

Dublin Coin Auction
5 St. Assam's Park, Raheny, Dublin 5
(00 353 868 714 880)

E2bid.com
PO Box 50, Sevenoaks TN14 6WD.
On-line auction.

Edinburgh Coin Shop
11 West Crosscauseway, Edinburgh EH8 9JW
(0131 668 2928 fax 0131 668 2926). (P)

Jean Elsen & ses Fils s.a.
Avenue de Tervueren 65, B–1040, Brussels
(0032 2 7346356, www.elsen.eu)

Fellows & Sons
Augusta House, 19 Augusta Street, Hockley,
Birmingham B18 6JA (0121-212 2131).
www.fellows.co.uk

B. Frank & Son
3 South Avenue, Ryton, Tyne & Wear NE40 3LD
(0191 413 8749 fax 0191 413 2957,
bfrankandson@aol.com).

T. Gillingham
42 Highbury Park, Warminster, Wilts BA12 9JF
(01985 216486).

Gillio Coins International
1013 State Street, Santa Barbara, CA 93101,
USA (805 9631345—
London contact Eric Green 020-7586 3964).

Goldberg Coins & Collectibles
350 South Beverly Drive, Ste. 350,
Beverly Hills CA 90212
(001 310.432.6688, fax: 001 310.551.2626,
www.goldbergcoins.com)

Graves, Son & Pilcher Fine Arts
71 Church Road, Hove, East Sussex BN3 2GL
(01273 735266, fax 01273 723813).

Helios Numismatik
Ottostrasse 5, D–80333, München, Germany
(+49 089 5527949 0, www.helios-numismatik.de)

Heritage World Coin Auctions
3500 Maple Avenue, 17th Floor, Dallas, Texas
75219–3941, USA (001 214 528 3500,
fax 001 214 443 8425, www.heritagecoins.com)

Kleeford Coin Auctions
19 Craythorns Crescent, Dishforth, Thirsk YO7 3LY (tel/fax 01845 577977). Ⓟ

Fritz Rudok Künker
Gutenbergstrasse 23, 49076, Osnabrück, Germany (0049 541 962020, fax: 0049 541 96 20222, www.kuenker.com)

Lakeland Coin Auctions
The Riverside Hotel, Penrith, Cumbria (venue). (01946 832693, www.lakelandcoinauctions.co.uk).

W. H. Lane & Son
65 Morrab Road, Penzance, Cornwall TR18 2QT (01736 61447 fax 01736 50097).

Lawrence Fine Art Auctioneers
South Street, Crewkerne, Somerset TA18 8AB (01460 73041).

Lockdale Coins
Shops at: 37 Upper Orwell Street, Ipswich IP4 1BR.(01473 218588, www.lockdales.com).

London Coins
4–6 Upper Street South, New Ash Green, Kent DA3 8JJ (01474 871464 , info@londoncoins.co.uk, www.londoncoins.co.uk)

Morton & Eden Ltd
45 Maddox Street, London W1S 2PE (020 7493 5344 fax 020 7495 6325, info@mortonandeden.com, www.mortonandeden.com)

Neales
192–194 Mansfield Road, Nottingham NG1 3HU (0115 9624141 fax 0115 9856890).

Numismatica Ars Classica NAC AG
3rd Floor, Genavco House, 17 Waterloo Place, London SW1Y 4AR (020 783 97270, info@arsclassicacoins.com).

Ponterio & Associates Inc
1818, Robinson Ave, San Diego, CA 92103, USA. (Fax: 001 619 299 6952, www.ponterio.com).

R & W Coin Auctions
307 Bretch Hill, Banbury, Oxon OX16 0JD (01295 275128).

Simmons Gallery
PO Box 104, Leytonstone, London. (Tel: 0207 8989 8097. www.simmonsgallery.co.uk info@simmonsgallery.co.uk) Ⓟ

Spink & Son Ltd
69 Southampton Row, Bloomsbury, London. WC1B 4ET (020 7563 4000, fax 020 7563 4066, www.spink.com, info@spink.com).

Spink Coins & Medals
47 The Shambles, York, YO1 7XL. (01904 654769, www.spink.com, info@spink.com)

Stacks
123 West 57th Sreet, New York NY 10019 USA. (001 866 811 1804, www.stacks.com).

St James's Auctions
43 Duke Street, St James's, London, SW1Y 6DD (020 7930 7597/7888/8215, www.sixbid.com.

Tennants Auctioneers
The Auction Centre, Leyburn, North Yorkshire DL8 5SG (01969 623780) www.tennants.co.uk.

The-saleroom.com
115 Shaftesbury Avenue, London WC2H 8AF. Live bidding in real-time auctions from around the world www.the-saleroom.com

Thomson Roddick & Metcalf
Coleridge House, Shaddongate, Carlisle CA2 5TU (01228 528939, www.thomsonroddick).com).

Mavin International
20 Kramat Lane, #01-04/05 United House, Singapore 228773 (+65 6238 7177, fax: +65 6238 7077, mail@mavininternational.com).

Warwick & Warwick
Chalon House, Scarbank, Millers Road, Warwick CV34 5DB (01926 499031 fax 01926 491906, richard.beale@warwickandwarwick.com, www.warwickandwarwick.com.)

directory of Fairs

Listed below are the names of the fair organisers, their venue details where known along with contact telephone numbers. Please call the organisers direct for information on dates etc.

Aberdeen
Jarvis Amatola Hotel, Great Western Road, also venues in **Glenrothes** and **Glasgow.** *Cornucopia Collectors Fairs. (01382 224946)*

Birmingham
National Motor Cycle Museum, Bickenhill, Birmingham. *Midland Stamp & Coin Fair. (01694 731439, www.midlandfair.co.uk)*

Birmingham
Collingwood Centre, Collingwood Drive, Great Barr, Birmingham. *Dave Burnett Fairs. (0776 5792998)*

Bristol
Patchway High School,Hempton Lane, Almondsbury, Bristol. *Avemart Fairs. (01626 859350, avemart@btopenworld.com).*

Britannia Medal Fair
Carisbrooke Hall, The Victory Services Club, 63/79 Seymour Street, London W2 2HF. *Token Publishing Ltd (01404 46972).*

Colchester
Stanway Football Club, New Farm Road, Colchester. *ClickCollect Fairs (01485 578117)*

Cardiff
City Hall, Cardiff. *M. J. Promotions. (01792 415293)*

Dublin
Serpentine Hall, RDS, Ballsbridge, Dublin 4. *Mike Kelly (00353 86 87 14 880)*

Dundee
15 King Street, Dundee. *Corncopia Collectors Fair. (01382 224946)*

East Grinstead
Large Parish Hall, De La Warr Road, East Grinstead. *John Terry Fairs. (01342 326317)*

Exeter
The America Hall, De La Rue Way, Pinhoe, Exeter. *Phoenix Fairs. (01761 414304)*

Harrogate
Old Swan Hotel, Swan Road, Harrogate HG1 2SR. *Simon Monks.* (01234 270260)

Leeds
Cedar Court Hotel, Denby Dale Road, Calder Grove, Wakefield *Eddie Smith. (01552 684681).*

Lichfield
Civic Hall, Castle Dyke, City Centre. *C. S. Fairs. (01562 710424)*

London
Holiday Inn, Coram St., Bloomsbury, London WC1. *London Coin Fair. (020 8989 8097)*

London
Jury's Hotel, 16-22 Great Russell Street, London WC1 3NN. *Linda Monk Fairs. (020 8656 4583)*

Plymouth
Lower Guildhall. *Bruce Stamps.* (01749 813324)

Stowmarket
Stowmarket Football Club, Bury Road, Stowmarket. *ClickCollect (01485 578117)*

Suttton Coldfield
Fellowship Hall, South Parade. *C. S. Fairs. (01562 710424)*

Newcastle upon Tyne
The Royal Station Hotel. *B. Frank & Son.* (0191 413 8749)

West Bromwich
Town Hall, High Street. *C. S. Fairs. (01562 710424)*

York
The Grandstand, York Race course. *York Coin Fair (01793 513431, 020 8946 4489 or 01425 656459)*

Important annual events

The B.N.T.A. (Coinex), Tel: 01797 229 988 for details

The I.B.N.S. (World Paper Money Fair), Email: mike@ogrady.clara.co.uk for details

Now available from Token Publishing Ltd. . .

A great range of accessories

BANKNOTE ALBUMS

a great way to keep your collection together!

	Price
Hendon	
An inexpensive 4-ring padded binder (270x315mm). Blue, wine, green or brown	*£4.50*
Matching slipcase.	*£4.50*
Clear pages, 1, 2, 3 or 4 pocket.	*£0.38*
Black card interleaves.	*£0.12*
Classic	
The popular budget 3-ring binder (275x310mm). Red, blue, green or black.	*£7.40*
Matching slipcase.	*£4.00*
Clear pages, 1, 2 or 3 pocket.	*£0.42*
White card interleaves.	*£0.10*
Lighthouse	
The ever-popular mid-range *Vario* 4-ring binder (255x320mm), with matching slipcase and 10 pages with black interleaves. Blue, green, red, black or brown.	*£29.95*
Clear pages, 1, 2, 3 or 4 pocket—in packs of 5.	*£2.25*
Black interleaves—in packs of 5.	*£1.15*
Multi-ring padded album (305x317mm) for the connoisseur. Red, blue, green, black or tan.	*£28.85*
Matching slipcase.	*£15.50*
Clear pages, 2, 3 or 4 pocket complete with cream interleaving, in packs of 10.	*£12.00*
Gift set—album, slipcase and 10 pages complete.	*£50.00*

BANKNOTE WALLETS

for individual notes

	Price
Medium rigid wallet, 208x136mm, pack of 50.	*£12.00*
Large rigid wallet, 229x144mm, pack of 10.	*£5.00*
Small archival wallet, 172x102mm, pack of 25.	*£8.00*
Medium archival wallet, 205x130mm, pack of 25.	*£10.00*
Large archival wallet, 229x144mm, Pack of 10.	*£8.00*

CHEQUE ALBUMS

a big album with a multitude of uses

	Price
Large 4-ring binder (375x350mm). Red, blue or black.	*£6.75*
Clear 3-pocket page.	*£0.35*

Ordering is easy!

- Call 01404 44166 with your credit or debit card details
- Write to Token Publishing Ltd, Orchard House, Duchy Road, Heathpark Honiton, Devon, EX14 1YD
- log on to www.tokenpublishing.com

ACCESSORIES

For all accessories (unless otherwise indicated) please add £3.50 for orders up to £25, £5 for orders from £26 to £75, £10 for all orders over £75. For airmail accessory orders please add an additional £5 to these prices.

Dealers directory

The dealers listed below have comprehensive stocks of coins and medals, unless otherwise stated. Specialities, where known, are noted. Many of those listed are postal dealers only, so to avoid disappointment always make contact by telephone or mail in the first instance, particularly before travelling any distance.

Abbreviations:
ADA— — Antiquities Dealers Association
ANA — American Numismatic Association
BADA — British Antique Dealers Association
BNTA — British Numismatic Trade Association
IAPN — International Association of Professional Numismatists
IBNS — International Bank Note Society
P — — Postal only
L — — Publishes regular lists

ABC Coins & Tokens
PO Box 52, Alnwick, Northumberland NE66 1YE (tel 01665 603851, email: d–stuart@d–stuart.demon.co.uk, www.abccoinsandtokens.com).

A. Ackroyd (IBNS)
62 Albert Road, Parkstone, Poole, Dorset BH12 2DB (tel/fax 01202 739039, website www.AAnotes.com). P L *Banknotes and cheques*

Airedale Coins (ANA, BNTA)
PO Box 7, Bingley, West Yorkshire, BD16 1XU (01535 272754 fax 01535 275727, website www.airedalecoins.co.uk email info@airedalecoins.com). P L *British and modern coins of the world.*

David Allen Coins and Collectables
PO Box 125, Pinner, Middlesex HA5 2TX (020 866 6796). P L *British and world coins, tokens.*

Joan Allen Electronics Ltd
190 Main Road, Biggin Hill, Kent TN16 3BB (01959 571255). Mon–Sat 09.00–17.00. **Metal detectors.**

Allgold of Sevenoaks
P.O Box 260, Wallington, SM5 4H (0844 5447952, email: sales@allgoldcoins.co.uk, website: www.allgoldcoins.co.uk) *Quality Sovereigns.*

Ancient & Gothic
PO Box 5390, Bournemouth, BH7 6XR (01202 431721). P L *Greek, Roman, Celtic and Biblical coins. English hammered coins & antiquities.*

Argentum Coins
Row Foot, SowerbyRow, Carlisle, Cumbria CA4 0QG. (01697 476990, website www.argentumandcoins.co.uk). *British milled coins from 1662 to date.*

Arghans
Unit 9, Callington Business Park, Tinners Way Moss side, Callington PL17 7SH (01579 382405, keithp44@waitrose.com). *British banknotes.*

ATS Bullion (BNTA)
2, Savoy Court, Strand. London WC2R 0EZ (020 7240 4040, email bullion@atslimited.fsnet.co.uk.). *Bullion and modern coins.*

Keith Austin (IBNS)
PO Box 89, Carlisle, Cumbria CA3 0GH (01228 819149, fax 01228 521176, email:kaustin@kabc.freeserve.co.uk). L *Banknotes.*

Mark Bailey
120 Sterte Court, Sterte Close, Poole, Dorset BH15 2AY (01202 674936). P L *Ancient, modern, world coins and antiquities.*

A. H. Baldwin & Sons Ltd (ANA, BADA, BNTA, IAPN)
11 Adelphi Terrace, London WC2N 6BJ. 09.00–17.00 weekdays. (email coins@baldwin.sh) *Coins, tokens, commemorative medals, war medals and decorations, numismatic books.*

Banking Memorabilia (IBNS)
PO Box 14, Carlisle, Cumbria (016974 76465). 09.00– 18.00 (not Sun). *Cheques, banknotes, related ephemera.*

G. Barrington Smith
Cross Street, Oadby, Leicestershire LE2 4DD (01533 712114). 08.30—17.15 weekdays. *Albums, catalogues and accessories.*

Bath Stamp and Coin Shop
Pulteney Bridge, Bath, Avon BA2 4AY (01225 463073). Mon–Sat 09.30–17.30. *British.*

Michael Beaumont
PO Box 8, Carlton, Notts NG4 4QZ (0115 9878361). P *Gold & Silver English/Foreign Coins.*

Beaver Coin Room (BNTA)
57 Philbeach Gardens, LondonSW5 9ED (020 7373 4553). P *European coins and medals.*

R. P. & P. J. Beckett
Maesyderw, Capel Dewi, Llandyssul, Dyfed SA44 4PJ. (Fax only 01559 395631, email becket@xin.co.uk). P *Coin sets and banknotes.*

Lloyd Bennett (BNTA)
PO Box 2, Monmouth, Gwent NP5 3YE (01600 890634). Abergavenny Market (Tue), Monmouth Market (Fri–Sat) 09.00–16.00. *English hammered, milled and coins of the world.*

Berkshire Coin Centre
35 Castle Street, Reading, Berkshire RG1 7SB (0118 957 5593). 0630–15.00 W, Th, Fri & Sat. Sat. *British British and world coins and militaria.*

Beron Coins
64 Rosewood Close, Glascote, Tamworth, Staffs B77 3PD (01827 54541). P L *British & world coins.*

Stephen J. Betts
4 Victoria Street, Narborough, Leics LE9 5DP (0116 2864434). P L *Medieval and modern coins, counters, jetons and tokens, countermarks and medals.*

Bigbury Mint
River Park, Ermington Mill, Ivybridge, Devon PL21 9NT (01548 830717. *Specialists in reproduction hammered coins*

Birchin Lane Gold Coin Company
6 Castle Court, St Michael's Alley (off Cornhill), London EC3V 9DS (020 7621 0370 and 020 7263 3981). Mon–Fri 10.00–16.30. *Gold and bullion coins.*

Barry Boswell
24 Townsend Lane, Upper Boddington, Daventry, Northants NN11 6DR (01327 261877, fax 01327 261391, email Barry.Boswell@btinternet.com). P L *British and world banknotes.*

Black Cat Coins
25 Weldon Road, New Marston, Oxford OX3 0HP. (01865 726939). *Milled gold and silver coins, proof sets and maundy money.*

James & C. Brett
17 Dale Road, Lewes, East Sussex BN7 1LH. P L *British and world coins.*

J. Bridgeman Coins
129a Blackburn Road, Accrington, Lancs (01254 384757). 09.30–17.00 (closed Wednesday). *British & World coins.*

Brighton Coin Company (ANA, BNTA)
The Hove Coin Shop, Church Road, Hove, (01273 737537) Mon–Fri 9.45–17.30, Sat 9.45–15.30 (closed alternate Wednesdays and Saturdays). *World coins.*

Britco
23 Orkney Close, Stenson Fields, Derby DE24 3LW. (Tel: 01332 760189. website: http://stores.ebay.co.uk/britcoins). *18th to 20th Century British coins.*

BRM Coins
3 Minshull Street, Knutsford, Cheshire WA16 6HG (01565 651480 and 0606 74522). Mon–Fri 11.00–15.00, Sat 11.00–1.00 or by appt. *British coins.*

A. F. Brock & Company
269 London Road, Hazel Grove, Stockport, Cheshire SK7 4PL (0161 456 5050/5112, email info@afbrock.co.uk, website: www.afbrock.co.uk). *Auctioneers and valuers.*

E. J. & C. A. Brooks (BNTA, IBNS)
44 Kiln Road, Thundersley, Essex SS7 1TB (01268 753835). Any time up to 23.00. L *British*

Bucks Coins
Jordan House, Jordan Lane, Whitwell, Norfolk NR10 4RQ. (07825 440085). *English milled coins.*

Iain Burn
2 Compton Gardens, 53 Park Road, Camberley, Surrey GU15 2SP (01276 23304). *Bank of England & Treasury notes.*

BBM Coins
8–9 Lion Street, Kidderminster, Hereford & Worcester, DY10 1PT (01562 515007). Wed, Th, Fri. 10.00–14.00 or by appointment. *World coins.*

Cambridge Coins
52 High Street, Biggleswade SG18 0LJ. 01767 90066/07787 358689. Email: shop@cambridgecoins.co.uk, website: www.cambridgecoins.co.uk). *Coins, medals, banknotes, bullion and jewellery.*

Cambridge Stamp Centre Ltd
9 Sussex Street, Cambridge CB4 4HU (01223 63980). Mon–Sat 09.00–17.30. *British coins.*

Castle Galleries
81 Castle Street, Salisbury, Wiltshire SP1 3SP (01722 333734). Tue, Thu Fri 09.00–17.00, Sat 09.30–16.00. *British coins, medals and tokens.*

Cathedral Coins
23 Kirkgate, Ripon, North Yorkshire HG4 1PB (01765 701400). Mon–Sat 10.00–17.00.

David L. Cavanagh
49 Cockburn Street, Edinburgh EH1 1BS (0131 226 3391). Mon–Sat 11.00–17.00. *British coins.*

Central Bank of Ireland
Currency Centre, Sandyford Road, Dublin 16, Ireland. *New coin and banknote issues of Ireland.*

Certified Coin Investment
PO Box 83, Longfield DA3 9AX. (01474 874895). *English milled coins.*

Lance Chaplin
17 Wanstead Lane, Ilford, Essex IG1 3SB (020 8554 7154. Website: www.shaftesburycoins.com). P L *Roman, Greek, Celtic, hammered coins and antiquities.*

Chard (BNTA)
521 Lytham Road, Blackpool, Lancs FY4 1RJ (01253 343081. Website: www.chards.co.uk). Mon–Sat 09.00–17.00. *British, Commonwealth and European coins.*

Chelsea Coins Ltd (BNTA)
PO Box 2, Fulham Road, London SW10 9PQ. (020 8870 5501 Fax 020 8875 1459). P *World coins.*

Nigel A. Clark
28 Ulundi Road, Blackheath, London SE3 7UG (020 8858 4020, email: nigel.a.clark@btinternet.com). Ⓟ Ⓛ *Tokens (Mainly 17th century) and British Farthings.*

Classical Numismatic Group
14 Old Bond Street, London W1X 4JL. (020 7495 1888 Fax 020 7499 5916, website www.cngcoins.com, email cng@cngcoins.com). Ⓟ *Ancient and world coins. Publishers of the Classical Numismatic Review.*

Paul Clayton (BNTA)
PO Box 21, Wetherby, West Yorkshire LS22 5JY. (01937 72441). *Modern gold coins.*

André de Clermont (BNTA)
PO Box 3615, London, SW10 0YD. (020 7351 5727, Fax 020 7352 8127). *World coins, especially Islamic & Oriental coins, Latin America.*

M. Coeshaw
PO Box 115, Leicester LE3 8JJ (0116 287 3808). Ⓟ *Coins, banknotes, coin albums and cases.*

Philip Cohen Numismatics (ANA, BNTA)
20 Cecil Court, Charing Cross Road, London WC2N 4HE (020 7379 0615). Mon–Sat 11.00–17.30.

Coin & Collectors Centre
PO Box 22, Pontefract, West Yorkshire WF8 1YT (01977 704112, website www.coincentre.co.uk, email sales@coincentre.co.uk). Ⓟ *British coins.*

Coincraft (ANA, IBNS)
44/45 Great Russell Street, London WC1B 3LU (020 7636 1188 and 020 7637 8785 fax 020 7323 2860, Website www.coincraft.com. Email info@coincraft.com). Mon–Fri 09.30–17.00, Sat 10.00–14.30. Ⓛ (newspaper format). *Coins and banknotes.*

Coinote Services Ltd
74–74a Elwick Road, Hartlepool TS26 9AP (01429 890894). Ⓟ Ⓛ *Coins and banknotes 1615 to date. Accessories and books.*

Coins Historic
PO Box 5043, Lower Quinton, Stratford Upon Avon, Warks CV37 8WH. (01789 721117). *Celtic, Roman, Greek and English hammered coins.*

Coins of Beeston
PO Box 19, Beeston, Notts BG9 2NE. Ⓟ Ⓛ *Tokens, medals and paranumismatics.*

Coins of Canterbury
PO Box 47, Faversham, Kent ME13 7HX (01795 531980). Ⓟ *English coins.*

Collectors' World
188 Wollaton Road, Wollaton, Nottingham NG8 1HJ. (01159 280347). *Coins, Tokens, Banknotes, Accessories.*

Constantia CB
15 Church Road, Northwood, Middlesex HA6 1AR. Ⓟ *Roman and medieval hammered coins.*

Colin Cooke
P.O. Box 602, Altrincham, WA14 5UN. (0161 927 9524 fax 0161 927 9540, website: www.colincooke.com, email coins@colincooke.com). Ⓛ *British coins.*

Colonial Coins & Medals
218 Adelaide Street, Brisbane, QLD 4001 (email:coinshop@bigpond.net.au). *Auctions of World coins*

Corbitts (BNTA)
5 Mosley Street, Newcastle Upon Tyne NE1 1YE (0191 232 7268 fax: 0191 261 4130). *Dealers and auctioneers of all coins and medals.*

David Craddock
PO Box 3785, Camp Hill, Birmingham B11 2NF. (0121 733 2259) Ⓛ *Crown to farthings. Copper and bronze specialist. Some foreign.*

Roy Cudworth
8 Park Avenue, Clayton West, Huddersfield HD8 9PT. *British and world coins.*

Mark Davidson
PO Box 197, South Croydon, Surrey, CR3 0ZD (020 8651 3890). *Ancient, hammered coinage.*

Paul Davis
PO Box 418, Birmingham, B17 0RZ. (0121 427 7179). *British and World Coins.*

R. Davis
(01332 740828 evenings). *Maker of traditional coin cabinets.*

Linda Monk Fairs
PO Box 201, Croydon, Surrey CR9 7AQ (020 8656 4583). Organiser of monthly fairs at the Jury's Hotel, 16–22 Great Russell Street, London, WC1 3NN.

Paul Davies Ltd (ANA, BNTA, IAPN)
PO Box 17, Ilkley, West Yorkshire LS29 8TZ (01943 603116 fax 01943 816326). Ⓟ *World coins.*

Ian Davison
PO Box 256, Durham DH1 2GW (0191 3750808). Ⓛ *English hammered and milled coins 1066–1910.*

Patrick Deane
PO Box 800, Orpington, Kent BR6 7XE (01959 533737, fax: 01959 533388). *British coins, tokens.*

Decus Coins
The Haven, Brockweir, Chepstow, Gwent NP6 7NN (01291 689216). Ⓟ

Dei Gratia
PO Box 3568, Buckingham MK18 4ZS (01280 848000). Ⓟ Ⓛ *Pre–Roman to modern coins, antiquities, banknotes.*

Den of Antiquity
(01223 863002. Website: www.denof antiquity.co.uk.) *Ancient and medieval coins.*

Clive Dennett (BNTA)
66 St Benedicts Street, Norwich, Norfolk NR2 4AR (01603 624315). Mon–Fri 09.00–17.30, Sat 09.00–16.00 (closed 1.00–2.00 & Thu). Ⓛ *Paper money.*

C. J. Denton (ANA, BNTA, FRNS)
PO Box 25, Orpington, Kent BR6 8PU (01689 873690). Ⓟ *Irish coins.*

Detecnicks
3 Orchard Crescent, Arundel Road, Fontwell. West Sussex BN18 0SA (01243 545060 fax 01243 545922) *Retail shop. Wide range of detectors and accessories.*

Michael Dickinson (ANA, BNTA)
Ramsay House, 825 High Road Finchley, London N12 8UB (0181 441 7175). P
British and world coins.

Dorset Coin Co Ltd (BNTA)
193 Ashley Road, Parkstone, Poole, Dorset BH14 9DL (01202 739606, fax 01202 739230. Website: www.dorsetcoincompany.co.uk). P L
Separate coin and banknote lists.

Dyas Coins & Medals
30 Shaftmoor Lane, Acocks Green, Birmingham B27 7RS (0121 707 2808). Fri 10.30–18.30, Sun 10.30–13.00. *World coins and medals.*

Eagle Coins
Winterhaven, Mourneabbey, Mallow, Co. Cork, Ireland (010 35322 29385). P L *Irish coins.*

Early World Coins
7–9 Clifford Street, York, YO1 9RA (08454 900724).

Eden Coins
PO Box 77, Brierley Hill, West Midlands DY5 2GS (01384 834648). P *English coins, tokens and medals.*

Edinburgh Coin Shop (ANA)
11 West Crosscauseway, Edinburgh EH8 9JW (0131 668 2928 fax 0131 668 2926). Mon–Sat 10.00–17.30. L *World coins and medals. Postal auctions.*

Educational Coin Company
Box 892, Highland, New York 12528, USA. (+ 845 691 6100.) *World banknotes.*

Christopher Eimer (ANA, BNTA)
PO Box 352 London NW11 7RF (020 8458 9933 fax 020 8455 3535, email art@christophereimer.co.uk). P *Commemorative medals.*

Malcolm Ellis Coins
Petworth Road, Witley, Surrey, GU8 5LX (01428 685566, email: malcolm.ellis@wizardvideo.co.uk, website: www.malcolmelliscoins.co.uk) *Collectors and dealers of British and foreign coins and medals.*

Elm Hill Stamps & Coins
27 Elm Hill, Norwich, Norfolk NR3 1HN (01603 627413). Mon. 09.00–17.00, Tues–Wed. 09.00–17.00, Thur. 0900–13.00, Sat. 09.30–15.00. *Mainly stamps, occasionally coins.*

Europa Numismatics (ANA, BNTA)
PO Box 119, High Wycombe, Bucks HP11 1QL (01494 437307). P *European coins.*

Evesham Stamp & Coin Centre
Magpie Antiques, Paris House, 61 High Street, Evesham, Worcs WR11 4DA (01386 41631). Mon–Sat 09.00–17.30. *British coins.*

Michael E. Ewins
Meyrick Heights, 20 Meyrick Park Crescent, Bournemouth, Dorset BH3 7AQ (01202 290674). P
World coins.

I. Fine & Son Ltd
Victoria House, 93 Manor Farm Road, Wembley, Middlesex HA10 1XB (020 8997 5055). P *British & World coins.*

Robin Finnegan Stamp Shop
83 Skinnergate, Darlington, Co Durham DL3 7LX (01325 489820/357674). Mon–Sat 10.00–17.30 (closed Wed). *World coins.*

Richard N. Flashman
54 Ebbsfleet Walk, Gravesend, Kent, DA11 9EW. L P *British banknotes.*

David Fletcher (Mint Coins) (ANA, BNTA)
PO Box 64, Coventry, Warwickshire CV1 5YR (024 7671 5425, Fax 024 7601 0300). P
World new issues

Format of Birmingham Ltd (ANA, BNTA, IAPN, IBNS)
2nd Floor, Burlington Court, Lower Temple Street, Birmingham, B2 4JD (0121 643 2058 fax 0121 643 2210). Mon–Fri 09.30–7.00. L *Coins, tokens and medals.*

B. Frank & Son (ANA, IBNS)
3 South Avenue, Ryton, Tyne & Wear NE40 3LD (0191 413 8749). Website www.b-frank-and-son.co.uk. Email P L *Banknotes and cheques, coins of the world. Organiser of the North of England fair.*

Frank Milward (BNTA)
2 Ravensworth Road, Mortimer, Berks, RG7 3UU (01734 332843). Mon–Sat 09.00–18.00. *British and World coins.*

Galata Coins Ltd (ANA)
The Old White Lion, Market Street, Llanfylin, Powys SY22 5BX (01691 648 765). P *British and world coins.*

G. Gant
Glazenwood, 37 Augustus Way, Witham, Essex CM8 1HH. P *British and Commonwealth coins.*

John Gaunt
21 Harvey Road, Bedford MK41 9LF (01234 217685). By appointment. *Numismatic books.*

A. & S. Gillis
59 Roykilner Way, Wombwell, Barnsley, South Yorkshire S73 8DY. (01226 750371, website www.gilliscoins.com, email catalogues@gilliscoins.com) P L *Ancient coins.*

G. K. Coins
17 Hanover Square, London W1S 1HU (020 7518 0383, fax: 020 7518 0302, george@gkcoins.com, www.gkcoins.com). *Rare and common sovereigns. British and world coins.*

Richard Gladdle – Northamptonshire
(01327 858511), email: gladdle@plumpudding.org. *Tokens.* P L

Glance Back Books
17 Upper Street, Chepstow, Gwent NP6 5EX (01291 626562). 10.30–17.30. *World coins, medals, banknotes.*

Glendining's (Bonhams) (ANA, BNTA)
101 New Bond Street, London W1Y 9LG (020 7493 2445). Mon–Fri 08.30–17.00, Sat 08.30–13.00. *Auctioneers.*

Glenely Coins
73 Ladymead, Cricklade, Swindon, Wiltshire SN6 6EP. Tel: 01793 750307. Email: chris kellow@hotmail.com. *British coins.*

GM Coins
www.gmonlinecoins.co.uk/gmcoins, email: gmcoins@blueyonder.co.uk, (01242 701144) *Hammered and milled coins.*

Phil Goodwin (ANA)
PO Box 69, Portsmouth, Hants PO1 5SH (02392 423267 or 02392 752006 incl. fax. Email: phil.goodwin.coins@cwctv.net). P *or by appointment.* L *Ancient coins and antiquities.*

Goulborn
PO Box 122, Rhyl LL18 3XR. (Tel: 01745 338112). *Coins and banknotes.*

Ian Gradon
PO Box 359, Durham DH7 6WZ (0191 3719 700, email: ian@worldnotes.co.uk, www.worldnotes.co.uk). L *World banknotes.*

Grantham Coins (BNTA)
PO Box 60, Grantham, Lincs (01476 870565). P L *English coins and banknotes.*

Eric Green—Agent in UK for Ronald J. Gillio Inc
1013 State Street, Santa Barbara, California, USA 93101 (020 8907 0015, Mobile 0468 454948). *Gold coins, medals and paper money of the world.*

Philip Green
Suite 207, 792 Wilmslow Road, Didsbury, Manchester M20 6UG (0161 440 0685). *World gold coins.*

R. I. Groves
8 Catherine Street, Dumfries DG1 1JA (01387 266617, website: www.worldcoins.biz, email: richard@I–groves.demon.co.uk). P *British & world coins.*

Ian Haines
PO Box 45, Hereford, HR2 7YP (01432 268178). P L *British and foreign coins and banknotes.*

Anthony Halse
PO Box 1856, Newport, Gwent NP6 2JN (01633 413238). P L *English and foreign coins and tokens.*

A. D. Hamilton & Co (ANA)
7 St Vincent Place, Glasgow G1 5JA (0141 221 5423, fax 0141 248 6019, website www.adhamilton.co.uk, email jeffineman@hotmail.com). Mon–Sat 10.00–17.00. *British and World coins.*

Peter Hancock
40–41 West Street, Chichester, West Sussex PO19 1RP (01243 786173). Tues–Sat. *World coins, medals and banknotes.*

Munthandel G. Henzen
PO Box 42, NL – 3958ZT, Amerogngen, Netherlands. (0031 343 430564 fax 0031 343 430542, web www.henzen.org, email henzen.coins@tiscali.nl). L *Ancients, Dutch and foreign coins.*

History In Coins.com
www.historyincoins.com (01949 836988). *World coins.*

Craig Holmes
6 Marlborough Drive, Bangor, Co Down BT19 1HB. P L *Low cost banknotes of the world.*

R. G. Holmes
11 Cross Park, Ilfracombe, Devon EX34 8BJ (01271 864474). P L *Coins, world crowns and banknotes.*

John L. Homan
Oxford Grange, Marsh Lane, Barrow Haven, Barrow-on-Humber, South Humberside DN19 7ER (01469 32109). P *Greek, Roman and Byzantine coins.*

Homeland Holding Ltd (IBNS)
Homeland, St John, Jersey, Channel Islands JE3 4AB (01534 65339). Mon–Fri 09.00–2.00. *World coins.*

HTSM Coins
26 Dosk Avenue, Glasgow G13 4LQ. P L *British and foreign coins and banknotes.*

T. A. Hull
15 Tangmere Crescent, Hornchurch, Essex RM12 5PL. P L *British coins, farthings to crowns, tokens.*

J. Hume
107 Halsbury Road East, Northolt, Middlesex UB5 4PY (020 8864 1731). P L *Chinese coins.*

D. A. Hunter
www.dahunter.co.uk/coins, email coins@dahunter.co.uk. P L *UK and World Coins.*

D. D. & A. Ingle
380 Carlton Hill, Nottingham (0115 9873325). Mon–Sat 09.30–17.00. *World coins.*

R. Ingram Coins
206 Honeysuckle Road, Bassett, Southampton, Hants SO16 3BU. (023 8032 4258, website: www.ringramcoins.com, email: info@ringramcoins.com. P L *Dealers in UK coins.*

Intercol London (ANA, IBNS)
43 Templars Cresent, London N3 3QR (020 8349 2207) P *Paper money of the World.*

Peter Ireland Ltd (BNTA, IBNS)
31 Clifton Street, Blackpool, Lancs FY1 1JQ (01253 621588 fax 01253 621589). Mon–Sat 09.00–17.30. *British and world coins, medals and tokens.*

F. J. Jeffery & Son Ltd
Haines Croft, Corsham Road, Whitley, Melksham, Wilts SN12 8QF. (01225 703143). P *British, Commonwealth and foreign coins.*

Richard W. Jeffery
Trebehor, Porthcurno, Penzance, Cornwall TR19 6LS (01736 871263). P *British and world coins.*

Jersey Coin Co Ltd
26 Halkett Street, St Helier, Jersey, Channel Islands (01534 25743). Mon–Sat 09.00–17.00. *World coins.*

J. G. Coins
PO Box 206, Southshore, Blackpool FY1 6GZ. (01253 349138). P L *British Coins.*

www.johnpettit.com
On-line banknote auction.

Robert Johnson Coin Co
Zeilerviertel 6, 8232, Grafendorf, Steiermark, Austria (06644 882 301, email: rjcoinco@aol.com). *British and world coins.*

Jumbo Coins
22 Woodend Lane, Stalybridge, Cheshire SK15 2SR (0161 338 5741). Fri–Sat 14.00–19.00. *World coins, medals and tokens.*

Kates Paper Money
Kate Gibson, PO Box 819, Camberley, Surrey, GU16 6ZU. www.katespapermoney.co.uk (01276 64181) *Banknotes.*

KB Coins (BNTA)
50 Lingfield Road, Martins Wood, Stevenage, Herts SG1 5SL (01438 312661, fax 01438 311990). 09.00–18.00 by appointment only. L *Mainly British coins.*

K&M Coins
PO Box 3662, Wolverhampton WV10 6ZW (0771 2381880/079719 50246, email:M_Bagguley@hotmail.com).*Englishmilledcoins.*

Knightsbridge Coins (ANA, BNTA, IAPN, PNG)
43 Duke Street, St James's, London SW1Y 6DD (020 7930 8215/7597 Fax 020 7930 8214). Mon–Fri 10.00–17.30. *Quality coins of the world.*

Lancashire Coin & Medal Co
31 Adelaide Street, Fleetwood, Lancs FY7 6AD (01253 779308). P *British coins and medals.*

Lennox Gallery Ltd
K12/13, 4 Davies Mews, London, W1Y 1AR. (020 7629 9119 fax 020 7629 9119). Ancient coins.
Lighthouse Publications (Duncannon Partnership)
4 Beaufort Road, Reigate, Surrey RH2 9DJ (01737 244222 Fax 01737 224743. Website: www.duncan non.co.uk). L *Manufacturers and stockists of coin albums, cabinets and numismatic accessories.*

Lindner Publications Ltd
3a Hayle Industrial Park, Hayle, Cornwall TR27 5JR (01736 751914 fax: 01736 751911, email lindner@prinz.co.uk). Mon–Fri 09.00–13.00. L *Manufacturers of coin albums, cabinets and accessories.*

Jan Lis (BNTA)
Beaver Coin Room, 57 Philbeach Gardens, London SW5 9ED (020 7373 4553 fax 020 7373 4555). By appointment only. *European coins.*

Keith Lloyd
45 Bramblewood, The Beeches, Ipswich, Suffolk IP8 3RS (01473 603067). P L *Greek, Roman coins.*

Lockdale Coins (BNTA)
Shops at: 37 Upper Orwell Street, Ipswich IP4 1BR.(01473 218588), 168 London Road South, Lowestoft NR33 0BB (01502 568468) & 23 Magdalene Street, Cambridge, CB3 OAF. (01223 361163). L (Shops open 9.30–4.30 Mon–Sat). *World coins, medals, banknotes and accessories.*

Stephen Lockett (BNTA)
4–6 Upper Street, New Ash Green, Kent, DA3 8JJ (01474 871464). *British and world coins.*

The London Coin Company
(0800 085 2933, 020 8343 2231. Email: sales@thelondoncoincompany.com. website: www.thelondoncoincomany.com). *Modern gold and silver coins.*

Mike Longfield Detectors
83 Station Road, Balsall Common, nr Coventry, Warwickshire CV7 7FN (01676 533274). Mon–Sat 09.30–17.00. *Metal detectors.*

Richard M. Lubbock (ANA, BNTA, IAPN, IBNS)
PO Box 352, London E14 7WB (020 7790 5115 fax 020 7790 5445). *World coins and medals.*

Don MacRae Coins
PO Box 233, Uxbridge, Middlesex UB9 4HY (01895 832625). P *British and world coins.*

David & Georgina Magnay
11 Lake Hill Drive, Cowbridge, Vale of Glamorgan, Wales UK CF71 7HR. (01446 774335) *Toy and Model Coins, Imitation Spade Guineas.*

MA Shops
www.mashops.com. On-line coin mall. *Coins, medals, banknotes and saccessories.*

Mannin Collections Ltd
5 Castle Street, Peel, Isle of Man, IM5 1AN (01624 843897, email: manncoll@advsys.co.uk). Mon–Sat 10.00–16.00. Closed Thu. *IOM coins, tokens, etc.*

Manston Coins of Bath
Bartletts St. Antique Centre, Bath (01761 416133. *Coins, tokens and medals.*

I. Markovits
1–3 Cobbold Mews, London W12 9LB (020 8749 3000). *Enamelled coins.*

C. J. Martin Coins (BNTA)
85 The Vale, Southgate, London N14 6AT (020 8882 1509, www.ancientart.co.uk). P L Bi–monthly catalogue. *Greek, Roman & English hammered coins.*

M. G. Coins & Antiquities
12 Mansfield, High Wych, Herts CM21 0JT. (01279 721719). L *Ancient and hammered coins, antiquities.*

Giuseppe Micelli
204 Bants Lane, Duston, Northampton NN5 6AH (01604 581533). P L *British coins and medals.*

Michael Coins
6 Hillgate Street, London W8 7SR (020 7727 1518). Mon–Fri 10.00–17.00. *World coins and banknotes.*

David Miller Coins & Antiquities (ANA, BNTA)
PO Box 711, Hemel Hempstead, HP2 4UH (tel/fax 01442 251492). *Ancient and hammered English coins.*

Timothy Millett
PO Box 20851, London SE22 0YN (tel: 020 8693 1111, fax: 020 8299 3733. Website www.historicmedals.com). L *Historical medals.*

Nigelmills.net
(020 8504 2569. Website: www.nigelmills.net, email: nigelmills@onetel.com). *Coins and antiquities.*

Frank Milward (ANA, BNTA)
2 Ravensworth Road, Mortimer, Berkshire RG7 3UU (01734 322843). P *European coins.*

Mis-struck World Coins
Storhojdgstan 17, 416 71 Gothenburg, Sweden. Email: mawett@hotmail.com. *Gold coins.*

Graeme & Linda Monk (ANA, BNTA)
PO Box 201, Croydon, Surrey, CR9 7AQ (020 8656 4583 fax 020 8656 4583). P *Fair organisers.*

Moore Antiquities
Unit 12, Ford Lane Industrial Estate, Ford, nr. Arundel, West Sussex BN18 0AA (01243 824 232, email moore.antiquities@virgin.net). *Coins and artefacts up to the 18th Century.*

Mike Morey
19 Elmtrees, Long Crendon, Bucks HP18 9DG. P L
British coins, halfcrowns to farthings.

Peter Morris (BNTA, IBNS)
1 Station Concourse, Bromley North Station, Bromley, BR1 1NN or PO Box 223, Bromley, BR1 4EQ (020 8313 3410 fax 020 8466 8502, website www.petermorris.co.uk, email info@petermorris.co.uk). Mon–Fri 10.00–18.00, Sat 0900–14.00 or by appointment. L *British and world coins, proof sets and numismatic books.*

James Murphy
PO Box 122, Chorley, Lancashire PR7 2GE. (01257 274 381). P L *Ancient coins and antiquities.*

N3 Coins—London
(07768 795575, website www.n3coins.com, email: mail@n3coins.com).
High quality Roman and Ancient coins.

Colin Narbeth & Son Ltd (ANA, IBNS)
20 Cecil Court, Leicester Square, London WC2N 4HE (020 7379 6975 fax 01727 811 244, website http://www.colin-narbeth.com). Mon–Sat 10.30–17.00. *World banknotes.*

New Forest Leaves
Bisterne Close, Burley, Ringwood, Hants BH24 4BA (014253 3315). *Publishers of numismatic books.*

Peter Nichols
2 Norman Road, St Leonards on Sea, East Sussex TN37 6NH. (01424 436682, website www.coincabinets.com, email coincabinets@freezone.co.uk).

Wayne Nicholls
PO Box 44, Bilston, West Midlands. (01543 45476). L *Choice English coins.*

Northeast Numismatics (BNTA)
10 Concord Crossing Suite 220, Concord MA 01742, USA (001 978 369 9155, fax: 001 978 369 9619, website: www.northeastcoin.com). *British and world coins.*

North Wales Coins Ltd (BNTA)
1b Penrhyn Road, Colwyn Bay, Clwyd (01492 533023/532129). Mon–Sat (closed Wed) 09.30–17.30. *British coins.*

NP Collectables
9 Main Street, Gedney Dyke, Spalding, Lincs PE12 0AJ (01406 365211Ireland (010 35322 29385). P L
English Hammered and Milled coins.

Glenn S. Ogden
53 Chestnut Crescent, Culver Green, Chudleigh, Devon TQ13 OPT. (01626 859350 or 07971 709427, website: www.glenogdencoins.com). P L
English milled coins.

John Ogden Coins
Hodge Clough Cottage, Moorside, Oldham OL1 4JW (0161 678 0709) P L *Ancient and hammered.*

Michael O'Grady (IBNS)
PO Box 307, Pinner, Middlesex HA5 4XT (020 428 4002). P *British and world paper money.*

Colin James O'Keefe
5 Pettits Place, Dagenham, Essex RM10 8NL. P
British and European coins.

Don Oliver Gold Coins
Stanford House, 23 Market Street, Stourbridge, West Midlands DY8 1AB (01384 877901). Mon–Fri 10.00–17.00. *British gold coins.*

Onewebby.com
PO Box 6219, Basildon, Essex, SS14 0AS. *World and British copper and silver.*

Ongar Coins
14 Longfields, Marden Ash, Ongar, Essex IG7 6DS. P *World coins.*

Orpington Coins and Medals
242 High Street, Orpington, Kent BR6 0LZ (01689 890045). Mon–Sat 09.45–17.30 (closed Tue). *Coins, medals, banknotes, badges, militaria, cigarette cards, etc.*

Roger Outing
PO Box 123, Huddersfield HD8 9WY (www.banknotes4u.co.uk email: rogerandlizbanknotes4u.co.uk. 01484 60415). *World banknotes.*

Tim Owen Coins
63 Allerton Grange Rise, Leeds 17, West Yorkshire P L *Quality hammered coins.*

P&D Medallions
PO Box 269, Berkhampstead, Herts HP4 3FT. (01442 865127, website: www.pdmedallions.co.uk). *Historical and Commemorative medals of the world.* P

Del Parker
PO Box 998, Mercer Island, WA 98040, USA. Tel: + 1 206 232 2560. Email: Irishcoins2000@hotmail.com). *Irish and American Coins.*

Pavlos S. Pavlou
Stand L17, Grays Antique Market, 1–7 Davies Mews, Mayfair, London W1Y 2LP (020 7629 9449) email: pspavlou@hotmail.com. *Ancient, Medieval & Modern Coins.*

Penrith Coin & Stamp Centre
37 King Street, Penrith, Cumbria CA11 7AY (01768 64185). Mon–Sat 09.00–17.30. *World coins.*

Pentland Coins (IBNS)
Pentland House, 92 High Street, Wick, Caithness KW14 L5. P *British and world coins and world banknotes.*

Gary Phelps
PO Box 136, Benfleet, Essex SS7 4WG (garyph@blueyonder.co.uk, www.garyphelps.co.uk) *Modern patterns and crowns.*

John Phillimore
The Old Post Office, Northwood, Shropshire SY4 5NN. L *Foreign coins 1600–1950.*

Philip. P. Phipps
PO Box 139, Tiverton, Devon EX16 0AU (tel 07850 864554, email p.p.phipps@tesco.net). P L *World and German banknotes.*

David C. Pinder
20 Princess Road West, Leicester LE1 6TP (0116 2702439). P *Greek, Roman and Byzantine coins.*

Pobjoy Mint Ltd (ANA)
Millennium House, Kingswood Park, Bonsor Drive, Kingswood, Surrey KT20 6AY (01737 818181 fax 01737 818199). Mon–Fri 09.00–17.00. Europe's largest private mint. *New issues.*

David Pratchett
UCCE, PO Box 57648, Mill Hill, London NW7 0FE (07831 662594, fax 020 7930 1152, website www.coinsonline.co.uk, email uccedcp@aol.com). Mon–Fri 10.00–7.30. *Specialist in gold and silverworld coins.*

Pykerleys Collectables
PO Box 649, Whitley Bay NE26 9AF (pykereley@yahoo.co.uk, www.pykerley.worldonline.co.uk). *Western European and US coins.*

Predecimal.com
Hauptstr. 33, Burkhardsdorf, 09235, Germany. (+491741 477182) www.predecimal.com. *British coins.*

George Rankin Coin Co Ltd (ANA)
325 Bethnal Green Road, London E2 6AH (020 7729 1280 fax 020 7729 5023). Mon–Sat 10.00–18.00 (half-day Thu). *World coins.*

Mark Rasmussen (BNTA)
PO Box 42, Betchworth RH3 7YR (01737 84100, website www.rascoins.com, email mark.rasmussen@rascoins.com). L *Hammered and milled coins.*

Mark T. Ray (Collectors World)
188 Wollaton Road, Wollaton, Nottingham, NG8 1HJ. (0115 928 0347). Mon–Sat. P *British coins.*

Regency Coins (UK) Lrd
First Floor, Unit 1, The Capricorn Centre, Cranes Farm Road, Basildon, Essex SS14 3JA. (0871 423 8871). *Milled gold and silver coins.*

Rhyl Coin Shop
12 Sussex Street, Rhyl, Clwyd (01745 338112). Mon–Sat 10.00–17.30. *World coins and banknotes.*

Chris Rigby
PO Box 181, Worcester WR1 1YE (01905 28028). P L *Modern British coins.*

Roderick Richardson (BNTA)
The Old Granary Antiques Centre, King's Staithe Lane, King's Lynn, Norfolk. (01553 670833, www.roderickrichardson.com) L *English, Hammered and early milled coins.*

Charles Riley (BNTA)
P.O Box 733, Aylesbury HP22 9AX (01296 747598 charles.riley@virgin.net). *Coins, medals and medallions.*

F. J. Rist
PO Box 4, Ibstock, Leics LE67 6ZJ (01530 264278). P L *Ancient and medieval coins, British coins and antiquities.*

Robin–on–Acle Coins
Parkeston House, Parkeston Quay, Harwich, Essex CO12 4PJ (01255 554440, email: enquiries@robin–on–acle–coins.co.uk). *Ancient to modern coins and paper money.*

S. J. Rood & Co Ltd
52–53 Burlington Arcade, London W1V 9AE (0171 493 0739). Mon–Sat 09.30–17.00. *World gold coins.*

Royal Gold
PO Box 123, Saxonwold, 2132, South Africa, (+27 11 483 0161, email: royalg@iafrica.com). *Gold coins.*

Royal Mint Coin Club
PO Box 500, Cardiff CF1 1YY (01443 623456). P *New issues struck by the Royal Mint.*

Colin de Rouffignac (BNTA)
57, Wigan Lane, Wigan, Lancs WN1 2LF (01942 237927). *P. English and Scottish hammered.*

R. P. Coins
PO Box 367, Prestwich, Manchester, M25 9ZH. Tel: 07802 713444. www.rpcoins.co.uk. *Coins, books, catalogues and accessories.*

Chris A. Rudd (IAPN, BNTA)
PO Box 222, Aylsham, Norfolk, NR11 6TY (01263 735007 fax 01263 731777, website www.celticcoins.com). P L *Celtic coins.*

Colin Rumney (BNTA)
PO Box 34, Denbighshire, North Wales, LL16 4YQ. (01745 890621). *All world including ancients.*

R & J Coins
21b Alexandra Street, Southend–on–Sea, Essex SS1 1DA (01702 345995). Mon–Sat 10.00–16.00 (closed Wed). *World coins.*

Safe Albums (UK) Ltd
16 Falcon Business Park, 38 Ivanhoe Road, Finchampstead, Berkshire RG40 4QQ. (0118 932 8976 fax 0118 932 8612).

Saltford Coins
Harcourt, Bath Road, Saltford, Bristol, Avon BS31 3DQ (01225 873512, www.saltfordcoins.com, email: info@saltfordcoins.com). P *British, Commonwealth and world coins.*

Satin Coins
PO Box 63, Stockport, Cheshire SK4 5BU. (07940 393583 answer machine).

David Seaman
PO Box 449, Waltham Cross EN9 3WZ. (01992 719723, email davidseamancoins@lineone.net). P L *Hammered, Milled, Maundy.*

Patrick Semmens
3 Hospital Road, Half Key, Malvern, Worcs WR14 1UZ (0886 33123). P *European and British coins.*

Mark Senior
553 Falmer Road, Woodingdean, Brighton, Sussex (01273 309359). By appointment only. P L *Saxon, Norman and English hammered coins.*

S. E. Sewell
PO Box 149, Stowmarket, IP14 4WD (01449 782185 or 07739 071822, www.sewellmedals.co.uk, email: sewellmedals@hotmail.com). *Mainly British milled.*

Shepshed Coins & Jewellery
24 Charnwood Road, Shepshed, Leics LE12 9QF (01509 502511). Mon, Wed–Sat 09.15–16.30. *British coins.*

Simmons Gallery (ANA, BNTA, IBNS)
PO Box 104, Leytonstone, London E11 1ND (020 8989 8097, email info@simmonsgallery.co.uk, www.simmonsgallery.co.uk). Organisers of the London Coin Fair, Holiday Inn, Bloomsbury, London W1. L *Coins, tokens and medals.*

E. Smith (ANA, IBNS)
PO Box 348, Lincoln LN6 0TX (01522 684681 fax 01522 689528). Organiser of the Morley, Leeds, monthly coin fair. P *World coins and paper money.*

J. Smith (BNTA)
47 The Shambles, York YO1 2LX (01904 654769). Mon–Sat 09.30–17.00. *World coins.*

Neil Smith
PO Box 774, Lincoln LN4 2WX (01522 522772 fax 01522 689528). *GB and World Gold coins 1816 to date, including modern proof issues.*

Jim Smythe
PO Box 6970, Birmingham B23 7WD (e-mail Jimdens@aol.com). P L *19th/20th century British and world coins.*

S&B Coins
Suite 313, St Loyes House, 20 Loyes Street, Bedford MK40 1ZL (01234 270260). P L *British coins and medallions.*

Spink & Son Ltd (ANA, BNTA, IAPN, IBNS)
69 Southampton Row, Bloomsbury, London. WC1B 4ET (020 7563 2820, fax 020 7563 4066, website www.spink.com, email info@spinkandson.com). *Ancient to modern world coins, orders, medals, banknotes and books.*

SPM Jewellers (BNTA)
112 East Street, Southampton, Hants SO14 3HD (023 80 223255/020 80 227923, fax 023 80 335634, wwbsite www.spmgoldcoins.co.uk, email user@spm.in2home.co.uk). Tue–Sat 09.15–17.00, Sat 09.15–16.00. *World coins and medals.*

Stamp & Collectors Centre
404 York Town Road, College Town, Camberley, Surrey GU15 4PR (01276 32587 fax 01276 32505). Mon, Tue, Thu, Sat 09.00–17.00, Wed, Fri 09.00–1900. *World coins and medals.*

St Edmunds Coins & Banknotes
PO Box 118, Bury St Edmunds IP33 2NE. (01284 761894)

Sterling Coins & Medals
2 Somerset Road, Boscombe, Bournemouth, Dorset BH7 6JH (01202 423881). Mon–Sat 09.30–16.30 (closed Wed). *World coins and medals.*

Strawbridge
Tanglewood, Ivy Tree Hill, Stokeinteignhead, Newton Abbott, Devon TQ12 4QH (01626 873783, emailjim@strawbridge.co.uk). P L *Coins, tokens, medals, banknotes.*

Studio Coins (ANA, BNTA)
16 Kilham Lane, Winchester, Hants SO22 5PT (01962 853156 fax 01962 624246). P *English coins.*

Time Line Originals
PO Box 193, Upminster, RM14 3WH Tel: (01708 222384. Mobile 07775 651218, Email: sales@time–lines.co.uk).

Stuart J. Timmins
Smallwood Lodge Bookshop, Newport, Salop (01952 813232). Mon–Sat 09.30–17.00. *Numismatic literature.*

R. Tims
39 Villiers Road, Watford, Herts WD1 4AL. P L *Uncirculated world banknotes.*

D. A. Travis
8 Cookridge Drive, Leeds LS16 7LT. P L *US coins.*

Michael Trenerry Ltd
PO Box 55, Truro, Cornwall TR1 2YQ (01872 277977 fax 01872 225565, email veryfinecoins@aol.com). By appointment only. L *Roman, Celtic and English hammered coins, tokens.*

Vera Trinder Ltd
38 Bedford Street, Strand, London WC2E 9EU (020 7257 9940). Mon–Fri 08.30–17.30. L *Coin catalogues and books, albums, envelopes, cases etc.*

Robert Tye
7–9 Clifford Street, York, YO1 9RA (0845 4 900 724 e-mail: orders@earlyworlscoins.com. P *European and Oriental hammered coins.*

Universal Currency Coin Exhange
PO Box 57648, Mill Hill, London, NW7 0FE. (07831 662594. Email: uccedcp@aol.com.) *German, Canadian and American Coins.*

Valda Coins
80 Aberfan Road, Aberfan, Mid Glamorgan CF48 4QJ. (01443 690452). P L

Vale (ADA)
21 Tranquil Vale, Blackheath, London SE3 0BU (020 8852 9817. Mon–Sat 10.00–17.30 (closed Thu). *British coins and medals.*

Valued History
27 Elm Hill, Norwich, NR3 1HN. (01603 627413. website www.valuedhistory.co.uk). *Coins and antiquities.*

Tony Vaughan Collectables
PO Box 364, Wolverhampton, WV3 9PW (01902 27351). (P) (L) *World coins and medals.*

Victory Coins (BNTA)
184 Chichester Road, North End, Portsmouth, Hants PO2 0AX (023 92 751908/663450). Thurs–Sat 09.00–17.00. *British and world coins.*

Viking Metal Detectors
1 angela Street, Mill Hill, Blacburn, Lancashire BB2 4DJ (01254 55887 fax 01254 676901, email viking@metaldetectors.co.uk)). *Metal detectors and accessories.*

Mark J. Vincenzi (BNTA)
Rylands, Earls Colne, Essex. CO6 2LE (01787 222555). (P) *Greek, Roman, Hammered.*

Vista World Banknotes
5 Greenfields Way, Burley-in-Wharfedale, Ilkley, W. Yorks LS29 7RB. (Email vistabanknotes@barclays.net).

Mike Vosper
PO Box 32, Hockwold, Brandon IP26 4HX (01842 828292, website www.vosper4coins.co.uk, email mikevosper@vosper4coins.co.uk).

B. M. & S. A. Weeks
PO Box 1447, Salisbury, Wilts SP5 2YG (01725 510311). (L) *British coins, world crowns and medals.*

Weighton Coin Wonders
E-shop www.weightoncoin.co.uk (01430 879740) *Modern gold, silver proofs and sets.*

John Welsh
PO Box 150, Burton-on-Trent, Staffs DE13 7LB (01543 73073 fax 0543 473234). (P) (L) *British coins.*

Pam West (IBNS, BNTA)
PO Box 257, Sutton, Surrey SM3 9WW (020 8641 3224, website www.brishnotes.co.uk, email pamwestbritnotes@aol.com). (P) (L) *English banknotes.*

West Essex Coin Investments (BNTA, IBNS)
Croft Cottage, Station Road, Alderholt, Fordingbridge, Hants SP6 3AZ (01425 656 459). *British and World coins and paper money.*

West Wicklow Coins
Blessington, Co Wicklow, Ireland. (00353 45 858767, email: westwicklowcoins@hotmail.com)

R & J White (IBNS)
29 Shortacre, Basildon, Essex SS14 2LR (01268 522923). (P) (L) *Banknotes and world ephemera.*

Whitmore (BNTA)
Teynham Lodge, Chase Road, Upper Colwall, Malvern, Worcs WR13 6DT (01684 50651). (P) *World coins, tokens and medals.*

T. Wilkes
PO Box 150, Battle, East Sussex TN33 0FA (01424 773352, www.wilkescoins.com). *Specialist in English Hammered coins, European Medieval and Crusader coins, Islamic and Indian coins.*

World Coins
35–36 Broad Street, Canterbury, Kent CT1 2LR (01227 768887). Mon–Sat 09.30–17.30 (half-day Thu). World & British coins, tokens & banknotes.

Worldwide Coins (IBNS)
PO Box 11, Wavertree, Liverpool L15 0FG. email: sales@worldwidecoins.co.uk,website: www.worldwidecoins.co.uk. *World coins and paper money.*

World Treasure Books
PO Box 5, Newport, Isle of Wight PO30 5QE (01983 740712). (L) *Coins, books, metal detectors.*

WRB Notes—Rare Currency & Banknotes
PO Box 52, Downham Market, PE38 0WX. (P) *English and world banknotes.*

Barry Wright
54 Dooley Drive, Bootle, Merseyside. L3O 8RT. (P) (L) *World banknotes.*

I. S. Wright (Australia Numismatic Co)
208 Sturt Street, Ballarat, Vic. Australia 3350 (0061 3 5332 3856 fax 0061 3 5331 6426, email ausnumis@netconnect.comau. (P) *Coins, banknotes, medallions, tokens.*

D. Yapp
PO Box 4718, Shrewsbury SY1 9EA (01743 232557). *World and British Banknotes.*

B. N. Yarwood (ANA)
Yarwood Hall, Luttongate Road, Sutton St Edmund, Spalding, Lincs PE12 0LH. (P) *British and US coins.*

Ye Olde Banknoteshop
Email: jim@oldbanknoteshop.co.uk. website www.oldbanknoteshop.co.uk. *British and world coins and banknotes, tokens and medals.*

York Coins
PO Box 160, Red Hook, New York 12571. Tel/fax: (718) 544 0120 email: antony@yorkcoins.com. *Ancient coins.*

York Coin and Stamp Centre
Cavendish Antique & Collectors Centre, 44 Stone gate, York, YO1 8AS.

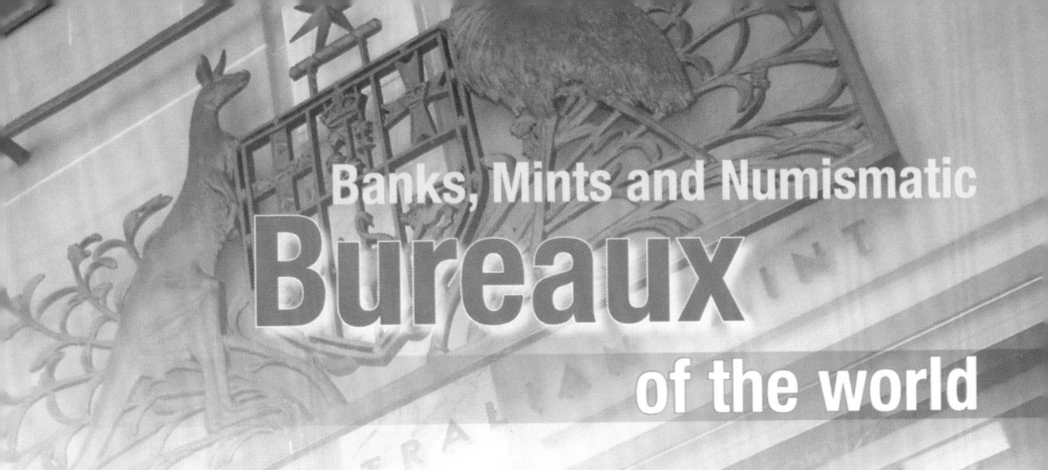

Banks, Mints and Numismatic Bureaux of the world

Many national banks and mints operate numismatic bureaux and sales agencies from which coins, medals and other numismatic products may be obtained direct. The conditions under which purchases may be made vary considerably. In many cases at the present time bureaux will accept orders from overseas customers quoting their credit card number and its expiry date; but in others payment can only be made by certified bank cheque, or international money order, or by girobank. Cash is seldom, if ever, acceptable. It is best to write in the first instance to enquire about

A

National Mint, Baghe Arg, Kabul, Afghanistan

Bank Mille Afghan, Kabul, Afghanistan

Banque d'Algerie, Sucursale d'Alger, 8 Boulevard Carnot, Alger, Algeria

Banco de Angola, Luanda, Daroal, Angola

Casa de Moneda de la Nacion, Avenida Antartica, Buenos Aires, BA, Argentina

Royal Australian Mint, Department of the Treasury, Canberra, ACT, Australia

GoldCorp Australia, Perth Mint Buildings, GPO Box M924, Perth, Western Australia 6001

Oesterreichsiches Hauptmunzamt, Am Heumarkt 1, A-1031 Wien, Postfach 225, Austria

Oesterreichische Nationalbank, A-1090 Wien, Otto Wagner-platz 3, Austria

B

Treasury Department, PO Box 557, Nassau, Bahamas (*coins*)

Ministry of Finance, PO Box 300, Nassau, Bahamas (*banknotes*)

Bank of Bahrain, PO Box 106, Manama, Bahrain

Eastern Bank, PO Box 29, Manama, Bahrain

Monnaie Royale de Belgique, Avenue de Pacheco 32, B-1000 Bruxelles, Belgium

Banque Nationale de Belgique SA, Caisse Centrale, Bruxelles, Belgium

Banque de Bruxelles SA, 2 Rue de la Regence, Bruxelles 1, Belgium

Casa de la Moneda, Potosi, Bolivia

Banco Central de Bolivia, La Paz, Bolivia

Casa da Moeda, Praca da Republica 173, Rio de Janeiro, Brazil

Hemus FTO, 7 Vasil Levski Street, Sofia C-1, Bulgaria

Banque de la Republique, Bujumbura, Burundi

C

Banque Centrale, Douala, Boite Postale 5.445, Cameroun

Royal Canadian Mint, 320 Sussex Drive, Ottawa 2, Ontario, Canada K1A 0G8

Casa de Moneda, Quinta Normal, Santiago, Chile

Casa de Moneda, Calle 11 no 4-93, Bogota, Colombia

Numismatic Section, The Treasury, Avarua, Rarotonga, Cook Islands

Banco Centrale de Costa Rica, Departamento de Contabilidad, San Jose, Costa Rica, CA

Central Bank of Cyprus, PO Box 1087, Nicosia, Cyprus

Artia, Ve Smekach 30, PO Box 790, Praha 1, Czech Republic

D

Den Kongelige Mønt, Amager Boulevard 115, København S, Denmark

Danmarks Nationalbank, Holmens Kanal 17, 1060 København K, Denmark

Banco Central de Santo Domingo, Santo Domingo, Dominican Republic

E

Banco Central, Quito, Ecuador

Mint House, Abbassia, Cairo, Egyptian Arab Republic

Exchange Control Department, National Bank of Egypt, Cairo, Egyptian Arab Republic

Banco Central de la Republica, Santa Isabel, Equatorial Guinea

Commercial Bank of Ethiopia, Foreign Branch, PO Box 255, Addis Ababa, Ethiopia

F

Currency Board, Victoria Parade, Suva, Fiji

Suomen Rahapaja, Katajanokanlaituri 3, Helsinki 16, Finland

Suomen Pankki, PO Box 10160, Helsinki 10, Finland

Hotel de Monnaie, 11 Quai de Conti, 75-Paris 6e, France

G

Banque Centrale Libreville, Boite Postale 112, Gabon

Verkaufstelle fur Sammlermunzen, D-638 Bad Homburg vdH, Bahnhofstrasse 16–18, Germany

Staatliche Munze Karlsruhe, Stephanienstrasse 28a, 75 Karlsruhe, Germany

Staatliche Munze Cannstatt, Taubenheimerstrasse 77, 7 Stuttgart-Bad, Germany

Bayerisches Hauptmunzamt, Hofgraben 4, 8 Munich, Germany

Hamburgische Munze, Norderstrasse 66, 2 Hamburg 1, Germany

Bank of Ghana, PO Box 2674, Accra, Ghana

Pobjoy Mint, Millennia House, Kingswood Park, Bonsor Drive, Kingswood, Surrey KT20 6AY

Royal Mint, Llantrisant, Mid Glamorgan, Wales, CF7 8YT

Royal Mint Coin Club, PO Box 500, Cardiff, CF1 1HA

Bank of Greece, Treasury Department, Cash, Delivery & Despatch Division, PO Box 105, Athens, Greece

Casa Nacional de Moneda, 6a Calle 4-28, Zona 1, Ciudad Guatemala, Republica de Guatemala CA

States Treasury, St Peter Port, Guernsey, Channel Islands

Bank of Guyana, PO Box 658, Georgetown, Guyana

H

Banque Nationale de la Republique d'Haiti, Rue Americaine et Rue Fereu, Port-au-Prince, Haiti

Banco Central de Honduras, Tegucigalpa DC, Honduras CA

State Mint, Ulloi utca 102, Budapest VIII, Hungary

Artex, PO Box 167, Budapest 62, Hungary

Magyar Nemzeti Bank, Board of Exchange, Budapest 54, Hungary

I

Sedlabanki Islands, Reykjavik, Iceland

Indian Government Mint, Bombay 1, India

Arthie Vasa, Keabajoran Baru, Djakarta, Indonesia

Perum Peruri, Djakarta, Indonesia

National Mint, Tehran, Iran

Bank Markazi Iran, Tehran, IranCentral Bank of Iraq, PO Box 64, Baghdad, Iraq

Central Bank of Ireland, Dublin 2, Republic of Ireland

The Treasury, Government Buildings, Prospect Hill, Douglas, Isle of Man

Israel Stamp and Coin Gallery, 4 Maze Street, Tel Aviv, Israel

Istituto Poligraphico e Zecca dello Stato, Via Principe Umberto, Roma, Italy

J

Decimal Currency Board, PO Box 8000, Kingston, Jamaica

Mint Bureau, 1 Shinkawasakicho, Kita-ku, Osaka 530, Japan

Numismatic Section, Treasury Department, St Helier, Jersey

Central Bank of Jordan, Amman, Jordan

Banque Nationale du Liban, Rue Masraf Loubnan, Beirut, Lebanon

K

Central Bank, PO Box 526, Kuwait

L

Bank of LatviaK. Valdemara iela 2A, LV-1050, Riga, Latvia

Bank of Lithuania, Cash Department, Gedimino av. 6, 2001 Vilius, Lithuania

Caisse Generale de l'Etat, 5 Rue Goethe, Luxembourg-Ville, Grande Duche de Luxembourg

M

Institut d'Emission Malgache, Boite Postale 205, Tananarive, Madagascar

Central Bank of Malta, Valletta 1, Malta

Casa de Moneda, Calle del Apartado no 13, Mexico 1, DF, Mexico

Le Tresorier General des Finances, Monte Carlo, Principaute de Monaco

Banque de l'Etat du Maroc, Rabat, Morocco

Banco Nacional Ultramarino, Maputo, Republica de Mocambique

British Bank of the Middle East, Muscat

N

Royal Mint, Dharahara, Katmandu, Nepal

Nepal Rastra Bank, Katmandu, Nepal

Rijks Munt, Leidseweg 90, Utrecht, Netherlands

Hollandsche Bank-Unie NV, Willemstad, Breedestraat 1, Curacao, Netherlands Antilles

Central Bank of Curacao, Willemstad, Curacao, Netherlands Antilles

New Zealand Post Stamps Centre, Private Bag 3001, Wanganui 4540, New Zealand

Banco de Nicaragua, Departamento de Emison, La Tresoria, Apartada 2252, Managua, Nicaragua

Nigerian Security Printing and Minting Corporation, Ahmadu Bello Road, Victoria Island, Lagos, Nigeria

Central Bank of Nigeria, Tinubu Square LB, Lagos, Nigeria

Norges Bank, Oslo, Norway

Den Kongelige Mynt, Hyttegaten, Konigsberg, Norway

P

Pakistan State Mint, Baghban Pura, Lahore 9, Pakistan

National Development Bank, Asuncion, Paraguay

Casa Nacional de Moneda, Calle Junin 791, Lima, Peru

Central Bank of the Philippines, Manila, Philippines

Bank Handlowy w Warszawie, Ul. Romuald Traugutta 7, Warsaw, Poland

Desa Foreign Trade Department, Al. Jerozolimskie 2, Warszawa, Poland

Casa da Moeda, Avenida Dr Antonio Jose de Almeida, Lisbon 1, Portugal

R

Cartimex, 14-18 Aristide Briand St, PO Box 134-135, Bucharest, Roumania

Bank of Foreign Trade, Commercial Department, Moscow K 16, Neglinnaja 12, Russian Federation

Banque Nationale du Rwanda, Boite Postale 351, Kigali, Republique Rwandaise

S

Numismatic Section, Box 194, GPO, Apia, Samoa

Azienda Autonoma di Stato Filatelica-Numismatica, Casalla Postale 1, 47031 Repubblica di San Marino

Banque Internationale pour le Commerce, 2 Avenue Roume, Dakar, Senegal

Bank of Yugoslavia, PO Box 1010, Belgrade, Serbia

The Treasury, PO Box 59, Victoria, Seychelles

Bank of Sierra Leone, PO Box 30, Freetown, Sierra Leone

The Singapore Mint, 20 Teban Gardens Crescent, Singapore 608928

South African Mint, PO Box 464, Pretoria, South Africa

Government Printing Agency, 93 Bukchang Dong, Chungku, Seoul, Republic of South Korea

Fabrica Nacional de Moneda y Timbre, Jorge Juan 106, Madrid 9, Spain

Bank of Sri Lanka, PO Box 241, Colombo, Sri Lanka

Hong Kong and Shanghai Banking Corporation, PO Box 73, Colombo 1, Sri Lanka

Sudan Mint, PO Box 43, Khartoum, Sudan

Bank of Sudan, PO Box 313, Khartoum, Sudan

Bank of Paramaribo, Paramaribo, Suriname

Kungelige Mynt och Justeringsverket, Box 22055, Stockholm 22, Sweden

Eidgenossische Staatskasse, Bundesgasse 14, CH-3003, Berne, Switzerland

Central Bank of Syria, Damascus, Syrian Arab Republic

T

Central Mint of China, 44 Chiu Chuan Street, Taipei, Taiwan, ROC

Royal Thai Mint, 4 Chao Fah Road, Bangkok, Thailand

Numismatic Section, The Treasury, Nuku'alofa, Tonga

Central Bank of Trinidad and Tobago, PO Box 1250, Port of Spain, Trinidad

Banque Centrale de Tunisie, Tunis, Tunisia

State Mint, Maliye Bakanligi Darphane Mudurlugu, Istanbul, Turkey

U

Bank of Uganda, PO Box 7120, Kampala, Uganda

Numismatic Service, US Assay Office, 350 Duboce Avenue, San Francisco, CA, 94102, USA

Office of the Director of the Mint, Treasury Department, Washington, DC, 20220, USA

Philadelphia Mint, 16th and Spring Garden Streets, Philadelphia, PA, 19130, USA

Franklin Mint, Franklin Center, Pennsylvania, 19063, USA

Banco Central del Uruguay, Cerrito 351, Montevideo, RO del Uruguay

V

Ufficio Numismatico, Governatorato dello Stato della Citta de Vaticano, Italy

Banco Central de Venezuela, Caracas, Venezuela

Y

Yemen Bank, Sana'a, Yemen.

Z

Bank of Zambia, PO Box 80, Lusaka, Zambia

Chief Cashier, Reserve Bank, PO Box 1283, Harare,

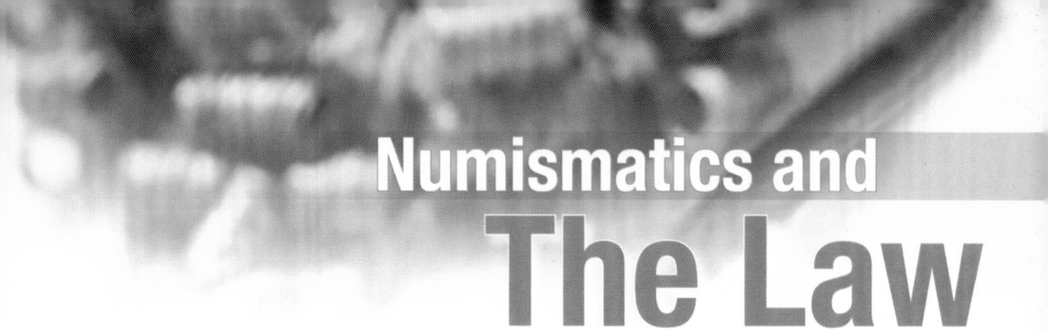

Numismatics and The Law

Counterfeit Currency

A counterfeit is a forgery or imitation of a coin or banknote produced with the intention of defrauding the revenue of the State or deceiving members of the public. By the Coinage Offences Act (1861) it was a felony to counterfeit gold or silver coins. Lesser offences included the gilding of farthings and sixpences to pass them off as half-sovereigns, the possession of moulds, machines or tools clandestinely removed from the Royal Mint, the impairment or diminution of gold or silver coins by filing or clipping (or even the possession of such filings and clippings).

The Coinage Act of 1870 made provision for the counterfeiting of base-metal coins, or the stamping of letters or words on coins of any kind, or the forging of colonial coinage. The most celebrated prosecution under this Act occurred in 1930 when Martin Coles Harman was convicted and fined £5 for issuing bronze coins resembling the British penny and halfpenny for the island of Lundy of which he was then the proprietor. Interestingly, no attempt was made to prosecute the Birmingham Mint which actually struck the coins (prudently omitting the H mintmark).

The making of medals or coins resembling current coin became a misdemeanour under the Counterfeit Medal Act of 1883.This Act is invoked from time to time against manufacturers or distributors of medallic pieces or coin jewellery. Such pieces, often struck in 9 carat gold, are deemed to infringe the Act if, for example, they have a figure even vaguely resembling St George and the Dragon on one side. The use of the royal effigy, however, without due authorisation, is regarded as a misdemeanour punishable by an unlimited fine and the confiscation of tools, dies and instruments. At the present time it is a serious offence to make a counterfeit of a currency note or coin with the intention of passing it off or tendering it as genuine. This offence carries a maximum penalty of ten years' imprisonment or an unlimited fine, or both. Making a counterfeit of a currency note or coin without lawful authority incurs a penalty up to two years' imprisonment or an unlimited fine, or both.

Passing or tendering as genuine anything which is known or believed to be a counterfeit of a currency note or coin renders the criminal on conviction to a term of ten years' imprisonment or an unlimited fine, or both. The mere possession of any forged note or coin is itself a criminal offence. Possessing countertfeits without authority or permission so to do, and doing so knowingly, renders the possessor liable to two years' imprisonment or an unlimited fine, or both. The Act also stipulates that the reproduction of a current banknote—of the Bank of England or of the Scottish and Northern Irish banks is a serious offence. This clause covers even such apparently innocent acts as making a photocopy (whether in black and white or full colour) of a current banknote, the photography of such a note or the illustration of such a note in any book, magazine or newspaper. Strict regulations are laid down concerning the legitimate illustration of notes, whether current or not, in books and periodicals; such illustrations must be either greatly reduced or enlarged *and* must bear a prominent defacement, such as SPECIMEN or CANCELLED. It is also a serious offence to utilise a reproduction of a current British banknote in any medium. Theoretically this includes such things as tea-towels, T-shirts, mugs, plates and other souvenirs in glass or ceramics, but in practice the law seems to turn a blind eye to such practices. Imitations and parodies of notes and coins are also regarded as infringements of the law, but in these instances prosecution of the offender seldom proceeds; a warning is generally regarded as sufficient, provided that the offending article or articles are withdrawn and suppressed.

The advent of high-definition colour photo-copying in recent years has brought the offence of reproduction into prominence once more. The regulations have been tightened considerably and there have been several cases of successful prosecution. In each case, however, the intent deliberately to deceive the public by uttering a colour photocopy as a genuine note was proved. Technically the offence takes places as soon as the photocopy is made, for whatever purpose, but as a rule only those cases in which an element of fraudulent deception subsequently arose are pursued with the full rigour of the law. The law is quite clear, however, and it is a criminal offence to make a photocopy or photograph of any current British note unless permission to do so has been obtained from the Treasury. The maximum penalty on conviction is an unlimited fine.

The note-issuing banks have, of course, taken steps in recent years to incorporate further security devices into their notes, notably the use of latent images and underprints in colours which are difficult, if not impossible to photocopy accurately. At the same time, the adoption of metal strips and more complex watermark devices has theoretically made the task of the forger much more difficult. If, by some unlucky chance, someone passes a dud note on to you, you must make no attempt to pass it in turn. To do so renders you liable to prosecution for uttering a forgery. Forged notes must be handed over to the police as soon as possible. If you receive a forged note in payment for goods or services you are entitled to claim its face value from the person who gave it to you. Even if the person giving you the note did not realise that it was counterfeit, it is assumed in law that he or she represented to you that the note was worth its face value at the time the note was passed. If the tenderer knew that the note was forged, he can be prosecuted; but at the end of the day he is still liable to you for the fraud and can be sued in the civil courts for the recovery of the sum involved. If, on the other hand, you received the money as a gift, you have no legal claim against the person who gave it to you. If you pay someone with a counterfeit note or coin unknowingly, you have committed no offence, but you must pay again. The degree of culpability is often difficult to prove or disprove, but it is unlikely that a prosecution would be initiated on the basis of a single note or coin.

It is also a serious offence to manufacture blanks, discs or washers which are intended to defraud the proprietors of vending machines, or to possess tools and equipment for the dishonest manufacture or alteration of such blanks for this purpose. Under the Gold and Silver Export Control Act (1920) melting down gold or silver coins to extract their precious metal content is an offence punishable by a fine of £100 or two years' imprisonment, or both.

Legal Tender

The dictionary defines this as currency which a creditor is bound by law to accept as payment of a money debt. Debts and purchases must be paid for in cash of legal tender unless the creditor or seller is willing to accept payment in another form, such as a postal order, money order, cheque or, nowadays, credit card. Bank of England notes of any denomination are legal tender in England and Wales. Formerly Bank of England pound notes (but no other) were legal tender in Scotland. Technically, since the demise of the one pound note, no Bank of England notes are legal tender in Scotland, although in practice they circulate freely north of the Border. Even more surprisingly, Scottish banknotes are not legal tender anywhere, not even in Scotland! The subtle difference is reflected in the actual wording of the promise on English and Scottish banknotes. Thus English notes are inscribed "*I promise to pay the bearer on demand the sum of . . .*" without stipulating any specific place, the promise being made by the Chief Cashier. Scottish notes, on the other hand, have the promise in the third person. It is the bank itself which makes the promise "*to pay the bearer on demand . . . pounds sterling at their head office here in Edinburgh, by order of the Board*". In practice, however, Scottish banknotes are accepted without question, not only throughout Scotland but also in parts of England, and are generally accepted in London, although there is no obligation on the part of a creditor so to do.

Apart from gold coins, the base-metal pound coin is legal tender for payment of any amounts. So, too, presumably, are the various two-pound and five-pound base-metal coins of recent years, even though they have been struck as commemoratives and not intended for general circulation in the ordinary sense. Smaller denominations are only legal tender up to a maximum value in each case. In the case of 50p coins, 25p crowns and 20p coins, they may be used alone, or in combination with each other, in payment of amounts up to £10. 10p and 5p coins, alone or in combination, may be used for sums up to £5. Bronze 1p and 2p coins, however, can only be used for payment of amounts up to 20p. In practice, of course, you can probably get away with making payment in larger quantities (within reason!) although strictly speaking there is no obligation on the part of your creditor to accept them.

An Offence to Possess Legal Tender Coins

From the foregoing it will be seen that gold coins are, and always have been, legal tender. Since 1817 the legal tender gold coin of the United Kingdom has been the sovereign (with its sub-division and multiples). Yet there have been times when actual possession of these legal tender coins has been, *per se*, an illegal act. The first attempt to regulate the movement and possession of gold coins arose in 1947 with the passage of the Exchange Control

Act which made it illegal to buy, borrow, lend or sell any gold or foreign currency, unless authorised to deal in gold. Moreover it was stipulated that "*any person possessing gold should offer it for sale to an authorised dealer at a price not exceeding the authorised price, unless the Treasury consented to this retention of the gold*".

The serious implications of this Act were mitigated in the case of numismatists by the Exchange Control (Collectors' Pieces Exemption) Order 1947, which allowed collectors to hold on to "*any gold coin which was minted in 1816 or earlier, and any gold coin which was minted after 1816 and which has a numismatic value greater than the value of the gold content which would have been received if the coin had been sold to an authorised (bullion) dealer*". In effect this meant that numismatists and coin dealers were not hindered from buying and selling gold coins as long as the coins were in collectable condition and possessed numismatic interest. This loophole was brazenly breached in the 1960s and led to the Exchange Control (Gold Coins Exemption) Order of 1966 which aimed to prevent the loss of currency reserves caused by the import of gold coins from abroad, and to eliminate the hoarding of gold by speculators. By the terms of this Order no one was permitted to hold more than four gold coins minted after 1837 unless they had received express permission from the Treasury. The maximum was set at four coins so that people who had one or two sovereigns as mementoes could keep them without breaking the law. Numismatists who possessed more than four post-1837 gold coins on April 27, 1966 had to apply to the Treasury for permission to retain them. To do so they had to prove that they were *bona fide* collectors by completing form GC 1, providing a detailed list of the coins in their possession—not only in gold, but also in silver (pre-1816, 1816–1919 and post-1919) and base metals (before and after 1860). Several individuals were successfully prosecuted under this draconian legislation and their holdings of gold sovereigns confiscated, although no one was imprisoned or heavily fined as the legislation provided. The 1966 order was rescinded in 1970, re-imposed in a modified form in 1975, and finally revoked in 1979. Since that date numismatists and speculators alike have been free to collect (or hoard) gold to their hearts' content.

Value Added Tax

This is a matter which primarily concerns dealers, but it also applies to those who dabble in coins on a part-time basis, and has implications for collectors at all levels. Briefly, anyone conducting a business, or in self-employment, who has a turnover in excess of £64,000 per annum, must register with HM Customs and Excise for the collection and payment of Value Added Tax. Anyone whose turnover is less than £64,000 is exempt from the obligation to register, but is at liberty to register if he or she feels that this would be advantageous. It is nice to think that there is an element of choice in this, although one would be hard pressed to think why anyone would voluntarily register for VAT unless they absolutely had to! Incidentally, the government raised the VAT registration level by 40 per cent to £35,000 in March 1991 with the avowed intention of relieving a large number of businesses from this burden, at a time when the rate of tax was increased from 15 per cent to 17.5 per cent. Assuming that you are a dealer with a turnover above the magic limit, then you are committing a serious offence if you fail to register. Registration then lays you open to the full machinery of the system. You have to charge VAT on all goods and services, issuing VAT invoices and receipts and keeping detailed accounts which are liable to snap inspection at any time. You have to make quarterly returns to Customs and Excise of the amount of tax you have collected. From this you are allowed to deduct the VAT which you yourself have paid out in the course of your business, and you then have to remit the difference to the VAT collector. Of course, should the amount you have paid exceed the tax you have collected, you receive a repayment in due course. This arises in businesses which handle zero-rated goods and services, but coins and medals do not come within that category.

For dealers in gold bullion, coins or medals, there is a special VAT leaflet which covers regulations specific to such matters. Since January 2000 investment gold has been exempt from VAT. A coin is classified as investment gold if it satisfies the following conditions: 1. Minted after 1800; 2. At least .900 fine; 3. Is or has been legal tender of its country of origin; 4. Is of a description of coin that is normally sold at a price that does not exceed 180% of the open market value of the gold contained in the coin. This is a complicated issue and further advice can be obtained from Customs & Excise Public Notice 701/21/99. A list of coins qualifying as investment gold is published in Public Notice 701/21A/99. When VAT is applicable of course it needs to be accounted for on the profit margin. It is vital therefore to maintain accurate records of all buying and selling, and which coins and medals are subject to VAT and which are exempt. Furthermore, the onus is on you to ensure that the source of the gold you bring into the country is impeccable. There are extremely heavy penalties for smuggling gold, and ignorance of the law, or apparently innocent handling of smuggled gold subsequently, are no defence.

From January 1, 1995 the special margin scheme of accounting for VAT currently available for certain second-hand goods, such as cars, was extended to almost all second-hand goods. The scheme allows businesses buying and selling eligible goods to account for VAT only on the difference between the buying and selling prices of these items.

A special system of accounting exists which enables some dealers to account for VAT without the need to keep a detailed record of every transaction. Certain works of art, antiques and collector's items, including "secondhand" coins, defined in Notice 712 *Second-hand goods*, were exempt from VAT at import. From January 1, 1996 these items became subject to VAT at import at an effective rate of 2.5 per cent.

Export and Import

Some coins do require an export licence before they can be taken out of the country and unfortunately these controls have been extended during the past year. Following the lifting of the export regulations relating to gold coins in 1979, then prior to April 1, 1993 the only coins which required any export licence were those with a value in excess of £35,000. However the agreement by the UK to implement an EC directive on the removal of cultural goods has resulted in a fresh interpretation of previous UK legislation on these coins which are on the market as a result of an archaeological find. Therefore as from April 1, 1993, any coin *whatever its value* which has come from an archaeological source within the UK will require an export licence even to take it to another EC country. Certain other coins of EC provenance other than the UK will now require an EC export licence. The value limit for non-archaeological source coins has been increased to £39,600 (Ecu 50,000). Both types of licence are issued by the Department of National Heritage, 2–4 Cockspur Street, Trafalgar Square, London SW1Y 5DH who can also supply a handy flow-chart to enable you to tell at a glance whether a licence is needed and what type.

These new regulations are imposing an enormous additional burden on the trade and the British Numismatic Trade Association has held numerous meetings with the authorities in an attempt to reduce to a minimum the number of licence applications needed. Hopefully, by next year's edition there will be better news.

The restrictions applied to the importation of gold coins were removed in 1979, as previously mentioned. Coins of any kind are now permitted under Open General Import licence from any country and a specific or individual licence is no longer required. Details of any duties which may be payable on imported coins can be obtained from HM Customs and Excise, King's Beam House, Southwark, London SE1 or any local Customs and Excise office. Until recently, the only gold coins under embargo were Krugerrands. This was a political decision, aimed at tightening sanctions against South Africa, and applied to the importation of new gold coins from that country, but not to Krugerrands which had been brought into the United Kingdom, or any of the countries of the European Community, prior to the imposition of sanctions. In practice, it was very difficult to regulate the movement, let alone the importation, of Krugerrands, and with the relaxation of Apartheid this regulation has been lifted.

Importing Coins by Mail

Elsewhere in this volume will be found the names and addresses of mints, banks and numismatic bureaux around the world from whom it may be possible to obtain currency direct. It is a wise precaution to write to these bodies in the first instance for details of their sales and distribution. In some cases they appoint a dealer in Britain as an agent and this is a method of purchase that removes a great deal of the hassle and red tape. Nowadays, however, many mints and banks are quite happy to use the credit card system to make it easy to part you from your money. The problem arises, however, when the coins are despatched. As a rule, banks and mints stipulate quite clearly that they will not accept orders prepaid in cash, and it is an offence to send coins or banknotes out of the country as payment, except through banks authorised for this purpose. Cheques drawn on British banks should not be used. Indeed, this may be actively discouraged by the imposition of heavy clearance and handling charges at the other end. The converse is also true, although Americans seem to think that dollar cheques drawn on some obscure mid-West bank will be eagerly accepted here, and are consequently aggrieved when it is tactfully pointed out to them that this creates enormous problems—to say nothing of the swingeing bank charges incurred in converting such cheques to sterling. Other than credit cards, the Girobank system is probably the best method of remitting currency from one country to another; full details may be obtained from any post office. Details on the preferred method of sending remittances, or transferring cash to another country, as well as the transmission of coins by post to different countries, will be found in the *Royal Mail International Service Guide*. This also lists, among the prohibitions pertaining to each country, which countries accept gold or silver, and which ban the transmission of precious metals by post.

The receipt of postal packets containing coins from abroad makes you liable for Value Added Tax on their importation. As a rule, the despatching mint or bank will have affixed a Customs declaration to the packet, listing the contents, their weight and value, and it is on that basis that VAT will be calculated. The position regarding the import and export of coins by post is more complicated, and applies also to goods sent on approval. In such cases you must consult your Customs and Excise office who will advise you on the correct procedure and what your liabilities will be to tax in either case. This also applies to dealers taking stock out of the country to a coin show and then re-importing the unsold stock afterwards, or importing material purchased at the show.

Buying and Selling

When goods are sold, the seller and the buyer enter into a contract which confers rights and imposes obligations on both parties. The contract need not be in writing. There is no law governing the quality of goods sold by a private individual. If you purchase a coin from a fellow-collector as a result of an informal meeting at the local numismatic society it is incumbent on you to ensure that what you buy is what you think you are buying. If you purchase something from a dealer or shopkeeper, however, you are entitled under the Sale of Goods Act to goods of "merchantable quality" which means that they must be reasonably fit for their purpose. Items sold under a specific description, on the other hand, must correspond exactly with that description. If they do not, the seller *even a private individual* can be sued under the Sale of Goods Act. This is an important distinction because there is an erroneous notion that the Act does not apply to transactions between private individuals.

If A sells a coin to B, purporting it to be a rare date, and B subsequently discovers that the date has been deliberately altered, then B can sue A. Even if A claims that he made the sale in good faith, believing the coin to be a genuine rare date, he will still be liable for restitution (giving B his money back) and may also face a claim for damages. The Sale of Goods Act thus overturns the traditional adage *caveat emptor* which, in its full formula, translates as "let the buyer beware for he ought not to be ignorant of the nature of the property which he is buying from another party". Traditionally this was the maxim applicable at auctions. Once the auctioneer's gavel had dropped, the successful bidder had, in effect, made a contract with the vendor and was bound to pay for the lot, even if he subsequently discovered that what he had purchased was not what he had imagined. The view was that it was up to the purchaser to ensure beforehand that what he purchased was genuine and answered the description in the sale catalogue.

Because of vexatious disputes arising from questions of authenticity, and with the Sale of Goods Act breathing down their necks, many auctioneers now have a safety net, in the form of extensions. These enable successful bidders to delay payment for two or three weeks while they seek expertisation of doubtful material. In other words, the law allows a cooling-off period, but only for he legitimate purpose of verifying the authenticity of items over which there may be some doubt. This is only operative in cases where a coin or medal is sold as genuine, and described and estimated in value accordingly. In many doubtful cases, however, an auctioneer will cover himself by adding the crucial words "as is" to the description of a lot. Then, indeed, it is a case of *caveat emptor*. The auctioneer has done everything humanly possible to draw attention to the controversial nature of the item, and it must then rest on the judgment of the purchaser.

On the subject of auctions there are legal aspects which are not always apparent, as well as subtle differences in law and practice between England and Scotland. These tend to arise in cases where coins and medals come up for sale at provincial general mixed auctions, rather than in the sales conducted by numismatic auctioneers. Goods up for auction may be subject to an upset price which is made public as the price at which the bidding will start. A reserve price, on the other hand, is known only to the auctioneer, and if it is not reached, the goods will not be sold. Upset prices are common in Scotland, reserve prices in England. If no upset price is specified and the goods are not subject to a reserve price then the highest bid secures them, even though it may not be as high as the vendor hoped for. If a seller notifies other bidders that he is bidding for his own goods, or that he has employed an agent to bid for him, the bidding is legal. If he does not give notice and bids himself, or gets someone to bid for him, thus forcing up the price, the sale is fraudulent, and the buyer can purchase the goods for the amount of the last bid he made before fraudulent bidding started.

One frequently hears dark, but usually apocryphal, tales of "the ring" in action to depress the bidding and secure items below the price commensurate with their actual value. This is a fraudulent practice and in law is regarded as a criminal conspiracy. In practice, however, it would be very difficult for a group of dealers or other individuals to keep the bidding down merely by sitting on their hands. This practice could only operate successfully in sales which were largely, if not entirely, frequented by dealers. But coin sales, like other specialist collector-orientated auctions, are characterised by a high proportion of private bidders in attendance. Any conspiracy by a ring would merely allow some private bidder to step in and secure the lot at a bargain price. Rings are illegal, but in practice prosecutions are very rare as it is extremely difficult to obtain proof of their operations. What is more likely to happen is that dealers have been known to act in concert to force up the bidding to frighten off some unwelcome interloper. Here again, such tales are legion, but astonishingly lacking in specific details. The golden rule in attending auctions is to know what you are going after, and to have a pretty precise idea of how much you are prepared to pay. Do not be stampeded in the heat of the moment into going way beyond your limit.

Taxation of Profits on Disposal

The Inland Revenue define an asset as "any form of property (other than sterling) wherever situated". A disposal includes a sale, exchange or gift of an asset, or the receipt of a capital sum in respect of them. In layman's terms you dispose of an asset when you sell it, give it away, exchange it or lose it. A transfer of assets between husband and wife doesn't count (unless they are legally separated), nor does the transfer of an asset you leave when you die. If a disposal results in a profit you could be liable to tax. Any profit made on the sale of certain assets, including coins, medals and other collectables, constitutes a capital gain and is subject to Capital Gains Tax (CGT) which is now charged at the same 25% and 40% rates as income tax. However the government allows you to make a total capital gain in the current tax year of £5,500 before tax becomes chargeable. If this is the case, and the total proceeds from disposal do not exceed £10,000, then a simple declaration to this effect is all you need to make in the relevant section of your annual tax return.

In any one year you are allowed to dispose of items with a total value of no more than £6,000 without needing to declare the fact to the Inland revenue. Above that, Capital Gains Tax (CGT) is payable on the actual gain, although the Annual Exempt Amount (AEA) set for 2008-9 is £9,600. In practice, you would have to dispose of quite a valuable coin or collection before tax becomes liable. Computing the actual capital gain is a complicated matter. Suppose you purchased a coin in 1960 for £5,000 and sold it in 1993 for £12,000. On the face of it, you've made a capital gain of £7,000 and you might think that you were liable to CGT because the gain was over £5,500. However, the *length of time* you've held the asset also has to be taken into consideration. From April 6, 1988 the law was altered so that only gains made after March 31, 1982 are now taxable. In effect, you are taxed as if you acquired the coin on March 31, 1982. The initial value of the coin is deemed to be its market value at that date. If the gain from March 1982 to the time of disposal is greater than the overall gain from acquisition in 1960 to disposal in 1993, you take the lesser of the two figures. If this produces a gain, whereas the old method of working it out would have produced a loss, you will be regarded, for tax purposes, as having made neither a gain nor a loss on disposal. You have a choice of opting for computing from the time of actual acquisition or from March 1982, whichever seems the more advantageous; but once you've made your choice you cannot subsequently change your mind.

How do you establish what the coin was worth in March 1982? The Inland Revenue tend to regard Spink, Krause or other relevant catalogues as their yardstick. The difference between the nominal or catalogue value in 1982 and what you eventually got for the coin *assuming that the latter was greater,* might be regarded as the capital gain, but even then the position is complicated by inflation in the intervening years eroding the real value of the coin.

At this stage things get really complicated as you have to work out the indexation allowance. This is determined by the Retail Prices Index (RPI), and you need to know the RPI for (a) the month of disposal, and (b) the month in which you acquired the asset, or March 1982, if later. The RPI is announced each month by the Departmenrt of Employment and is published in its *Employment Gazette* which ought to be available in your local public library. Take the RPI for the month of the disposal and subtract the RPI for the month when indexation commenced. Then divide the result by the RPI for the month when indexation began, and work out this figure to the nearest third decimal place. This is known as the indexation factor, which you then multiply by the initial value of your coin. Simple isn't it? In most cases, however, I expect you will have made a capital loss in real terms, so these sums, though necessary to satisfy the Inland Revenue, are largely academic.

Treasure and the Law

Until the introduction of the new Treasure Act, the legal position regarding articles of gold, silver or bullion, found long after they were hidden or abandoned, was not as simple and straightforward as it might be supposed. Furthermore, this was a case where the law in England and Wales differed fundamentally from that in Scotland.

Treasure Trove was one of the most ancient rights of the Crown, deriving from the age-old right of the monarch to gold, silver or bullion treasure whose owner was not known. In England and Wales, the law applied only to objects made of, or containing, gold or silver, whether in the form of coin, jewellery, plate or bullion. Moreover, the object had to be shown to have been deliberately hidden with intent to retrieve and the owner could not be readily found. The English law therefore excluded precious stones and jewels set in base metals or alloys such as bronze or pewter. It also took no account of artifacts in pottery, stone, bone, wood or glass which might be of immense antiquarian value.

In recent years, as a result of the rise in metal-detecting as a hobby, the archaeological lobby brought pressure to bear on Parliament to change the law and bring it into line with Scotland where the rules on Treasure Trove were far more rigorously interpreted. In Scotland the Crown is entitled to *all* abandoned property, even if it has not been hidden and is of little value. This applies even to objects dumped in skips on the pavement. Strictly speaking you would be committing a criminal offence if you removed an old chair from a skip without the owner's permission, although in practice such helping oneself rarely proceeds to a prosecution. In 1958 an archaeological expedition from Aberdeen University found several valuable

Metal detecting can be fun—but be sure you know the rules!

artifacts on St Ninian's Isle, Shetland. These included silver vessels and ornaments, as well as a porpoise bone which had incised decoration on it. The archaeologists challenged the rights of the Crown to this treasure, arguing that the Crown would have to prove that the articles had been deliberately hidden, and that a porpoise bone was in any case not valuable enough to count as treasure. The High Court, however, decided that as long as the property had been abandoned, it belonged automatically to the Crown. Its value, intrinsic or otherwise, or whether or not it was hidden, did not make any difference. Since then, as a result of this decision in case law, the criteria for Treasure Trove have been very strictly applied in Scotland. It would have only required a similar test case in England or Wales to result in a similar tightening of the rules. This has been resisted, mainly by the detectorist lobby, but inevitably the government considered legislation to control the use of metal detectors, if not to ban them altogether.

In England and Wales a find of gold or silver coins, artifacts or ornaments, or objects which contain some of these metals, which appears to have been concealed by the original owner, was deemed to be Treasure Trove. It was not even necessary for the articles to be buried in the ground; objects concealed in thatched roofs or under the floorboards of buildings have been judged to be Treasure Trove. Such finds had to be notified immediately to the police who then informed the district coroner. He then convened an inquest which decided whether all or part of the find was Treasure Trove. Establishing the gold or silver content was straightforward, but the coroner's inquest had to decide whether the material was hidden deliberately and not just lost or abandoned, and that the owner could not be located. A gold coin found on or near a country footpath might reasonably have been dropped by the original possessor through a hole in pocket or purse and in such cases it was very unlikely that it would be deemed Treasure Trove, even if the coin turned out to be very rare. In this instance the coroner would then have had to determine who was the lawful owner of the find: the actual finder, the owner of the land where it was found or even the tenant of the land. As a rule, however, it was left to the finder and landowner to decide between them who the owner of the coin should be, and in some cases the matter could only be resolved by referring to a civil court. For this reason it was vital that metal detectorists should secure permission *in writing* from landowners before going on to their land, defining rights and obligations on both sides, in order to determine the disposal or share-out of any finds or proceeds from the sale of finds, *beforehand*.

The unique Coenwulf gold penny was found by an amateur metal detectorist next to a public footpath in Bedfordshire

If the coroner decided that the articles were deliberately concealed, and declared them to be Treasure Trove, the find automatically reverted to the Crown. In practice the find was considered by the Treasure Trove Reviewing Committee of the Treasury. They might decide that although the articles, *invariably coins,* were gold or silver, they were so common that they were not required by the British Museum or one of the other great national collections, and would return them to the finder to dispose of at their discretion. If some or all of the coins were deemed vital for inclusion in a national collection the finder was recompensed with the full market value of the material. On the other hand, if someone found gold or silver which might be Treasure Trove and failed to declare it at the time, that person was liable to prosecution under the Theft Act 1968 should the find subsequently come to light. Not only could they face a heavy fine but the articles would be forfeit to the Crown, and of course no reward or recompense was then payable either.

The anomalies and inconsistencies of existing law on Treasure Trove were eliminated and the position considerably tightened up by the passage, on July 5, 1996, of the Treasure Act.

Announcing that the Treasure Act had received the Royal Assent, Lord Inglewood, National Heritage Minister, said, "This represents the first legislation on Treasure Trove to be passed in England and Wales and will replace Common Law precedents and practices dating back to the Middle Ages. The Act, which offers a clearer definition of treasure and simplified procedures for dealing with finds, will come into force after a code of practice has been drawn up and agreed by both Houses of Parliament". The Act came into force in England, Wales and Northern Ireland on September 24, 1997, replacing the Common Law of Treasure Trove.

The act was introduced as a Private Member's Bill by Sir Anthony Grant, after the failure of an earlier attempt by Lord Perth. For the first time, it would be a criminal offence to fail to report within 14 days the discovery of an item which could be declared Treasure Trove. Finders will continue to be rewarded for reporting their discoveries promptly, while landowners and occupiers will also be eligible for rewards for the first time.

The Treasure Act covers man-made objects and defines treasure as objects other than coins which are at least 300 years old and contain at least 10 per cent by weight of gold or silver; coins more than 300 years old which are found in hoards (a minimum of two coins if the precious metal content is more than 10 per cent, and a minimum of 10 coins if the precious metal content is below 10 per cent). The act also embraces all objects found in clear archaeological association with items which are treasure under the above definitions. It also covers any object which would have been Treasure Trove under the previous definitions (e.g. hoards of 19th century gold or silver coins).

An extension to The Act from January 1992 provides that groups of prehistoric bronze implements are also deemed to be Treasure.

The maximum penalty for failing to report the discovery of treasure within 14 days will be a fine of £5,000 or three months imprisonment, or both.

In Scotland the police pass the goods on to the procurator fiscal who acts as the local representative of the Queen's and Lord Treasurer's Remembrancer. If the articles are of little value, historically or intrinsically, the finder will usually be allowed to keep them. If they are retained for the appropriate national collection then a reward equal to the market value is payable.

A favourite haunt of metal-detectorists these days is the beach, and many hobbyists make quite a lucrative living by sweeping the beaches

The Langtoft hoards were discovered by three keen metal detectorists—the larger of the hoards being found in its original pot.

Nothing quite beats the excitement of holding treasure in your hands

especially just after a Bank Holiday. It's surprising how much loose change gets lost from pockets and handbags over a holiday weekend. Technically the coins recovered from the beach are lost property, in which case they ought to be surrendered to the police, otherwise the finder may be guilty of theft. In practice, however, the law turns a blind eye to coins, on the sensible grounds that it would be impossible to prove ownership. On the other hand, banknotes are treated as lost property since someone could in theory at least identify a note as his by citing the serial number.

In the case of other objects, such as watches and jewellery, of course the law governing lost property is enforced, and the old adage of "finders keepers" does not apply. Any object of value, identifiable as belonging to someone, that is washed up on the foreshore or found in territorial waters is known technically as "wreck". This includes not just a wrecked ship, but any cargo that was being carried by a ship.

If wreck is not claimed by its owner, it falls to the Crown. In this case it is not necessary to prove deliberate concealment, as in the case of Treasure Trove. This law has a specific numismatic application in the case of the gold and silver coins washed up after storms around our shores, from Shetland to the Scillies. Such coins, emanating from wrecks of Spanish treasure ships and Dutch East Indiamen in particular, are well documented, and any such finds ought to be reported immediately to the police.

Stray finds of coins, as well as other objects of value, on public places, such as the street, a public park or a sports ground, are also subject to law. In this case the finder must take all reasonable steps to locate the owner. Anyone who keeps a coin without making reasonable effort to find the owner could be prosecuted for theft. As with the beach, however, such "reasonable effort" would clearly be impractical. Finding coins on private premises is another matter. In this case large bodies, such as the Post Office, British Rail, the British Airports Authority, bus companies, municipal authorities, hospitals, the owners of department stores, theatre and cinema proprietors and the like, may have bye-laws, rules and regulations for dealing with lost property found within their precincts, or in their vehicles. If you found a purse or wallet on a bus or train, or in a telephone kiosk or a shop, common sense (and your conscience) would tell you to hand it over to the driver, conductor, shopkeeper or official in charge. As a rule, unclaimed lost property reverts eventually to the finder, but not always; British Rail and some other organisations have a rule that in such cases the property reverts to the organisation. In any event, failure to disclose the find immediately might render you liable to prosecution for stealing by finding.

Treasure Act
Code of Practice
a summary

For easy reference a summary of the main points of the new law is reproduced here. Further information will be found in the *Code of Practice on the Treasure Act*, which can be obtained free of charge from the Department for Culture, Media and Sport (telephone: 020 7211 6200, email enquiries@culture.gov.uk). Metal detectorists are strongly advised to obtain a copy of the Code of Practice which, among other things, contains guidance for detectorists, sets out guidelines on rewards, gives advice on the care of finds and has lists of useful addresses.

What is the definition of treasure?

The following finds are treasure under the Act (*more detailed guidance is given in the Code of Practice*):

1. *Objects other than coins:* any object other than a coin provided that it contains at least 10 per cent of gold or silver and is a least 300 years old when found (objects with gold or silver plating normally have less than 10 per cent of precious metal).

2. *Coins:* all coins from the same find provided they are at least 300 years old when found (but if the coins contain less than 10 per cent of gold or silver there must be at least 10 of them; there is a list of these coins in the Code of Practice).

An object or coin is part of the same find as another object or coin if it is found in the same place as, or had previously been left together with, the other object. Finds may have become scattered since they were originally deposited in the ground.

Only the following groups of coins will normally be regarded as coming from the "same find":

(a) hoards that have been deliberately hidden;
(b) smaller groups of coins, such as the con tents of purses, that may have been dropped or lost and
(c) votive or ritual deposits.

Single coins found on their own are not treasure and groups of coins lost one by one over a period of time (for example those found on settlement sites or on fair sites) will not normally be treasure, but two coins over 300 years old found together can be deemed to be treasure.

3. *Associated objects:* any object, whether it is made of, that is found in the same place as, or that had previously been together with, another object that is treasure.

4. *Objects that would have been treasure trove:* any object that would previously have been treasure trove, but does not fall within the specific categories given above. These objects have to be made substantially of gold or silver; they have to have been buried with the intention of recovery and their owner or his/her heirs cannot be traced. The following types of find are not treasure:

(a) objects lost whose owners can be traced;
(b) unworked natural objects, including human and animal remains, even if they are found in association with treasure;
(c) objects from the foreshore, which are wreck.

If you are in any doubt, it will probably be safest to report your find.

What about objects found before the Act came into force?

You should report objects that come into any of the four categories just described (if found after September 23, 1997). There is no need to report any objects found before that date unless they may be treasure trove (see 4 above).

What should I do if I find something that may be treasure?

You must report all finds of treasure to the coroner for the district in which they are found *either* within 14 days after the date on which you made the find *or* within 14 days after the day on which you realised that the find might be treasure (for example, as a result of having it identified). The obligation to report finds applies to everyone, including archaeologists.

How do I report a find of treasure?

Very simply. You may report your find to the coroner in person, by letter, telephone or fax. The coroner or his officer will send you an acknowledgement and tell you where you should deliver your find. The Code of Practice has a list of all coroners' addresses, telephone and fax numbers.

There are special procedure for objects from a few areas for which treasure franchises exist, but they should be reported to the coroner in the usual way. The main franchise-holders (the Duchies of Lancaster and Cornwall, the Corporation of London and the City of Bristol) have confirmed that they will pay rewards for finds of treasure from their franchises in the normal way.

Where will I have to take my find?

You will normally be asked to take your find to a local museum or archaeological body. Local agreements have been drawn up for each coroner's district in England and Wales to provide the coroner with a list of such museums and archaeological organisations. The Department is publishing a series of leaflets, roughly one for each county of England and one for Wales, listing the relevant coroners, museums and archaeological services in each area.

The body which receives the find on behalf of the coroner will give you a receipt. Although they will need to know where you made the find, they will keep this information confidential if you or the landowner wish—and you should do so too.

The body receiving the find will notify the Sites and Monuments Record as soon as possible (if that has not already happened), so that the site where the find was made can be investigated by archae-ologists if necessary. A list of Sites and Monuments Records is in Appendix 3 of the Code of Practice.

What if I do not report a find of treasure?

If you fail to report a find that you believe or have reasonable grounds for believing to be treasure without a reasonable excuse you may be imprisoned for up to three months or receive a fine of up to level 5 on the standard scale (currently £5,000) or both. You will not be breaking the law if you do not report a find because you do not initially recognise that it may be treasure, but you should report it once you do.

What happens if the find is not treasure?

If the object is clearly not treasure, the museum or archeological body will inform the coroner, who may then decide to give directions that the find should be returned without holding an inquest.

What happens if the find is treasure?

If a museum curator or archaeologist believes the find may be treasure, they will inform the British Museum or the National Museums & Galleries of Wales. The museums will then decide whether they or any other museum may wish to acquire it.

If no museum wishes to acquire the find, the Secretary of State will be able to disclaim it. When this happens, the coroner will notify the occupier and landowner that he intends to return the object to the finder after 28 days unless he receives an objection. If the coroner receives an objection, the find will be retained until the dispute is settled.

What if a museum wants to acquire my find?

If a museum wants to acquire part or all of a find, then the coroner will hold an inquest to decide whether it is treasure. The coroner will inform the finder, occupier and landowner and they will be able to question witnesses at the inquest. Treasure inquest will not normally be held with a jury.

If the find is declared to be treasure, then it will be taken to the British Museum or the National Museums & Galleries of Wales, so that it can be valued by the Treasure Valuation Committee.

How do I know I will receive a fair price for my find?

Any find of treasure that a museum wishes to acquire must be valued by the Treasure Valuation Committee, which consists of independent experts. The Committee will commission a valuation from one or more experts drawn from the trade. You, together with the museum that wishes to acquire the find and any other interested party, will have an opportunity to comment on the valuation and to send in a separate valuation of your own, before the Committee makes its recommendation. If you are dissatisfied you can appeal to the Secretary of State.

What if the coroner or museum loses or damages my find?

They are required to take reasonable steps to ensure that this does not happen; but, if it does, you should nonetheless be compensated.

Who will receive the reward?

This is set out in detail in the Code of Practice. To summarise:

- where the finder has permission to be on the land, rewards should continue to be paid in full to him or her (the burden of proof as to whether he or she has permission will rest with the finder). If the finder makes an agreement with the occupier/landowner to share a reward, the Secretary of State will normally follow it;
- if the finder does not remove the whole of a find from the ground but allows archaeologists to excavate the remainder of the find, the original finder will normally be eligible for a reward for the whole find;
- rewards will not normally be payable when the find is made by an archaeologist;
- where the finder has committed an offence in relation to a find, or has trespassed, or has not followed best practice as set out in the Code of Practice, he or she may expect no reward at all or a reduced reward. Landowners and occupiers will be eligible for rewards in such cases.

How long will it take before I receive my reward?

The Code of Practice states that you should receive a reward within one year of you having delivered your find, although this may take longer in the case of very large finds or those that present special difficulties. If no museum wants to acquire the find it should be disclaimed within six months or within three months if it is a single object.

From the man who signed the banknotes!

INSIDE MAFEKING

The diary of Captain Herbert Greener

Step inside the walls of Mafeking with this exciting new publication from Token Publishing Ltd.

- The personal diary of Herbert Greener the Paymaster General for Baden-Powell during the famous siege of Mafeking
- Illustrated with numerous photographs taken during the siege
- The fascinating story of the famous stamps and banknotes produced under the noses of the Boer enemy, by Captain Greener, the man who helped design, print them and actually signed the originals.

An outstanding factual account of an exciting, dramatic and sometimes harrowing period in British Colonial history where the idea for the foundation of the Boy Scout Movement first became a reality. A not to be missed publication for anyone interested in the story of the siege and the stamps and banknotes that are today avidly sought after.

Limited edition now available

Order your copy today! £29.95 +£3.00p&p
(Europe & World Surface £5.00, Airmail £8)

Call 01404 44166, log on to www.tokenpublishing.com
or write to Token Publishing, Orchard House, Duchy Road, Heathpark, Honiton, Devon EX14 1YD
www.tokenpublishing.com

New Title

Advertisers

Directory

Dealer Directory

See our website at tokenpublishing.com for up-to-date dealer entries, with hyperlinks taking you directly to their websites.